GW00646815

EZ SOLUTIONS
TEST PREP SERIES

MATH PRACTICE

BASIC WORKBOOK

EZ SIMPLIFIED SOLUTIONS – THE BREAKTHROUGH IN TEST PREP!

LEADERS IN TEST PREP SOLUTIONS – WE MAKE IT EZ FOR YOU!

AUTHOR: PUNIT RAJA SURYACHANDRA

WWW.EZMETHODS.COM

EZ SOLUTIONS
USA

EZ SOLUTIONS
P.O. Box 10755
Silver Spring, MD 20914
USA

Conceived, conceptualized, written, and edited by:
Punit Raja SuryaChandra, EZ Solutions

PRINTED AND MANUFACTURED IN THE UNITED STATES OF AMERICA

TABLE OF CONTENTS

THIS PAGE HAS BEEN INTENTIONALLY LEFT BLANK

PREFACE

▪ABOUT EZ SOLUTIONS

EZ Solutions – *the breakthrough in test-preparation*!

EZ Solutions is an organization formed to provide **simplified solutions** for test-preparation and tutoring. Although EZ Solutions is a fairly new name in the publishing industry, it has quickly become a respected publisher of test-prep books, study guides, study aids, handbooks, and other reference works. EZ publications and educational materials are highly respected, and they continue to receive an unprecedented amount of praise from professionals, instructors, librarians, parents, and students.

OBJECTIVE: Our ultimate objective is to help you **achieve academic and scholastic excellence**. We possess the right blend and matrix of skills and expertise that are required to not only do justice to our programs and publications, but also to handle them most effectively and efficiently. We are confident that our state-of-the-art programs/publications will give you a completely **new dimension** by enhancing your skill set and improving your overall performance.

MISSION: Our mission is to foster continuous knowledge to develop and enhance each student's skills through innovative and methodical programs/publications coupled with our add-on services – leading to a **better career and life** for our students.

OUR PHILOSOPHY: We subscribe to the traditional philosophy that everyone is equally capable of learning and that the natural, though sometimes unfulfilled and unexplored impetus of people is towards growth and development. We know that the human brain is undoubtedly a very powerful and efficient problem-solving tool, and every individual is much more capable than they realize. We strive to implement this philosophy throughout our books by helping our students explore their **potential** so that they can **perform at their optimum level**.

OUR COMMITMENT TOWARDS YOUR SATISFACTION: Reinventing, Redesigning, and Redefining Success: We are committed to providing **total customer satisfaction** that exceeds your expectations! Your satisfaction is extremely important to us, and your approval is one of the most important indicators that we have done our job correctly.

Long-Term Alliance: We, at EZ, look forward to forming a **long-term alliance** with all our readers who buy our book(s), for the days, months, and years to come. Moreover, our commitment to client service is one of our most important and distinguished characteristics. We also encourage our readers to contact us for any further assistance, feedback, suggestions, or inquiries.

EZ Solutions publishing series include books for the following major standardized tests:
- GMAT
- SAT
- PSAT
- ASVAB
- PRAXIS Series
- GRE
- ACT
- CLEP
- TOEFL
- Other (national and state) Standardized Tests

EZ Solutions aims to provide good quality study aides in a wide variety of disciplines to the following:
- Students who have not yet completed high school
- High School students preparing to enter college
- College students preparing to enter graduate or post-graduate school
- Anyone else who is simply looking to improve their skills

Students from every walk of life, of any background, at any level, in any field, with any ambition, can find what they are looking for among EZ Solutions' publications.

FOREIGN STUDENTS: All of our books are designed, keeping in mind the unique needs of students from North and South America, U.K., Europe, Middle East, Far East, and Asia. Foreign students from countries around the world seeking to obtain education in the United States will find the assistance they need in EZ Solutions' publications.

CONTACT US: Feel free to contact us, and one of our friendly specialists will be more than happy to assist you with your queries, or feel free to browse through our website for lots of useful information.
E-Mail: info@EZmethods.com
Phone: (301) 622-9597
Mail: EZ Solutions, P.O. Box 10755, Silver Spring, MD 20914, USA
Website: www.EZmethods.com

FEEDBACK: The staff of EZ Solutions hopes that you find our books helpful and easy to use. If you have any specific suggestions, comments, or feedback, please email us at: feedback@EZmethods.com

BUSINESS DEVELOPMENT: If you are interested in exploring business development opportunities, including forming a partnership alliance with us, kindly email us at: partners@EZmethods.com.

PRODUCT REGISTRATION: In order to get the most up-to-date information about this and our other books, you must register your purchase with EZ solutions by emailing us at: products@EZmethods.com, or by visiting our website www.EZmethods.com.

ERRORS AND INACCURACIES: We are not responsible for any typographical errors or inaccuracies contained in this publication. The information, prices, and discounts given in this book are subject to change without prior notice. To report any kind of errors or inaccuracies in this publication, kindly email us at: errors@EZmethods.com.

▪ABOUT OUR AUTHOR

The name of the man behind EZ publication series is **Punit Raja SuryaChandra**, who is also the founder of our company. He holds a Bachelors in Business and an MBA. It took him many years to write and publish these unique books. He researched every single book available in the market for test-preparation, and actually realized there is not even one book that is truly complete with all the content and concepts. This was the single most important reason that prompted him to write these books, and hence our **EZ prep guidebooks were born**. He has made every effort to make these books as comprehensive and as complete as possible. His expertise and experience are as diverse as the subjects that are represented in our books. He has the breadth and depth of experience required to write books of this magnitude and intensity. Without his unparalleled and unmatched skills and determination, none of this would have been possible.

In developing these books, his primary goal has been to give everyone the same advantages as the students we tutor privately or students who take our classes. Our tutoring and classroom solutions are only available to a limited number of students; however, with these books, any student in any corner of the world can benefit the same level of service at a fraction of the cost. Therefore, you should take this book as your personal EZ tutor or instructor, because that's precisely how it has been designed.

ACKNOWLEDGEMENTS:
Our author would like to extend his vote of appreciation and gratitude to all his family members for their unconditional and continuous support, to all his close friends for their trust and confidence in him, and to all his colleagues for their helpful consultation and generous advice.

Our EZ books have benefited from dedicated efforts and labors of our author and other members of the editorial staff. Here at EZ, we all wish you the best as you get comfortable, and settle down with your EZ tutor to start working on preparing for your test. In pursuing an educational dream, you have a wonderful and an exciting opportunity ahead of you. All of us at EZ Solutions wish you the very best!

▪ABOUT EZ BOOKS

THE EZ NAME:

All our books have been written in a very easy to read manner, and in a very easy to understand fashion, so that students of any background, of any aptitude, of any capacity, of any skill-set, of any level, can benefit from them. These books are not specifically written for the **dummies** or for the **geniuses**; instead, they are written for students who fit into any category of intellectual acumen. This is how we acquired the name *"EZ Solutions"* for our publications – and as the name itself suggests, **we make everything EZ for you**!

THE EZ TUTOR:

Like any good tutor, EZ Tutor will work with you **individually and privately**, providing you with all the tools needed to improve your testing skills. It will assist you in recognizing your weaknesses, and enlighten you on how to improve upon them while transforming them into strengths. Of course, it will also point out your strengths as well, so that you can make them even stronger. By employing innovative techniques, EZ tutor will **stimulate, activate, and accelerate your learning process**. Soon after you start working with your EZ tutor, you will see **remarkable and noticeable improvement** in your performance by utilizing your newly acquired learning skills.

Whenever, Wherever, and However: EZ tutor also has the **flexibility** to work with you whenever you like – day or night, wherever you like – indoors or outdoors, and however you like – for as long or as short. While working with your EZ tutor, you can work at your own pace, you can go as fast or as slow as you like, repeat sections as many times as you need, and skip over sections you already know well. Your EZ tutor will also give you explanations, not just correct answers, and it will be **infinitely patient and adaptable**. Hence, our EZ Tutor will make you a more intelligent and smarter test-taker, and will help you maximize your score!

ADD-ON OPTIONS: *Turn your EZ Virtual Tutor into a Real Tutor!*

EZ TUTORING OVER THE PHONE:

Along with buying the entire series of our modules, students can also add on services like email/online support and/or telephone support. In fact, you can get the best preparation for your test by blending our professional 1-on-1 tutoring with our state-of-the-art books. The most important feature of our add-on features is our individualized and personalized approach that works toward building your self-confidence, and enhancing your ability to learn and perform better. This will also invigorate your motivational, organizational, as well as your learning skills. Our phone specialists are highly qualified, experienced, innovative, and well trained. You can do all this in the exclusivity and comfort of your home. Students can get in touch with one of our specialists anytime they need help – we'll be there for you, whenever you need us! We offer several packages with different levels, features, and customizations for tutoring over the phone to suit your individualized needs. Contact us for more details.

EZ 1-ON-1 TEST-TAKING & ADMISSION CONSULTATION:

We understand that standardized tests and school/college admissions can sometimes become very stressful. Our 1-on-1 Test-Taking & Admission Consulting Program can dramatically reduce your stress and anxiety. One of our consultants can personally guide you through the entire process, starting from familiarizing you with a test to getting you successfully admitted into a school/college of your choice. Again, you can do all this in the exclusivity and comfort of your home. We offer several packages with different levels, features, and customizations for test-taking and admission consultation over the phone to suit your individualized needs. Contact us for more details.
The following are some of the features of our EZ 1-on-1 Test-Taking & Admission Consulting Program:
- Familiarize you with a particular test
- Equip you with test-taking skills for each section of your test
- Reduce test-taking anxiety, stress, nervousness, and test-fever with personal counseling
- Draft and edit your essays
- Re-design your resume
- Prepare you for a telephone or personal interview
- Select the right school/college & help with admission application procedures
- Presentation Skills – how to present and market yourself

EZ UNIQUE FEATURES:

Your EZ Tutor offers you the following unique features that will highlight important information, and will let you find them quickly as and when you need to review them.

EZ STRATEGIES: It provides you with many powerful, effective, proven, and time tested strategies for various concepts, and shows you exactly how to use them to attack different question types. Many of these test-taking strategies cannot be found in any other books!

EZ SHORTCUTS: It gives you many time-saving shortcuts you can apply to save yourself some very valuable testing-time while solving a question on your actual test.

EZ TACTICS: It shows you several important tactics to use so that you can solve problems in the smartest way.

EZ DEFINITIONS: It defines all the key definitions in an easy to understand manner so that you get a clear description and concise understanding of all the key terms.

EZ RULES: It presents all the important rules in an orderly manner so that you can learn the basic rules of all the concepts.

EZ STEPS: It walks you through hundreds of concepts, showing you how to tackle every question type in an organized user-friendly step-by-step easy-to-understand methodology that adapts to your understanding and needs so that you get the best procedural knowledge.

EZ MULTIPLE/ALTERNATE METHODS: It gives you a choice of multiple methods of answering the same question so that you can choose the method that seems easiest to you.

EZ SUMMARIES: It lists a complete summary of all the important concepts in an ordered and organized manner so that you will never have to hunt for them.

EZ FACTS: It provides you with numerous key facts about various principles so that you know all the facts-and-figures of the material you are reviewing.

EZ HINTS: It supplies you with innumerable hints and clues so that you can use them to become a smarter and wiser test-taker.

EZ TIPS: It also presents you with many tips and pointers that will prevent you from making any careless mistakes or falling into traps.

EZ NOTES: It reminds you to make notes of some important points that will come handy while answering a question.

EZ WARNINGS/CAUTIONS: It warns you of some obvious mistakes that will prevent you from making them while answering a question.

EZ EXCEPTIONS: It makes you aware of the exceptions and exclusions that apply to any particular rule.

EZ REFERENCES: It gives you references of related materials that you may want to refer to in other parts of the same or different modules, while learning a specific concept.

EZ SPOTS: It lists buzzwords and phrases that will help you easily spot some specific question types.

EZ PROBLEM SET-UP: It converts even some of the most complex problems into an easy to understand mathematical statement so that you understand accurately how to interpret the problems.

EZ PROBLEM EXPLANATIONS: It provides easy to understand explanations within square brackets for each step of the problem so that you know exactly what you need to do in each step.

EZ SOLVED EXAMPLES: It also throws several realistic solved examples with easy to understand detailed explanations for each and every question type explained so that you can understand and learn how to apply the concepts.

EZ PRACTICE EXERCISES: Last but not the least; it also includes intensive realistic practice exercises with easy to understand detailed explanations for each and every question type explained so that you can put to practice what you learned in an actual test question – solved examples will help you understand the concepts & practice will make you perfect!

GUESS WHAT!! No other book offers you so much. Your EZ tutor strives to provide you with the *best possible training* for your test, and *best value for your time and money*; and it is infinitely committed to providing you with *state-of-the-art* material.

Advantages: Amazing results in the first few days of the program!

Disadvantages: Only if you don't make use of our programs and publications!

THE EZ ADVANTAGE:

EZ TEST-PREP PROGRAM BROKEN INTO MODULES:
Instead of having a *big fat ugly scary all-in-one gigantic book*, we have broken our entire test-prep program into *small easy-to-use modules*.
- **Exclusivity:** Each module is exclusively dedicated to covering one major content area in extensive depth and breadth, allowing you to master each topic by getting an in-depth review.
- **More Content:** You will find many more topics and many more pages per topic than what you can find in all other books combined.
- **Tailored and Customized:** Separated modules offer test-takers of all levels with a more tailored and customized approach towards building specific foundational and advanced skills, and successfully preparing for the test.

EZ TO READ, CARRY, AND MANAGE:
EZ Modules are convenient – they are *easier to read, carry, and manage*.
- **EZ to Read:** EZ Modules are easier to read with text in spacious pages with a bigger font size than those other books with overcrowded pages with a small print.
- **EZ to Carry:** EZ Modules are easier to carry and hold than those other big fat bulky gigantic books.
- **EZ to Manage:** EZ Modules are overall easier to manage than those other all-in-one books.

BUY ONE MODULE OR THE ENTIRE SERIES:
The individually separated modules give you the flexibility to buy only those modules that cover the areas you think you need to work on; nevertheless, we strongly suggest you buy our entire series of modules. In fact, the most efficient and effective way to get the most out of our publications is to use our entire set of modules in conjunction with each other, and not just a few. Each module can be independently bought and studied; however, the modules are somehow connected with and complement the other modules. Therefore, if you are serious about getting a good score on your test, we sincerely recommend you purchase our entire series of modules. Contact us to order, or go to www.EZmethods.com, or check your local bookstore (look at the EZ Book Store on the last page for more information).

NO NEED TO REFER TO ANY OTHER BOOK:
Almost all other test-prep books contain a small disclaimer in some corner. They themselves spell it out very loud and clear, and admit that their book is only a brief review of some important topics; hence, it should not be considered to be an overall review of all the concepts. Most other test-preparation guides only include information for you to get familiar with the kind of topics that may appear on the test, and they suggest that you refer to additional textbooks, or consult other reference books if you want more detailed information and to get an in-depth knowledge of all the concepts. These books are not designed to be a one-stop book to learn everything you must know; instead, they are more like a

summary of some important points. Moreover, they assume that you already know everything, or at least most of the concepts.

However, if you are using our EZ modules to prepare for your test, it's the opposite case, you don't need to refer or consult any other book or text or any other source for assistance. On the contrary, we, in fact, discourage you from referring to any other book, just because there is absolutely no reason to. Our EZ modules contain everything that you need to know in order to do well on your test. We haven't left anything out, and we don't assume anything. Even if you don't know anything, you will find everything in our modules from topics that are frequently tested to topics that are rarely tested, and everything in between. The only topics that you won't find in our books are the topics that will probably never appear on your test!

Frequently Tested: Included in our review – topics that are repeatedly tested on your test, on a regularly basis
Occasionally Tested: Included in our review – topics that are sometimes tested on your test, every now and then
Rarely Tested: Included in our review – topics that are seldom tested on your test, very infrequently
Never Tested: Not included in our review – since these topics are never tested on your test, we don't even mention them anywhere in our review

The bottom line is, if something can be on your test, you'll find it in our modules; and if something is not going to be on your test, it's not going to be in our modules. Each and every math concept that even has the slightest possibility to be on the test can be found in our modules.

THE OFFICIAL REAL PRACTICE TESTS:
Although we don't suggest you refer to any other book, the only time we recommend using other books is for practicing previously administered tests to exercise your skills. The best resources for actual practice tests are the official guides published by the test makers that have several actual previously administered tests. One can *replicate* these tests as closely as one can, but no one other than the test administrators can *duplicate* them, and have the ability to reproduce or publish them. Therefore, to get the maximum effect of our approach, you must practice the actual tests from the official guide. You can also take a free online practice test by going to their website. EZ's practice tests are also based upon the most recently administered tests, and include every type of question that can be expected on the actual exam.

HOW OUR BOOKS CAN HELP YOU:
Our books are designed to help you identify your strengths and the areas which you need to work on. If you study all our modules, you will be fully equipped with all the tools needed to take your test head-on. Moreover, you'll also have the satisfaction that you did all you possibly could do to prepare yourself for the test, and you didn't leave any stone unturned. The amount of content covered in our books is far more than what you would learn by studying all the other test-prep books that are out there, put together, or by even taking an online or an actual prep course, and of course, spending thousands of dollars in the process. This will give you an idea of how material we have covered in our books.

STRUCTURE OF OUR MODULES:
All our modules are *structured in a highly organized and systematic manner*. The review is divided into different modules. Each module is divided into units. Each unit is further subdivided into chapters. Each chapter covers various topics, and in each specific topic, you are given all that you need to solve questions on that topic in detail – explaining key concepts, rules, and other EZ unique features. Also included in some topics are test-taking strategies specific to the topics discussed. Following each topic are solved sample examples with comprehensive explanations, which are exclusively based on that topic, and utilizing the concepts covered in that topic and section. Finally, there are practice exercises with thorough explanations containing real test-like questions for each topic and section, which are very similar to actual test questions. All units, chapters, and topics are chronologically numbered for easy reference.

Moreover, the modules, units, chapters, and topics are all arranged in sequence so that later modules, units, chapters, and topics assume familiarity with the material covered in earlier modules, units, chapters, and topics. Therefore, the best way to review is to work through from the beginning to the end.

SERIES > MODULES > UNITS > CHAPTERS > TOPICS > SUB-TOPICS > SOLVED EXAMPLES > PRACTICE EXERCISES

THE EZ DIFFERENCE:

DIFFERENCE BETWEEN EZ SOLUTIONS' PUBLICATIONS AND OTHER BOOKS:

Most of the other test-prep books suggest that your exam only tests your ability to take the test, and it does not test any actual content knowledge. In other words, they claim that your test is all about knowing the test-taking strategies, and it has very little to do with the actual knowledge of content; others claim that your test is all about knowing a few most commonly tested topics. While we have great respect for these books and the people who write or publish them, all these books have one thing in common: they all want to give their readers a quick shortcut to success. They actually want their readers to believe that just by learning a few strategies and memorizing some key formulas, they'll be able to ace their test. We are not sure if it's the fault of the people who write these books or the people who use them; but someone is definitely trying to fool someone – either those test-prep books for making the readers believe it, or the readers for actually believing it (no pun intended).

With a test as vast as this, it's simply not possible to cover the entire content in just a few pages. We all wish; however, in life, there really aren't any shortcuts to success, and your test is no exception to this rule. Nothing comes easy in life, and that is also precisely the case with your test. You have to do it the hard way by working your way through. Unfortunately, there is no magic potion, which we can give you to succeed in math! Therefore, if you want to do well on your test – be mentally, physically, and psychologically prepared to do some hard work. In this case, efforts and results are directly proportional, that is, greater the efforts you make, better your results are going to be.

While most test-preparation books present materials that stand very little resemblance to the actual tests, EZ's publication series present tests that accurately depict the official tests in both, degree of difficulty and types of questions.

Our EZ books are like no other books you have ever seen or even heard of. We have a completely different concept, and our books are structured using a totally different model. We have *re-defined the way test-prep books should be*.

STRATEGIES SEPARATED FROM CONTENT:
What we have done in our modules is, *separated the actual content-knowledge from the test-taking strategies*. We truly believe that a test-prep program should be more than just a *cheat-sheet of tricks, tips, and traps*. The test you are preparing for is not a simple game that you can master by learning these quick tactics. What you really need to do well on your test is a program that builds true understanding and knowledge of the content.

PERFECT EQUILIBRIUM BETWEEN STRATEGIES AND CONTENT:
In our modules, we've tried our best to present a *truly unique equilibrium* between two competing and challenging skills: test-taking strategies and comprehensive content-knowledge. We have *blended* the two most important ingredients that are essential for your success on your test. We have *enhanced* the old traditional approach to some of the most advanced forms of test-taking strategies. To top all this, we have *refined* our solved examples with detailed explanations to give you hands-on experience to real test-like questions before you take your actual test.

Other Books: Most of the other test-prep books primarily concentrate on teaching their readers how to *guess* and *use the process of elimination,* and they get so obsessed with the tactics that in the process they completely ignore the actual content. Majority of the content of these books consists of pages of guessing techniques.

EZ Books: With our EZ Content-Knowledge Modules, you'll find *100% pure content* that has a highly organized and structured approach to all the content areas, which actually teaches you the content you need to know to do well on your test. Therefore, if you are looking to learn more than just guessing by process of elimination, and if you are serious about developing your skills and confidence level for your exam, then our highly organized and structured test-prep modules is the solution. By studying our books, you'll learn a systematic approach to any question that you may see on your test, and acquire the tools that will help you get there.

EZ Solutions' publications are packed with important information, sophisticated strategies, useful tips, and extensive practice that the experts know will help you do your best on your test.

You should use whichever concept, fact, or tip from that section that you think is appropriate to answer the question correctly in the least possible time. If you've mastered the material in our review modules and strategy modules, you should be able to answer almost all (99.99%) of the questions.

LEARN BACKWARDS AND MOVE FORWARD: Smart students are the ones who make an honest attempt to learn what they read, and also learn from their mistakes, but at the same time, who moves ahead. Therefore, you should learn backwards, that is, learn from your past experiences, and move forward, that is, keep moving ahead without looking back!

ONE CONCEPT, EZ MULTIPLE METHODS:
Our books often give you a *choice of multiple methods* of answering the same question – you can pick the method that seems easiest to you. Our goal is not to *prescribe* any *hard-and-fast* method for taking the test, but instead, to give you the *flexibility and tools you can use to approach your test with confidence and optimism*.

STRATEGIES OR CONTENT?

In order to do well on your test, it is absolutely essential that you have a pretty good grasp of all the concepts laid out in our review modules. Our review modules contain everything you need to know, or must know to crack your test. They cover everything from basic arithmetic to logical reasoning, and everything in between. Nonetheless, that's not enough. You should be able to use these concepts in ways that may not be so familiar or well known to you. This is where our EZ Strategies kick in.

CONTENT VERSUS STRATEGIES:

There is a *succinct* difference between knowing the math content and knowing the math strategies.

Hypothetically speaking, let's assume there is a student named Alex, who learns only the test-taking strategies; and there is another student named Andria, who learns only the math-content. Now when the test time comes, Andria who learns only the math-content is extremely likely to do a lot better than Alex, who learns only the test-taking strategies.

The truth is that someone who has the knowledge of all the math content, but doesn't know anything about the strategies, will almost always do better on the test than someone who knows all the strategies but doesn't know the content properly.

Now let's assume there is another student named Alexandria, who learns both, the test-taking strategies and the math-content. Yes, now we are talking! This student, Alexandria, who knows both the strategies and the content, is guaranteed to do a lot better than Alex, who only knows the strategies, or Andria who only knows the content.

This brings us to our conclusion on this topic: don't just study the strategies, or just the content; you need to know both simultaneously – the strategies and the content, in order to do well on your test. How quickly and accurately you can answer the math questions will depend on your knowledge of the content and the strategies, and that will have an overall effect on your success on the test.

Hence, the equation to succeed on your test is: **Strategies + Content = Success!**

We are confident that if you study our books on test-taking strategies along with our books on content-knowledge, you'll have everything you possibly need to know in order to do well on your test, in fact, to ace your test, and come out with flying colors!

The good thing is that you made the smart decision to buy this book, or if you are reading this online, or in a bookstore, or in a library, you are going to buy one soon!

CONTENT-KNOWLEDGE REVIEW MODULES:

THOROUGH IN-DEPTH REVIEW:

Most other test-prep books briefly touch upon some of the concepts sporadically. On the other hand, our books start from the basics, but unlike other books, they do not end there – *we go deep inside, beyond just touching up the surface* – all the way from fundamental skills to some of the most advanced content that many other prep books choose to ignore. *Each concept is first explained in detail, and then analyzed for most effective understanding* – each and every concept is covered, and we haven't left any stone unturned. Overall, our program is more challenging – you simply get the *best-of-the-best*, and you get more of everything!

COMPREHENSIVE REVIEW:

Our Content-Knowledge Review Modules provide the *most comprehensive and complete review* of all the concepts, which you need to know to excel in your test. Each module is devoted to one of the main subject areas so that you can focus on the most relevant material. The ideal way to review our modules is to go through each topic thoroughly, understand all the solved examples, and work out all of the practice exercises. You must review each topic, understand every solved example, and work out all of the practice exercises. If you don't have enough time, just glimpse through a section. If you feel comfortable with it, move on to something else that may potentially give you more trouble. If you feel uncomfortable with it, review that topic more thoroughly.

Moreover, if you carefully work through our review, you will probably find some topics that you already know, but you may also find some topics that you need to review more closely. You should have a good sense of areas with which you are most comfortable, and in which areas you feel you have a deficiency. Work on any weaknesses you believe you have in those areas. This should help you organize your review more efficiently. Try to give yourself plenty of time and make sure to review the skills and master the concepts that you are required and expected to know to do well on your test. Of course, the more time you invest preparing for your test and more familiar you are with these fundamental principles, the better you will do on your test.

There is a lot of content reviewed in our modules. Although the amount of material presented in our books may appear to be overwhelming, it's the most complete review to get prepared for your test. To some of you, this may seem like a great deal of information to assimilate; however, when you start reviewing, you'll probably realize that you are already comfortable with many concepts discussed in our review modules. We also suggest that you spread your use of our modules over several weeks, and study different modules at your own pace. Even if you are sure you know the basic concepts, our review will help to warm you up so that you can go into your test with crisp and sharp skills. Hence, we strongly suggest that you at least touch up on each concept. However, depending on your strengths and weaknesses, you may be able to move quickly through some areas, and focus more on the others that seem to be troublesome to you. You should develop a plan of attack for your review of the wide range of content. Work on your weaknesses, and be ready to take advantage of your strengths.

Finally, our main objective in the content review modules is to refresh your knowledge of key concepts on the test and we attempt to keep things as concrete and concise as possible.

PRACTICE MODULES:

BASIC WORKBOOK:

Our math practice basic workbook contains a variety of questions on each and every topic that is covered in our review modules. The best way is to first learn all the concepts from our review modules and then apply your skills to test your knowledge on the actual test-like questions in our basic workbook.

ADVANCED WORKBOOK:

Our math practice advanced workbook also contains a variety of questions on each and every topic that is covered in our review modules. Once you become comfortable with the questions in our basic workbook, you should try your hands on our advanced workbook so that you can gain more experience with some of the most difficult questions. For students who are aiming for a very high score, practicing from our advanced workbook is very important. For students who are aiming for a mediocre score, practicing from our advanced workbook is not so important.

▪ABOUT THIS BOOK

In order to excel on your test, it's important that you master each component of your test. That's why we have broken the entire test into different sections and each book focuses only on only one component. It's important to learn the art of tackling the questions you'll see on the test; nevertheless, it's equally important to get a strong hold of the mathematical fundamentals and principles. Apparently it's not enough to only know the test taking strategies, you also need to have a solid knowledge of the math content, and know how to solve the problems mathematically. This book is exclusively dedicated to the **Basic Problems** that apply to the math section of your test.

WHAT'S COVERED IN THIS BOOK:

In this book, you will learn everything related to **Basic problems** content that can be used on different types of questions throughout the math section. Mastering the content of this book will not only improve your performance on the math section, but will also make you a smarter and wiser test-taker. In this book, you'll learn all the strategies and the content related to basic problems, so that you can solve the basic quickly, correctly, and more efficiently. In fact, being able to solve basic problems is one of the most important factors to succeed on the math section.

WHAT'S NOT COVERED IN THIS BOOK:

This book does not cover any content other than Basic Problems – to learn about the content areas, you must refer to the other books in the series.

PRE-REQUISITES FOR THIS BOOK:

The pre-requisite for this book is your thorough familiarity with all the principles and concepts covered in all the review modules in the series. Hence, when you go through this book, you are already expected to know all the content covered in all of the other books in the series.

RELATED MODULES FOR THIS BOOK: You will get the best out of this book if you use it in conjunction with some of the other related books in the series that are listed below.

List of related modules for this book:
- EZ Solutions – Test Prep Series – General – Test Taker's Manual
- EZ Solutions – Test Prep Series – Math Review – Arithmetic
- EZ Solutions – Test Prep Series – Math Review – Algebra
- EZ Solutions – Test Prep Series – Math Review – Applications
- EZ Solutions – Test Prep Series – Math Review – Geometry
- EZ Solutions – Test Prep Series – Math Review – Word Problems
- EZ Solutions – Test Prep Series – Math Review – Logic & Stats
- EZ Solutions – Test Prep Series – Math Practice – Basic Workbook
- EZ Solutions – Test Prep Series – Math Practice – Advanced Workbook
- EZ Solutions – Test Prep Series – Math Strategies – Math Test Taking Strategies

Note: Look at the back of the book for a complete list of EZ books

PART 0.0: INTRODUCTION TO BASIC WORKBOOK:

Our Math Practice Basic Workbook contains a variety of questions on each and every topic that is covered in our review modules.

The best way is to first learn all the concepts from our review modules and then apply your skills to test your knowledge on the actual test-like questions in our basic workbook.

In our Math Practice Basic Workbook, you'll get to practice all the skills that you learned in our review books. All questions are given for each review book, and are arranged in the same order as in our review books.

After you get a firm control on all the concepts given in our math review books, its important that you practice the actual test-like questions given in this book. Each question is explained in detail.

THIS PAGE HAS BEEN INTENTIONALLY LEFT BLANK

PART 1.0: ARITHMETIC:

TOPICS COVERED:

- Integers

- Fractions

- Decimals

- Exponents

- Radicals

EZ REFERENCE: -To review arithmetic concepts, please refer to our EZ Review Arithmetic.
-To practice medium-to-difficult level questions, please refer to our EZ Practice Advanced Workbook.

PRACTICE EXERCISE:

Question #1:   Simplify: $\dfrac{\frac{5}{9} \times 18 \times 0.6}{0.24}$

Question #2:   Simplify: $\dfrac{100 + 2(25 \div 5)}{\frac{1}{5}}$

Question #3:   Simplify: $\dfrac{1 + \frac{2}{9}}{2 + \frac{1}{8}}$

Question #4:   Simplify: $\dfrac{\left[\frac{\frac{9}{5}}{\frac{8}{5}}\right]\left[\frac{\frac{7}{2}}{\frac{9}{2}}\right]}{\left[\frac{\frac{5}{9}}{\frac{5}{8}}\right]\left[\frac{\frac{2}{7}}{\frac{2}{9}}\right]}$

Question #5:   What is the value of $(0.1)^1 + (0.1)^2 + (0.1)^3 + (0.1)^4 + (0.1)^5$?

Question #6:   What is the decimal equivalent of $\left(\dfrac{1}{5}\right)^6$?

Question #7:   Simplify: $\left(\sqrt{6} + \sqrt{6}\right)^2$

Question #8:   Simplify: $8x^{\frac{2}{3}}y^{\frac{5}{3}}$

Question #9:   Simplify: $\sqrt[2]{\sqrt[3]{15625}}$

Question #10:   Simplify: $\sqrt[3]{\sqrt[2]{64}}$

Question #11:   Simplify: $(-125)^{\frac{2}{3}}$

Question #12:   Simplify: $\dfrac{\sqrt{1279}}{\sqrt{0.1279}}$

Question #13:   Simplify: $7^n + 7^n + 7^n + 7^n + 7^n + 7^n + 7^n$

Question #14:   Simplify: $4^{3/2} + 4^{3/2}$

Question #15:   Simplify: $8^{2/3} + 8^{2/3}$

PRACTICE EXERCISE – QUESTIONS & ANSWERS WITH EXPLANATIONS:

Question #1:   Simplify: $\dfrac{\frac{5}{9} \times 18 \times 0.6}{0.24}$

Solution:

$\Rightarrow \dfrac{\frac{5}{9^1} \times \cancel{18}^2 \times 0.6}{0.24}$ [Cancel the common factors in the numerator]

$\Rightarrow \dfrac{5 \times 2 \times 0.\cancel{6}}{0.\cancel{24}^4}$ [Cancel the common factors in the numerator and denominator]

$\Rightarrow \dfrac{10}{0.4}$ [Simplify the numerator and denominator]

$\Rightarrow 25$ [Do the division]

Question #2:   Simplify: $\dfrac{100 + 2(25 \div 5)}{\frac{1}{5}}$

Solution:

$\Rightarrow \dfrac{100 + 2(5)}{\frac{1}{5}}$ [Solve within the parentheses in the numerator]

$\Rightarrow \dfrac{100 + 10}{\frac{1}{5}}$ [Do the multiplication in the numerator]

$\Rightarrow \dfrac{110}{\frac{1}{5}}$ [Do the addition in the numerator]

$\Rightarrow 110 \div \dfrac{1}{5}$ [Divide the numerator by the fraction in the denominator]

$\Rightarrow 110 \times 5$ [Change the division sign to multiplication sign and flip the fraction]

$\Rightarrow 550$ [Do the multiplication]

Question #3:   Simplify: $\dfrac{1 + \frac{2}{9}}{2 + \frac{1}{8}}$

Solution:

$\Rightarrow \dfrac{\frac{9}{9} + \frac{2}{9}}{\frac{16}{8} + \frac{1}{8}}$ [In the numerator & denominator, scale-up the fractions to the LCD]

$\Rightarrow \dfrac{\frac{11}{9}}{\frac{17}{8}}$ [Add the fractions in the numerator and the denominator]

$\Rightarrow \dfrac{11}{9} \div \dfrac{17}{8}$ [Divide the fraction in numerator by the fraction in denominator]

$\Rightarrow \dfrac{11}{9} \times \dfrac{8}{17}$ [Switch the division to multiplication sign and flip the second fraction]

$\Rightarrow \dfrac{88}{153}$ [Multiply the two fractions straight across]

Question #4:   Simplify: $\dfrac{\left[\dfrac{\frac{9}{5}}{\frac{8}{5}}\right]\left[\dfrac{\frac{7}{2}}{\frac{9}{2}}\right]}{\left[\dfrac{\frac{5}{9}}{\frac{5}{8}}\right]\left[\dfrac{\frac{2}{7}}{\frac{2}{9}}\right]}$

Solution:

$\Rightarrow \dfrac{\left(\dfrac{9}{5}\div\dfrac{8}{5}\right)\bullet\left(\dfrac{7}{2}\div\dfrac{9}{2}\right)}{\left(\dfrac{5}{9}\div\dfrac{5}{8}\right)\bullet\left(\dfrac{2}{7}\div\dfrac{2}{9}\right)}$ [Rewrite fractions in numerator and denominator with division signs]

$\Rightarrow \dfrac{\left(\dfrac{9}{\cancel{5}}\times\dfrac{\cancel{5}}{8}\right)\bullet\left(\dfrac{7}{\cancel{2}}\times\dfrac{\cancel{2}}{9}\right)}{\left(\dfrac{\cancel{5}}{9}\times\dfrac{8}{\cancel{5}}\right)\bullet\left(\dfrac{\cancel{2}}{7}\times\dfrac{9}{\cancel{2}}\right)}$ [Switch the division to multiplication sign and flip the second fraction]

$\Rightarrow \dfrac{\left(\dfrac{\cancel{9}}{8}\right)\bullet\left(\dfrac{7}{\cancel{9}}\right)}{\left(\dfrac{8}{\cancel{9}}\right)\bullet\left(\dfrac{\cancel{9}}{7}\right)}$ [Reduce the fractions in the numerator and denominator]

$\Rightarrow \dfrac{\dfrac{7}{8}}{\dfrac{8}{7}}$ [Again, reduce the fractions in the numerator and denominator]

$\Rightarrow \dfrac{7}{8}\div\dfrac{8}{7}$ [Divide the fraction in numerator by the fraction in denominator]

$\Rightarrow \dfrac{7}{8}\times\dfrac{7}{8}$ [Switch the division to multiplication sign and flip the second fraction]

$\Rightarrow \dfrac{49}{64}$ [Multiply the two fractions straight across]

Question #5:   What is the value of $(0.1)^1 + (0.1)^2 + (0.1)^3 + (0.1)^4 + (0.1)^5$?
Solution: $\Rightarrow 0.1 + 0.01 + 0.001 + 0.0001 + 0.00001$ [Solve all the exponents]
              $\Rightarrow 0.11111$ [Add all the numbers]

Question #6:   What is the decimal equivalent of $\left(\dfrac{1}{5}\right)^6$?

Solution: $\Rightarrow (0.2)^6$ [Convert the fraction into a decimal number]
              $\Rightarrow (0.2)\,(0.2)\,(0.2)\,(0.2)\,(0.2)\,(0.2)$ [Expand the exponential term]
              $\Rightarrow 0.000064$ [Do the multiplication]

Question #7:   Simplify: $\left(\sqrt{6}+\sqrt{6}\right)^2$

Solution: $\Rightarrow \left(2\sqrt{6}\right)^2$ [Combine like terms]

              $\Rightarrow (2)^2\left(\sqrt{6}\right)^2$ [Split the term inside the parentheses]

              $\Rightarrow 4\times 6$ [Solve the exponent]
              $\Rightarrow 24$ [Do the multiplication]

Question #8:   Simplify: $8x^{\frac{2}{3}}y^{\frac{5}{3}}$

Solution: $\Rightarrow 8\sqrt[3]{x^2}\sqrt[3]{y^5}$ [Write each exponent in radical terms]

$\Rightarrow 8\sqrt[3]{x^2y^5}$ [Combine the radicals]

Question #9:   Simplify: $\sqrt[2]{\sqrt[3]{15625}}$

Solution: $\Rightarrow \sqrt[2]{25}$ [Solve for the inner radical]

$\Rightarrow 5$ [Solve for the outer radical]

Question #10:   Simplify: $\sqrt[3]{\sqrt[2]{64}}$

Solution: $\Rightarrow \sqrt[3]{8}$ [Solve for the inner radical]

$\Rightarrow 2$ [Solve for the outer radical]

Question #11:   Simplify: $(-125)^{\frac{2}{3}}$

Solution: $\Rightarrow \left(\sqrt[3]{-125}\right)^2$ [Write the exponent in radical terms]

$\Rightarrow (-5)^2$ [Solve the radical]

$\Rightarrow 25$ [Solve the exponent]

Question #12:   Simplify: $\dfrac{\sqrt{1279}}{\sqrt{0.1279}}$

Solution: $\Rightarrow \dfrac{\sqrt{10,000 \times 0.1279}}{\sqrt{0.1279}}$ [Factor the numerator so that one factor is same as denominator]

$\Rightarrow \dfrac{\sqrt{10,000} \times \sqrt{0.1279}}{\sqrt{0.1279}}$ [Separate the numbers in the numerator in radical sign]

$\Rightarrow \sqrt{10,000}$ [Cancel out the common factors]

$\Rightarrow 100$ [Solve the Square root]

Question #13:   Simplify: $7^n + 7^n + 7^n + 7^n + 7^n + 7^n + 7^n$

Solution: $\Rightarrow 7 \times 7^n$ [Factor out the common term]

$\Rightarrow 7^1 \times 7^n$ [Write the terms in exponential terms]

$\Rightarrow 7^{(n+1)}$ [Combine the terms using laws of exponents]

Question #14:   Simplify: $4^{3/2} + 4^{3/2}$

Solution: $\Rightarrow \sqrt{4^3} + \sqrt{4^3}$ [Write each exponent in radical terms]

$\Rightarrow \sqrt{64} + \sqrt{64}$ [Solve the exponents]

$\Rightarrow 8 + 8$ [Solve the radicals]

$\Rightarrow 16$ [Do the addition]

Question #15:   Simplify: $8^{2/3} + 8^{2/3}$

Solution: $\Rightarrow \sqrt[3]{8^2} + \sqrt[3]{8^2}$ [Write each exponent in radical terms]

$\Rightarrow \sqrt[3]{64} + \sqrt[3]{64}$ [Solve the exponents]

$\Rightarrow 4 + 4$ [Solve the radicals]

$\Rightarrow 8$ [Do the addition]

THIS PAGE HAS BEEN INTENTIONALLY LEFT BLANK

PART 2.0: ALGEBRA:

TOPICS COVERED:

- Algebraic Expressions

- Algebraic Factoring

- Linear Equations

- Unsolvable Equations

- Multiple Equations

- Quadratic Equations

- Inequalities

- Functions

EZ REFERENCE: -To review algebra concepts, please refer to our EZ Review Algebra.
-To practice medium-to-difficult level questions, please refer to our EZ Practice Advanced Workbook.

PRACTICE EXERCISE:

ALGEBRAIC EXPRESSIONS:

Question #1:   Simplify: $\{[(n \times n) + n] \div n\} - n$

Question #2:   Simplify: $\sqrt{\dfrac{x^2}{9} + \dfrac{x^2}{16}}$

Question #3:   If $abc \neq 0$, then what is the value of $\dfrac{a^2 bc + ab^2 c + abc^2}{abc}$?

Question #4:   If $y \neq z$, then what is the value of $\dfrac{xy - zx}{z - y}$?

Question #5:   What is the sum of the reciprocals of x^2 and y^2?

Question #6:   Evaluate $\dfrac{1 + x + x^2 - x^3 + x^4 - x^5}{x - 1}$ for $x = -1$.

ALGEBRAIC FACTORING:

Question #7:   Simplify: $\left(1 + \sqrt{6}\right)\left(1 - \sqrt{6}\right)$

Question #8:   Simplify: $\left(\sqrt{8} + 1\right)\left(\sqrt{8} - 1\right)$

Question #9:   Simplify: $\dfrac{2x^2 - 50}{x + 5}$

Question #10:   If $x^2 + 2xy + y^2 = 25$, simplify: $(x + y)^4$

Question #11:   If $x > 25$, simplify: $\dfrac{x - 25}{\sqrt{x} - 5}$

LINEAR EQUATIONS:

Question #12:   If $9(2x^2 + 1) = 8(2x^2 + 15) + 17$, then what is the value of x?

Question #13:   If $\dfrac{2x}{11 + \dfrac{5}{x}} = x$, then what is the value of x?

Question #14:   If $\dfrac{0.11}{0.2 + x} = 0.05$, then what is the value of x?

Question #15:   If $n \times n \times n = n + n + n + n$ such that $n > 0$, then what is the value of n?

Question #16:   If $n \times n \times n = n + n + n$ such that $n > 0$, then what is the value of n?

Question #17: If $\dfrac{x^2 - 81}{(x + 9)} = 7$, then what is the value of x?

Question #18: What positive number n satisfies the equation $(25)\ (25)\ (25)\ n = \dfrac{(125)(125)}{n}$?

Question #19: If $\dfrac{1}{n} + \dfrac{1}{n} + \dfrac{1}{n} = 12$, then what is the value of n?

Question #20: If $\dfrac{1}{n} + \dfrac{1}{n} + \dfrac{1}{n} + \dfrac{1}{n} = 20$, then what is the value of n?

Question #21: If $\left(9^{\frac{5}{7}} \right)^n = 9^{\frac{1}{2}}$, then what is the value of n?

Question #22: For how many integers does the inequality $|x| < \sqrt{5}$ satisfy?

Question #23: If $10^{2x+2} = 1,000,000$, then what is the value of 10^x?

Question #24: If $9x = 5$ and $5y = 9$, then what is the value of $\dfrac{x}{y}$?

Question #25: If $\dfrac{1}{x} = 7\dfrac{1}{2}$, then what is the value of $\dfrac{x}{x + 1}$?

Question #26: If x and y are positive numbers and if $xy = 125$ and $x = 5y$, then what is the value of $x - y$?

UNSOLVABLE EQUATIONS:

Question #27: If $p - q = \dfrac{p^2 - q^2}{q^2 - p^2}$ and $q - p \neq 0$, then what is the value of $q - p$?

Question #28: If $\dfrac{x}{y} = \dfrac{x + 5}{y + 5}$, then what is the value of $(x + y)(x - y)$?

Question #29: If $(7^p)\ (7^q) = \dfrac{7^r}{7^s}$, then what is the value of s in terms of p, q, and r?

Question #30: If x and y are positive integers and if $\sqrt{x^2 - y^2} = 5y - x$, then what is the value of $\dfrac{x}{y}$?

Question #31: If $\dfrac{x}{y} + x = 27$, then what is the value of $\sqrt{\dfrac{x + xy - 2y}{y}}$?

Question #32: If x is positive, and $y = 5x^2 + 2$, then what is the value of x in terms of y?

Question #33: If $\sqrt{x + 2y} - 2 = 9$, then what is the value of y in terms of x?

Question #34: If $\dfrac{a + 2b + c}{2} = \dfrac{6a + 2b}{5}$, then what is the value of c in terms of a and b?

Question #35: If $\dfrac{m+n}{mn} = 1$, then what is the value of n in terms of m?

Question #36: If $y = 5x$ and $z = 2y$, then in terms of x, then what is the value of $x + y + z$?

Question #37: If $y > 0$ and $\sqrt{\dfrac{x}{y}} = y^2$, then what is the value of x in terms of y?

Question #38: If x and y are positive integers and $2(2^x) = 2^y$, then what is the value of x in terms of y?

Question #39: If $z^2 y^5 = xy^{-1}$, what is the value of x in terms of y and z?

Question #40: If $\dfrac{p}{q} = \dfrac{r-p}{s-q}$, then what is the value of s in terms of p, q, and r?

Question #41: If $s = \dfrac{r-q}{p-q}$, then what is the value of q in terms of p, r, and s?

MULTIPLE LINEAR EQUATIONS:

Question #42: If $ab + ac = 112$ and $b + c = 7$, then what is the value of a?

Question #43: If $x + y = 60$, $y + z = 80$, and $x + z = 120$, what is the value of z?

Question #44: If $5x + 5y = 10$ and $x + y + z = 100$, what is the value of z?

Question #45: If $n + n = m + m + m$ and $n + m = 25$, what is the value of $n - m$?

Question #46: If $x^2 - y^2 = 99$ and $x + y = 11$, what is the value of x?

QUADRATIC EQUATIONS:

Question #47: If $\dfrac{x^2 - 7x - 18}{x^2 - 8x - 9} = \dfrac{9}{8}$, what is the value of x?

Question #48: What is the smallest possible value of x for which $(81 - x^2)\left(\dfrac{15}{x} + 2\right) = 0$?

INEQUALITIES:

Question #49: If $x + 7 > 2$ and $x - 1 < 6$, what should be the value of x?

Question #50: What is the solution set to the inequality $|5x - 1| < 8$?

FUNCTIONS:

Question #51: If $f(x) = x^2 - \sqrt{x}$, what is the value of $f(16)$?

Question #52: If $f(x) = x^8 - 8^x$, what is the value of $f(2)$?

Question #53: What is the minimum value of the function $f(x) = x^2 - 8$?

Question #54: If $f(x) = (x + 1)^2$ and $g(x) = \sqrt{x-1}$, then what is the value of $\dfrac{f(9)}{g(5)}$?

Question #55: A function is defined as $f(x) = 2x^5 - 6$. When $f(x) = -70$, what is the value of $2 - 2x$?

Question #56: If $f(x) = x^2 + x - 56$ and $f(y - 1) = 0$, what is the positive value of y?

Question #57: A function is defined as $f(x) = x^2 + 50$. If n is a positive number such that $2f(n) = f(2n)$, what is the value of n?

Question #58: If $f(x) = 2x + 9$ and $g(x) = f(-x)$, then what is $f(x) + g(x)$?

Question #59: If $f(x) = x + 7$, then for what value of n is it true that $f(2n + 1) = f(n + 2)$?

Question #60: If $f(x) = 6x + 8$, and if the domain of x consists of all real numbers defined by the inequality $-6 < x < 2$, then what is the range of $f(x)$?

Question #61: If $f(x) = 5x + 9$, and if the domain of x consists of all real numbers defined by the inequality $-7 < x < 2$, then what is the range of $f(x)$?

Question #62: If $f(x) = \sqrt{x+1}$, and if the domain of the function is the set {3, 8, 15, 24}, then define the set that indicates the range of $f(x)$.

Question #63: If $f(x) = \sqrt{x-1}$, and if the domain of the function is the set {5, 10, 17, 26}, then define the set that indicates the range of $f(x)$.

Question #64: What is the domain of $f(x) = \sqrt{121 - x^2}$?

Question #65: What is the domain of $f(x) = \dfrac{x}{\sqrt{10 - x}}$?

PRACTICE EXERCISE – QUESTIONS & ANSWERS WITH EXPLANATIONS:

ALGEBRAIC EXPRESSIONS:

Question #1:   Simplify:$\{[(n \times n) + n] \div n\} - n$

Solution:
$\Rightarrow \{[(n \times n) + n] \div n\} - n$ [Given]

$\Rightarrow \{[(n^2) + n] \div n\} - n$ [Solve within parentheses]

$\Rightarrow \dfrac{n^2 + n}{n} - n$ [Rewrite the expression within square brackets as a fraction]

$\Rightarrow \dfrac{n(n+1)}{n} - n$ [Factor out the numerator of the fraction]

$\Rightarrow n + 1 - n$ [Cancel-out the common term in the fraction]

$\Rightarrow 1$ [Combine like-terms]

Question #2:   Simplify: $\sqrt{\dfrac{x^2}{9} + \dfrac{x^2}{16}}$

Solution:
$\Rightarrow \sqrt{\dfrac{x^2}{9} + \dfrac{x^2}{16}}$ [Given]

$\Rightarrow \sqrt{\dfrac{(16)x^2}{(16)9} + \dfrac{(9)x^2}{(9)16}}$ [Scale up the fractions to their LCD, which is 16×9]

$\Rightarrow \sqrt{\dfrac{16x^2 + 9x^2}{(9)(16)}}$ [Combine fractions with the same denominator]

$\Rightarrow \sqrt{\dfrac{25x^2}{144}}$ [Combine like-terms]

$\Rightarrow \dfrac{5x}{12}$ [Take the square root]

Question #3:   If $abc \neq 0$, then what is the value of $\dfrac{a^2bc + ab^2c + abc^2}{abc}$?

Solution:
$\Rightarrow \dfrac{a^2bc + ab^2c + abc^2}{abc}$ [Given]

$\Rightarrow \dfrac{a(abc) + b(abc) + c(abc)}{abc}$ [Rewrite the numerator with common terms in the parentheses]

$\Rightarrow \dfrac{(abc)(a + b + c)}{abc}$ [Factor out the common terms in the numerator]

$\Rightarrow a + b + c$ [Cancel-out common terms in the numerator and denominator]

Question #4:   If $y \neq z$, then what is the value of $\dfrac{xy - zx}{z - y}$?

Solution:
$\Rightarrow \dfrac{xy - zx}{z - y}$ [Given]

$\Rightarrow \dfrac{x(y - z)}{z - y}$ [Factor out x in the numerator]

$\Rightarrow \dfrac{x(y - z)}{(-1)(y - z)}$ [Factor out -1 in the denominator]

$\Rightarrow -x$ [Cancel-out common terms in the numerator and denominator]

Question #5: What is the sum of the reciprocals of x^2 and y^2?

Solution: The common denominator of x^2 and y^2 is x^2y^2.

Reciprocal of $x^2 \Rightarrow \dfrac{1}{x^2} \times \dfrac{y^2}{y^2} = \dfrac{y^2}{x^2y^2}$ $\quad$ [Write the reciprocal of x^2 in terms of x^2y^2]

Reciprocal of $y^2 \Rightarrow \dfrac{1}{y^2} \times \dfrac{x^2}{x^2} = \dfrac{x^2}{x^2y^2}$ $\quad$ [Write the reciprocal of y^2 in terms of x^2y^2]

Sum of Reciprocal of x & $y \Rightarrow \dfrac{1}{x^2} + \dfrac{1}{y^2} = \dfrac{y^2}{x^2y^2} + \dfrac{x^2}{x^2y^2} = \dfrac{x^2 + y^2}{x^2y^2}$ $\quad$ [Add and simplify]

Question #6: Evaluate $\dfrac{1 + x + x^2 - x^3 + x^4 - x^5}{x - 1}$ for $x = -1$.

Solution:

$\Rightarrow \dfrac{1 + x + x^2 - x^3 + x^4 - x^5}{x - 1}$ $\quad$ [Given]

$\Rightarrow \dfrac{1 + (-1) + (-1)^2 - (-1)^3 + (-1)^4 - (-1)^5}{(-1) - 1}$ $\quad$ [Substitute $x = -1$]

$\Rightarrow \dfrac{1 + (-1) + (1) - (-1) + (1) - (-1)}{(-1) - 1}$ $\quad$ [Solve all the exponents]

$\Rightarrow \dfrac{1 + (-1) + (1) + (1) + (1) + (1)}{(-1) - 1}$ $\quad$ [Convert all negative signs]

$\Rightarrow \dfrac{5 + (-1)}{(-1) - 1}$ $\quad$ [Group all positives and negatives]

$\Rightarrow \dfrac{4}{-2}$ $\quad$ [Combine terms in the numerator and denominator]

$\Rightarrow -2$ $\quad$ [Do the division]

ALGEBRAIC FACTORING:

Question #7: Simplify: $\left(1 + \sqrt{6}\right)\left(1 - \sqrt{6}\right)$

Solution:

$\Rightarrow \left(1 + \sqrt{6}\right)\left(1 - \sqrt{6}\right)$ $\quad$ [Given]

$\Rightarrow 1^2 - \left(\sqrt{6}\right)^2$ $\quad$ [Factor $(a + b)(a - b) = a^2 - b^2$]

$\Rightarrow 1 - 6 = -5$ $\quad$ [Apply rules of exponents]

Question #8: Simplify: $\left(\sqrt{8} + 1\right)\left(\sqrt{8} - 1\right)$

Solution:

$\Rightarrow \left(\sqrt{8} + 1\right)\left(\sqrt{8} - 1\right)$ $\quad$ [Given]

$\Rightarrow \left(\sqrt{8}\right)^2 - 1^2$ $\quad$ [Factor $(a + b)(a - b) = a^2 - b^2$]

$\Rightarrow 8 - 1 = 7$ $\quad$ [Apply rules of exponents]

Question #9: Simplify: $\dfrac{2x^2 - 50}{x + 5}$

Solution:

$\Rightarrow \dfrac{2x^2 - 50}{x + 5}$ $\quad$ [Given]

$\Rightarrow \dfrac{2(x^2 - 25)}{x + 5}$ $\quad$ [Factor out 2 in the numerator]

$\Rightarrow \dfrac{2(x^2 - 5^2)}{x + 5}$ [Rewrite the numerator in $a^2 - b^2$ form]

$\Rightarrow \dfrac{2(x + 5)(x - 5)}{x + 5}$ [Expand $a^2 - b^2 = (a + b)(a - b)$]

$\Rightarrow 2(x - 5) = 2x - 10$ [Cancel-out the common terms in the numerator and denominator]

Question #10: If $x^2 + 2xy + y^2 = 25$, simplify: $(x + y)^4$

Solution:
$\Rightarrow x^2 + 2xy + y^2 = 25$ [Given]
$\Rightarrow (x + y)^2 = 25$ [Factor the trinomial]
$\Rightarrow (x + y)^4 = 625$ [Square both sides]

Question #11: If $x > 25$, simplify: $\dfrac{x - 25}{\sqrt{x} - 5}$

Solution: $\Rightarrow \dfrac{x - 25}{\sqrt{x} - 5}$ [Given]

$\Rightarrow \dfrac{\left(\sqrt{x}\right)^2 - (5)^2}{\sqrt{x} - 5}$ [Rewrite the numerator in the $a^2 - b^2$ form]

$\Rightarrow \dfrac{\left(\sqrt{x} + 5\right)\left(\sqrt{x} - 5\right)}{\sqrt{x} - 5}$ [Expand $a^2 - b^2 = (a + b)(a - b)$]

$\Rightarrow \sqrt{x} + 5$ [Cancel-out the common terms in the numerator and denominator]

LINEAR EQUATIONS:

Question #12: If $9(2x^2 + 1) = 8(2x^2 + 15) + 17$, then what is the value of x?

Solution:
$\Rightarrow 18x^2 + 9 = 16x^2 + 120 + 17$ [Apply distributive property]
$\Rightarrow 18x^2 + 9 = 16x^2 + 137$ [Combine like-terms]
$\Rightarrow 2x^2 + 9 = 137$ [Subtract $16x^2$ from both sides]
$\Rightarrow 2x^2 = 128$ [Subtract 9 from both sides]
$\Rightarrow x^2 = 64$ [Divide both sides by 2]
$\Rightarrow x = 8$ [Square root both sides]

Question #13: If $\dfrac{10x}{11 + \dfrac{5}{x}} = x$, then what is the value of x?

Solution: $\Rightarrow 10x = x\left(11 + \dfrac{5}{x}\right)$ [Cross multiply]

$\Rightarrow 10x = 11x + 5$ [Apply distributive property]
$\Rightarrow -x = 5$ [Subtract $11x$ from both sides]
$\Rightarrow x = -5$ [Multiply both sides by -1]

Question #14: If $\dfrac{0.11}{0.2 + x} = 0.05$, then what is the value of x?

Solution:
$\Rightarrow (0.2 + x)\, 0.05 = 0.11$ [Cross multiply]
$\Rightarrow 0.01 + 0.05x = 0.11$ [Apply distributive property]
$\Rightarrow 0.05x = 0.1$ [Subtract 0.01 from both sides]
$\Rightarrow x = 0.1 \div 0.05 = 2$ [Divide both sides by 0.05]

Question #15: If $n \times n \times n = n + n + n + n$ such that $n > 0$, then what is the value of n?

Solution:
$\Rightarrow n \times n \times n = n + n + n + n$ [Given]
$\Rightarrow n^3 = 4n$ [Combine terms on both sides]
$\Rightarrow n^2 = 4$ [Divide both sides by n]

$\Rightarrow n = 2$ [Square root both sides]

Question #16: If $n \times n \times n = n + n + n$ such that $n > 0$, then what is the value of n?

Solution:
$\Rightarrow n \times n \times n = n + n + n$ [Given]
$\Rightarrow n^3 = 3n$ [Combine terms on both sides]
$\Rightarrow n^2 = 3$ [Divide both sides by n]
$\Rightarrow n = \sqrt{3}$ [Square root both sides]

Question #17: If $\dfrac{x^2 - 81}{(x+9)} = 7$, then what is the value of x?

Solution:

$\Rightarrow \dfrac{x^2 - 81}{(x+9)} = 7$ [Given]

$\Rightarrow \dfrac{(x-9)(x+9)}{(x+9)} = 7$ [Factor the numerator]

$\Rightarrow x - 9 = 7$ [Cancel-out the common terms in the numerator and denominator]
$\Rightarrow x = 16$ [Add 9 to both sides]

Question #18: What positive number n satisfies the equation $(25)(25)(25)\, n = \dfrac{(125)(125)}{n}$?

Solution:

$\Rightarrow (25)(25)(25)\, n = \dfrac{(125)(125)}{n}$ [Given]

$\Rightarrow (25)(25)(25)\, n^2 = (125)(125)$ [Cross Multiply]

$\Rightarrow n^2 = \dfrac{(125)(125)}{(25)(25)(25)}$ [Divide both sides by $(25)(25)(25)$]

$\Rightarrow n^2 = \dfrac{(25 \times 5)(25 \times 5)}{(25)(25)(25)}$ [Factor 125 into 25×5]

$\Rightarrow n^2 = \dfrac{(25)(25)(5 \times 5)}{(25)(25)(25)}$ [Rearrange the factors in the numerator]

$\Rightarrow n^2 = \dfrac{(25)(25)(25)}{(25)(25)(25)}$ [Rewrite $5 \times 5 = 25$]

$\Rightarrow n^2 = 1$ [Cancel-out common terms]
$\Rightarrow n = 1$ [Square root both sides]

Question #19: If $\dfrac{1}{n} + \dfrac{1}{n} + \dfrac{1}{n} = 12$, then what is the value of n?

Solution:

$\Rightarrow \dfrac{1}{n} + \dfrac{1}{n} + \dfrac{1}{n} = 12$ [Given]

$\Rightarrow \dfrac{3}{n} = 12$ [Combine like-terms]

$\Rightarrow 12n = 3$ [Multiply both sides by n]
$\Rightarrow n = \tfrac{1}{4}$ [Divide both sides by 12]

Question #20: If $\dfrac{1}{n} + \dfrac{1}{n} + \dfrac{1}{n} + \dfrac{1}{n} = 20$, then what is the value of n?

Solution:

$\Rightarrow \dfrac{1}{n} + \dfrac{1}{n} + \dfrac{1}{n} + \dfrac{1}{n} = 20$ [Given]

$\Rightarrow \dfrac{4}{n} = 20$ [Combine like-terms]

$\Rightarrow 20n = 4$ [Multiply both sides by n]

$$\Rightarrow n = \frac{4}{20} = \frac{1}{5} \qquad \text{[Divide both sides by 20]}$$

Question #21: If $\left(9^{\frac{5}{7}}\right)^n = 9^{\frac{1}{2}}$, then what is the value of n?

Solution:
$$\Rightarrow \left(9^{\frac{5}{7}}\right)^n = 9^{\frac{1}{2}} \qquad \text{[Given]}$$

$$\Rightarrow 9^{\frac{5}{7}n} = 9^{\frac{1}{2}} \qquad \text{[Apply distributive property in exponents]}$$

$$\Rightarrow \frac{5}{7}n = \frac{1}{2} \qquad \text{[Since both sides have the same base, equate the powers]}$$

$$\Rightarrow n = \frac{1}{2} \times \frac{7}{5} = \frac{7}{10} \qquad \text{[Multiply both sides by 7/5]}$$

Question #22: For how many integers does the inequality $|x| < \sqrt{5}$ satisfy?

Solution:
$$\Rightarrow |x| < \sqrt{5}$$
$$\Rightarrow -\sqrt{5} < x < \sqrt{5}$$
$$\Rightarrow -2.2 < x < 2.2$$
$$\Rightarrow x = -2, -1, 0, 1, 2$$

Question #23: If $10^{2x+2} = 1,000,000$, then what is the value of 10^x?

Solution:
$$\Rightarrow 10^{2x+2} = 1,000,000 \qquad \text{[Given]}$$
$$\Rightarrow 10^{2x+2} = 10^6 \qquad \text{[Rewrite the right side so that both sides have the same base]}$$
$$\Rightarrow 2x + 2 = 6 \qquad \text{[Since the bases on both sides are the same, equate the exponents]}$$
$$\Rightarrow 2x = 4 \qquad \text{[Subtract 2 from both sides]}$$
$$\Rightarrow x = 2 \qquad \text{[Divide both sides by 2]}$$
Value of $10^x \Rightarrow 10^2 = 100$

Question #24: If $9x = 5$ and $5y = 9$, then what is the value of $\frac{x}{y}$?

Solution:
Solve for x $\Rightarrow 9x = 5 \qquad \text{[Given]}$

$$\Rightarrow x = \frac{5}{9} \qquad \text{[Divide both sides by 9]}$$

Solve for y $\Rightarrow 5y = 9 \qquad \text{[Given]}$

$$\Rightarrow y = \frac{9}{5} \qquad \text{[Divide both sides by 5]}$$

Value of $\frac{x}{y}$ $\Rightarrow \frac{5}{9} \div \frac{9}{5} \qquad \text{[Substitute the value of x and y from above]}$

$$\Rightarrow \frac{5}{9} \times \frac{5}{9} \qquad \text{[Switch to multiplication sign and flip the second fraction]}$$

$$\Rightarrow \frac{25}{81} \qquad \text{[Do the multiplication]}$$

Question #25: If $\frac{1}{x} = 7\frac{1}{2}$, then what is the value of $\frac{x}{x+1}$?

Solution: Solve for x $\Rightarrow \frac{1}{x} = 7\frac{1}{2} \qquad \text{[Given]}$

$$\Rightarrow \frac{1}{x} = \frac{15}{2} \qquad \text{[Convert the mixed number into improper fraction]}$$

$$\Rightarrow x = \frac{2}{15} \qquad \text{[Invert both sides]}$$

Value of $\dfrac{x}{x+1}$ $\qquad \Rightarrow \dfrac{\dfrac{2}{15}}{\dfrac{2}{15}+1}$ [Substitute the value of x from above]

$$\Rightarrow \frac{\dfrac{2}{15}}{\dfrac{2}{15}+\dfrac{15}{15}} \qquad \text{[Scale up the fractions in the denominator to their LCD]}$$

$$\Rightarrow \frac{\dfrac{2}{15}}{\dfrac{17}{15}} \qquad \text{[Combine like-fractions in the denominator]}$$

$$\Rightarrow \frac{2}{15} \div \frac{17}{15} \qquad \text{[Divide the numerator by the denominator]}$$

$$\Rightarrow \frac{2}{15} \times \frac{15}{17} \qquad \text{[Switch to multiplication sign and flip the second fraction]}$$

$$\Rightarrow \frac{2}{17} \qquad \text{[Cancel-out the common terms]}$$

Question #26: If x and y are positive numbers and if $xy = 125$ and $x = 5y$, then what is the value of $x - y$?

Solution:
$\Rightarrow xy = 125$ [Given]
$\Rightarrow (5y)y = 125$ [Substitute $x = 5y$]
$\Rightarrow 5y^2 = 125$ [Apply distributive property]
$\Rightarrow y^2 = 25$ [Divide booth sides by 5]
$\Rightarrow y = 5$ [Square root both sides]
$\Rightarrow xy = 125$ [Given]
$\Rightarrow x = 125/y$ [Divide both sides by y]
$\Rightarrow x = 125/5$ [Substitute $y = 5$]
$\Rightarrow x = 25$ [Simplify right hand side]
Value of $x - y \Rightarrow 25 - 5 = 20$ [Substitute $x = 25$ and $y = 5$]

UNSOLVABLE EQUATIONS:

Question #27: If $p - q = \dfrac{p^2 - q^2}{q^2 - p^2}$ and $q - p \neq 0$, then what is the value of $q - p$?

Solution:
$$\Rightarrow p - q = \frac{p^2 - q^2}{q^2 - p^2} \qquad \text{[Given]}$$

$$\Rightarrow p - q = \frac{(p-q)(p+q)}{(q-p)(q+p)} \qquad \text{[Expand } a^2 - b^2 = (a+b)(a-b)]$$

$$\Rightarrow p - q = \frac{(p-q)}{(q-p)} \qquad \text{[Cancel-out the common terms in the numerator and denominator]}$$

$$\Rightarrow p - q = \frac{(p-q)}{-(p-q)} \qquad \text{[Take out the negative sign out of the denominator]}$$

$\Rightarrow p - q = -1$ [Cancel-out the common terms in the numerator and denominator]
$\Rightarrow (-1)(p-q) = (-1)(-1)$ [Multiply both sides by -1]
$\Rightarrow (q - p) = +1$ [Apply distributive property]

Question #28: If $\dfrac{x}{y} = \dfrac{x+5}{y+5}$, then what is the value of $(x+y)(x-y)$?

Solution: $\Rightarrow \dfrac{x}{y} = \dfrac{x+5}{y+5}$ [Given]

$\Rightarrow x(y + 5) = y(x + 5)$ [Cross Multiply]
$\Rightarrow xy + 5x = xy + 5y$ [Apply distributive property]
$\Rightarrow 5x = 5y$ [Subtract xy from both sides]
$\Rightarrow x = y$ [Divide both sides by 5]
Value of $(x + y)(x - y) \Rightarrow (x + x)(x - x) = (2x)(0) = 0$ [Substitute $y = x$]

Question #29:   If $(7^p)(7^q) = \dfrac{7^r}{7^s}$, then what is the value of s in terms of p, q, and r?

Solution: $\Rightarrow (7^p)(7^q) = \dfrac{7^r}{7^s}$ [Given]

$\Rightarrow 7^{p+q} = 7^{r-s}$ [Rewrite the terms on both sides so that they have the same base]
$\Rightarrow p + q = r - s$ [Since the bases on both sides are the same, equate the exponents]
$\Rightarrow -s = p + q - r$ [Subtract r from both sides]
$\Rightarrow s = r - p - q$ [Multiply both side by –1]

Question #30:   If x and y are positive integers and if $\sqrt{x^2 - y^2} = 5y - x$, then what is the value of $\dfrac{x}{y}$?

Solution: $\Rightarrow \sqrt{x^2 - y^2} = 5y - x$ [Given]

$\Rightarrow \left(\sqrt{x^2 - y^2}\right)^2 = (5y - x)^2$ [Square both sides]

$\Rightarrow x^2 - y^2 = (5y - x)^2$ [Take the square of left hand side]
$\Rightarrow x^2 - y^2 = 25y^2 + x^2 - 10xy$ [Expand right side $(a - b)^2 = a^2 + b^2 - 2ab$]
$\Rightarrow -y^2 = 25y^2 - 10xy$ [Subtract x^2 from both sides]
$\Rightarrow -26y^2 = -10xy$ [Subtract $25y^2$ from both sides]
$\Rightarrow 26y^2 = 10xy$ [Multiply both sides by –1]
$\Rightarrow 26y = 10x$ [Divide both sides by y]
$\Rightarrow \dfrac{x}{y} = \dfrac{26}{10} = \dfrac{13}{5}$ [Divide both sides by 10y]

Question #31:   If $\dfrac{x}{y} + x = 27$, then what is the value of $\sqrt{\dfrac{x + xy - 2y}{y}}$?

Solution: $\Rightarrow \sqrt{\dfrac{x + xy - 2y}{y}}$ [Given]

$\Rightarrow \sqrt{\dfrac{x}{y} + \dfrac{xy}{y} + \dfrac{-2y}{y}}$ [Split the fractions under the radical sign]

$\Rightarrow \sqrt{\dfrac{x}{y} + x - 2}$ [Simplify each fraction]

$\Rightarrow \sqrt{27 - 2}$ [Substitute $\dfrac{x}{y} + x = 27$]

$\Rightarrow \sqrt{25}$ [Simplify within the radical sign]
$\Rightarrow 5$ [Take the square root]

Question #32:   If x is positive, and $y = 5x^2 + 2$, then what is the value of x in terms of y?
Solution: $\Rightarrow y = 5x^2 + 2$ [Given]
$\Rightarrow 5x^2 = y - 2$ [Subtract 2 from both sides]
$\Rightarrow x^2 = \dfrac{y - 2}{5}$ [Divide both sides by 5]

$$\Rightarrow x = \sqrt{\frac{y-2}{5}}$$ [Take square root of both sides]

Question #33:   If $\sqrt{x+2y} - 2 = 9$, then what is the value of y in terms of x?

Solution:

$\Rightarrow \sqrt{x+2y} - 2 = 9$	[Given]
$\Rightarrow \sqrt{x+2y} = 11$	[Add 2 to both sides]
$\Rightarrow \left(\sqrt{x+2y}\right)^2 = (11)^2$	[Square both sides]
$\Rightarrow x + 2y = 121$	[Take the square of both sides]
$\Rightarrow 2y = 121 - x$	[Subtract x from both sides]
$\Rightarrow y = \dfrac{121-x}{2}$	[Divide both sides by 2]

Question #34:   If $\dfrac{a+2b+c}{2} = \dfrac{6a+2b}{5}$, then what is the value of c in terms of a and b?

Solution:

$\Rightarrow \dfrac{a+2b+c}{2} = \dfrac{6a+2b}{5}$	[Given]
$\Rightarrow 5(a + 2b + c) = 2(6a + 2b)$	[Cross multiply]
$\Rightarrow 5a + 10b + 5c = 12a + 4b$	[Apply distributive property]
$\Rightarrow 5c = 7a - 6b$	[Subtract $5a + 10b$ from both sides]
$\Rightarrow c = \dfrac{7a-6b}{5}$	[Divide both sides by 5]

Question #35:   If $\dfrac{m+n}{mn} = 1$, then what is the value of n in terms of m?

Solution:

$\Rightarrow \dfrac{m+n}{mn} = 1$	[Given]
$\Rightarrow m + n = mn$	[Cross multiply]
$\Rightarrow m = mn - n$	[Subtract n from both sides]
$\Rightarrow m = n(m - 1)$	[Factor out n on the right side]
$\Rightarrow n = \dfrac{m}{m-1}$	[Divide both sides by $(m - 1)$]

Question #36:   If $y = 5x$ and $z = 2y$, then in terms of x, what is the value of $x + y + z$?
Solution: Find the value of all three variables in terms of x:

$\Rightarrow x = x$	[]
$\Rightarrow y = 5x$	[]
$\Rightarrow z = 2y = 2(5x) = 10x$	[]
$\Rightarrow x + y + z = x + 5x + 10x = 16x$	[Substitute the values from above]

Question #37:   If $y > 0$ and $\sqrt{\dfrac{x}{y}} = y^2$, then what is the value of x in terms of y?

Solution:

$\Rightarrow \sqrt{\dfrac{x}{y}} = y^2$	[Given]
$\Rightarrow \dfrac{x}{y} = y^4$	[Square both sides]
$\Rightarrow x = y^5$	[Multiply both sides by y]

Question #38:   If x and y are positive integers and $2(2^x) = 2^y$, then what is the value of x in terms of y?
Solution:

$\Rightarrow 2(2^x) = 2^y$	[Given]
$\Rightarrow (2^1)(2^x) = 2^y$	[Rewrite all terms as exponential terms]

$$\Rightarrow (2)^{1+x} = 2^y \qquad \text{[Combine exponents using laws of exponents]}$$
$$\Rightarrow 1 + x = y \qquad \text{[Since the bases on both sides are the same, equate the exponents]}$$
$$\Rightarrow x = y - 1 \qquad \text{[Subtract 1 from both sides]}$$

Question #39: If $z^2y^5 = xy^{-1}$, what is the value of x in terms of y and z?

Solution:

$$\Rightarrow z^2y^5 = xy^{-1} \qquad \text{[Given]}$$

$$\Rightarrow \frac{x}{y} = z^2y^5 \qquad \text{[Rewrite the terms with positive exponents]}$$

$$\Rightarrow x = z^2y^6 \qquad \text{[Multiply both sides by } y\text{]}$$

Question #40: If $\dfrac{p}{q} = \dfrac{r-p}{s-q}$, then what is the value of s in terms of p, q, and r?

Solution:

$$\Rightarrow \frac{p}{q} = \frac{r-p}{s-q} \qquad \text{[Given]}$$

$$\Rightarrow p(s-q) = q(r-p) \qquad \text{[Cross multiple both fractions]}$$
$$\Rightarrow ps - pq = qr - pq \qquad \text{[Apply distributive property]}$$
$$\Rightarrow ps = qr \qquad \text{[Add } pq \text{ to both sides]}$$

$$\Rightarrow s = \frac{qr}{p} \qquad \text{[Divide both sides by } p\text{]}$$

Question #41: If $s = \dfrac{r-q}{p-q}$, then what is the value of q in terms of p, r, and s?

Solution:

$$\Rightarrow \frac{s}{1} = \frac{r-q}{p-q} \qquad \text{[Given]}$$

$$\Rightarrow s(p-q) = r - q \qquad \text{[Cross multiply]}$$
$$\Rightarrow ps - qs = r - q \qquad \text{[Apply distributive property]}$$
$$\Rightarrow ps - qs - r = -q \qquad \text{[Subtract } r \text{ from both sides]}$$
$$\Rightarrow ps - r = qs - q \qquad \text{[Add } qs \text{ to both sides]}$$
$$\Rightarrow ps - r = q(s - 1) \qquad \text{[Factor out } q \text{ on the right side]}$$

$$\Rightarrow q = \frac{ps - r}{s - 1} \qquad \text{[Divide both sides by } (s-1)\text{]}$$

MULTIPLE LINEAR EQUATIONS:

Question #42: If $ab + ac = 112$ and $b + c = 7$, then what is the value of a?

Solution:
$$\Rightarrow ab + ac = 112 \qquad \text{[Given]}$$
$$\Rightarrow a(b + c) = 112 \qquad \text{[Factor out } a \text{ from the left side]}$$
$$\Rightarrow a(7) = 112 \qquad \text{[Substitute } b + c = 7\text{]}$$
$$\Rightarrow a = 16 \qquad \text{[Divide both sides by 7]}$$

Question #43: If $x + y = 60$, $y + z = 80$, and $x + z = 120$, what is the value of z?

Solution: Add all three given equations:

$$
\begin{array}{lllll}
& x & + & y & = 60 \qquad \Rightarrow \text{Equation \#1} \\
+ & y & + & z & = 80 \qquad \Rightarrow \text{Equation \#2} \\
+ & x & + & z & = 120 \qquad \Rightarrow \text{Equation \#3} \\
\hline
\end{array}
$$

$$\Rightarrow x + y + y + z + x + z = 60 + 80 + 120 = 260$$
$$\Rightarrow 2x + 2y + 2z = 260 \qquad \text{[Combine like-terms]}$$
$$\Rightarrow 2(x + y + z) = 260 \qquad \text{[Factor out 2 on the left side]}$$
$$\Rightarrow x + y + z = 130 \qquad \text{[Divide both sides by 2]} \qquad \Rightarrow \text{Equation \#4}$$

Substitute the value of $x + y$ from Equation #1 into Equation #4:
$$\Rightarrow x + y + z = 130 \qquad \text{[Equation \#4]}$$
$$\Rightarrow 60 + z = 130 \qquad \text{[Substitute } x + y = 60\text{]}$$
$$\Rightarrow z = 130 - 60 = 70 \qquad \text{[Subtract 60 from both sides]}$$

Question #44: If $5x + 5y = 10$ and $x + y + z = 100$, what is the value of z?

Solution:

Simplify the first equation	$\Rightarrow 5x + 5y = 10$	[Given]
	$\Rightarrow 5(x + y) = 10$	[Factor out 5 on the left side]
	$\Rightarrow x + y = 2$	[Divide both sides by 5]
Solve the second equation	$\Rightarrow x + y + z = 100$	[Given]
	$\Rightarrow 2 + z = 100$	[Substitute $x + y = 2$]
	$\Rightarrow z = 98$	[Subtract 2 from both sides]

Question #45: If $n + n = m + m + m$ and $n + m = 25$, what is the value of $n - m$?

Solution: Solve for the first equation for n in terms of m:

$\Rightarrow n + n = m + m + m$ $\Rightarrow$ Equation #1

$\Rightarrow 2n = 3m$ [Combine like-terms]

$\Rightarrow n = \dfrac{3}{2}m$ [Divide both sides by 2]

Substitute the value of n in the second equation to solve for the numerical value of m:

$\Rightarrow n + m = 25$ $\Rightarrow$ Equation #2

$\Rightarrow \dfrac{3}{2}m + m = 25$ [Substitute $n = 3/2m$]

$\Rightarrow \dfrac{5}{2}m = 25$ [Combine like-terms]

$\Rightarrow m = 10$ [Multiply both sides by 2/5]

Substitute the value of m in the second equation to solve for the numerical value of n:

$\Rightarrow n + m = 25$ $\Rightarrow$ Equation #2

$\Rightarrow n + 10 = 25$ [Substitute $m = 10$]

$\Rightarrow n = 25 - 10 = 15$ [Subtract 10 from both sides]

Finally, Substitute the value of n and m to solve for $n - m$:

$\Rightarrow n - m = 15 - 10 = 5$

Question #46: If $x^2 - y^2 = 99$ and $x + y = 11$, what is the value of x?

Solution:

$\Rightarrow x + y = 11$ $\Rightarrow$ Equation #1

$\Rightarrow x^2 - y^2 = 99$ $\Rightarrow$ Equation #2

$\Rightarrow (x + y)(x - y) = 99$ [Factor the left side]

$\Rightarrow (11)(x - y) = 99$ [Substitute $x + y = 11$ from Equation #1]

$\Rightarrow x - y = 9$ [Divide both sides by 11] $\Rightarrow$ Equation #3

Add Equation #1 and Equation #3:

$x + y$	$= 11$	$\Rightarrow$ Equation #1
$+\quad x - y$	$= 9$	$\Rightarrow$ Equation #3
$\Rightarrow 2x$	$= 20$	[Add the two equations]
$\Rightarrow x$	$= 10$	[Divide both sides by 2]

QUADRATIC EQUATIONS:

Question #47: If $\dfrac{x^2 - 7x - 18}{x^2 - 8x - 9} = \dfrac{9}{8}$, what is the value of x?

Solution:

$\Rightarrow \dfrac{x^2 - 7x - 18}{x^2 - 8x - 9} = \dfrac{9}{8}$ [Given]

$\Rightarrow \dfrac{(x - 9)(x + 2)}{(x - 9)(x + 1)} = \dfrac{9}{8}$ [Factor the trinomials on the left side into binomials]

$\Rightarrow \dfrac{(x + 2)}{(x + 1)} = \dfrac{9}{8}$ [Cancel-out the common terms on the left side]

$\Rightarrow 8(x + 2) = 9(x + 1)$ [Cross multiply]

$\Rightarrow 8x + 16 = 9x + 9$ [Apply distributive property]

$\Rightarrow x + 9 = 16$ [Subtract 8x from both sides]
$\Rightarrow x = 7$ [Subtract 9 from both sides]

Question #48: What is the smallest possible value of x for which $(81 - x^2)\left(\dfrac{15}{x} + 2\right) = 0$?

Solution: We are asked to find the smallest possible value of x that will satisfy the given equation.

Solve the first factor $\Rightarrow (81 - x^2) = 0$ [Equate the first factor to zero and solve for x]
$\Rightarrow x^2 = 81$ [Subtract 81 from both sides]
$\Rightarrow x = +9$ or -9 [Square root both sides]

Solve the second factor $\Rightarrow \left(\dfrac{15}{x} + 2\right) = 0$ [Equate the second factor to zero and solve for x]

$\Rightarrow \dfrac{15}{x} = -2$ [Subtract 2 from both sides]

$\Rightarrow -2x = 15$ [Cross multiply]
$\Rightarrow x = -7.5$ [Divide both sides by –2]

The possible values of x are +9 or –9 or –7.5; and the smallest value of x is –9.

INEQUALITIES:

Question #49: If $x + 7 > 2$ and $x - 1 < 6$, what should be the value of x?
Solution: Solve for both inequalities:
$\Rightarrow x + 7 > 2$ and $\Rightarrow x - 1 < 6$
$\Rightarrow x > -5$ $\Rightarrow x < 7$
Value of x must be $-5 < x < 7$.

Question #50: What is the solution set to the inequality $|5x - 1| < 8$?
Solution: $\Rightarrow |5x - 1| < 8$ [Given]
$\Rightarrow -8 < 5x - 1 < 8$ [Write the absolute value inequality in general inequality form]
$\Rightarrow -7 < 5x < 9$ [Add 1 to all parts of the inequality]
$\Rightarrow -\dfrac{7}{5} < x < \dfrac{9}{5}$ [Divide all part of the inequality by 5]

FUNCTIONS:

Question #51: If $f(x) = x^2 - \sqrt{x}$, what is the value of $f(16)$?
Solution: $f(x)$ $\Rightarrow x^2 - \sqrt{x}$ [Given function]
$f(16)$ $\Rightarrow 16^2 - \sqrt{16} = 256 - 4 = 252$ [Find the value of the function when $x = 16$]

Question #52: If $f(x) = x^8 - 8^x$, what is the value of $f(2)$?
Solution: $f(x)$ $\Rightarrow x^8 - 8^x$ [Given function]
$f(2)$ $\Rightarrow 2^8 - 8^2 = 256 - 64 = 192$ [Find the value of the function when $x = 2$]

Question #53: What is the minimum value of the function $f(x) = x^2 - 8$?
Solution: If you use some common sense, you can figure out that the function will be at a minimum when x^2 is as small as possible. As x^2 gets larger, the farther x will be from 0, x^2 is as small as possible when $x = 0$. Therefore, the smallest value of the function occurs when $x = 0$. So plug in $x = 0$ in the given function to get the minimum value of the function.
$f(1)$ $\Rightarrow 1^2 - 8 = 1 - 8 = -7$ $\Rightarrow$ this is not the smallest value of the function
$f(-1)$ $\Rightarrow -1^2 - 8 = 1 - 8 = -7$ $\Rightarrow$ this is also not the smallest value of the function
$f(0)$ $\Rightarrow 0 - 8 = -8$ $\Rightarrow$ this is the smallest value of the function

Question #54: If $f(x) = (x + 1)^2$ and $g(x) = \sqrt{x - 1}$, then what is the value of $\dfrac{f(9)}{g(5)}$?

Solution:

$f(x)$	$\Rightarrow (x + 1)^2$	[Given function]
$f(9)$	$\Rightarrow (9 + 1)^2 = 10^2 = 100$	[Find the value of the function when $x = 9$]
$g(x)$	$\Rightarrow \sqrt{x - 1}$	[Given function]
$g(5)$	$\Rightarrow \sqrt{5 - 1} = \sqrt{4} = 2$	[Find the value of the function when $x = 5$]
$\dfrac{f(9)}{g(5)}$	$\Rightarrow \dfrac{100}{2} = 50$	[Find the quotient of the two functions]

Question #55: A function is defined as $f(x) = 2x^5 - 6$. When $f(x) = -70$, what is the value of $2 - 2x$?

Solution:

$f(x) = 2x^5 - 6$	[Given function]
$f(x) = -70$	[Value of the given function]
$\Rightarrow 2x^5 - 6 = -70$	[Equate the given function with the given value]
$\Rightarrow 2x^5 = -64$	[Add 6 to both sides]
$\Rightarrow x^5 = -32$	[Divide both sides by 2]
$\Rightarrow x^5 = (-2)^5$	[Write both sides with the same exponent]
$\Rightarrow x = -2$	[Take the 5th root of both sides]

Value of $2 - 2x \Rightarrow 2 - 2(-2) = 2 + 4 = 6$

Question #56: If $f(x) = x^2 + x - 56$ and $f(y - 1) = 0$, what is the positive value of y?

Solution:

$f(x) = x^2 + x - 56$	[Given function]
$f(y - 1) = 0$	[Given function]
$\Rightarrow (y - 1)^2 + (y - 1) - 56 = 0$	[Equate the given function with the given value]
$\Rightarrow y^2 + 1 - 2y + y - 1 - 56 = 0$	[Apply distributive property]
$\Rightarrow y^2 - y - 56 = 0$	[Combine like-terms]
$\Rightarrow (y + 7)(y - 8)$	[Factor the trinomial into two binomials]
$\Rightarrow y = -7$ or $+8$	[Solve for the two values of x]

Positive value of $y \Rightarrow 8$

Question #57: A function is defined as $f(x) = x^2 + 50$. If n is a positive number such that $2f(n) = f(2n)$, what is the value of n?

Solution:

$f(x) \Rightarrow x^2 + 50$	[Given function]
$2f(n) \Rightarrow 2[(n)^2 + 50] = 2n^2 + 100$	[Find two times the value of the function]
$f(2n) \Rightarrow (2n)^2 + 50 = 4n^2 + 50$	[Find the value of the function when $x = 2n$]
EZ Problem Set-Up $\Rightarrow 2f(n) = f(2n)$	
$\Rightarrow 2n^2 + 100 = 4n^2 + 50$	[Set up the equation]
$\Rightarrow 100 = 2n^2 + 50$	[Subtract $2n^2$ from both sides]
$\Rightarrow 2n^2 = 50$	[Subtract 50 from both sides]
$\Rightarrow n^2 = 25$	[Divide both sides by 2]
$\Rightarrow n = 5$	[Square root both sides]

Question #58: If $f(x) = 2x + 9$ and $g(x) = f(-x)$, then what is $f(x) + g(x)$?

Solution:

$f(x)$	$\Rightarrow 2x + 9$	[Given function]
$g(x)$	$\Rightarrow f(-x)$	[Given function]
	$\Rightarrow 2(-x) + 9 = -2x + 9$	[Replace x with $-x$]
$f(x) + g(x)$	$\Rightarrow (2x + 9) + (-2x + 9) = 18$	[Add the two functions]

Question #59: If $f(x) = x + 7$, then for what value of n is it true that $f(2n + 1) = f(n + 2)$?

Solution:

$f(x)$	$\Rightarrow x + 7$	[Given function]
$f(2n + 1)$	$\Rightarrow (2n + 1) + 7 = 2n + 8$	[Find the value of the function when $x = 2n + 1$]
$f(n + 2)$	$\Rightarrow (n + 2) + 7 = n + 9$	[Find the value of the function when $x = n + 2$]
EZ Problem Set-Up $\Rightarrow f(2n + 1) = f(n + 2)$		
	$\Rightarrow 2n + 8 = n + 9$	[Set up the equation]
	$\Rightarrow n + 8 = 9$	[Subtract n from both sides]
	$\Rightarrow n = 1$	[Subtract 8 from both sides]

Question #60: If $f(x) = 6x + 8$, and if the domain of x consists of all real numbers defined by the inequality $-6 < x < 2$, then what is the range of $f(x)$?

Solution: To determine the function's range, apply the rule $f(x) = 6x + 8$ to -6 and to 2. The range will consist of all real numbers between the two results:

$f(-6)$ $\Rightarrow 6x + 8 = 6(-6) + 8 = -36 + 8 = -28$ [Find the value of the function when $x = -6$]

$f(2)$ $\Rightarrow 6x + 8 = 6(2) + 8 = 12 + 8 = 20$ [Find the value of the function when $x = 2$]

The set that indicates the range of $f(x) \Rightarrow \{r \mid -28 < r < 20\}$

Question #61: If $f(x) = 5x + 9$, and if the domain of x consists of all real numbers defined by the inequality $-7 < x < 2$, then what is the range of $f(x)$?

Solution: To determine the function's range, apply the rule $f(x) = 5x + 9$ to -7 and to 2. The range will consist of all real numbers between the two results:

$f(-7)$ $\Rightarrow 5x + 9 = 5(-7) + 9 = -35 + 9 = -26$ [Find the value of the function when $x = -7$]

$f(2)$ $\Rightarrow 5x + 9 = 5(2) + 9 = 10 + 9 = 19$ [Find the value of the function when $x = 2$]

The set that indicates the range of $f(x) \Rightarrow \{r \mid -26 < r < 19\}$

Question #62: If $f(x) = \sqrt{x+1}$, and if the domain of the function is the set $\{3, 8, 15, 24\}$, then define the set that indicates the range of $f(x)$.

Solution: To determine the range of the function, apply the rule $f(x) = \sqrt{x+1}$ to all the domain values of the function:

$f(3)$ $\Rightarrow \sqrt{x+1} = \sqrt{3+1} = \sqrt{4} = 2$ [Find the value of the function when $x = 3$]

$f(8)$ $\Rightarrow \sqrt{x+1} = \sqrt{8+1} = \sqrt{9} = 3$ [Find the value of the function when $x = 8$]

$f(15)$ $\Rightarrow \sqrt{x+1} = \sqrt{15+1} = \sqrt{16} = 4$ [Find the value of the function when $x = 15$]

$f(24)$ $\Rightarrow \sqrt{x+1} = \sqrt{24+1} = \sqrt{25} = 5$ [Find the value of the function when $x = 24$]

The set that indicates the range of $f(x) \Rightarrow \{2, 3, 4, 5\}$

Question #63: If $f(x) = \sqrt{x-1}$, and if the domain of the function is the set $\{5, 10, 17, 26\}$, then define the set that indicates the range of $f(x)$.

Solution: To determine the range of the function, apply the rule $f(x) = \sqrt{x+1}$ to all the domain values of the function:

$f(5)$ $\Rightarrow \sqrt{x-1} = \sqrt{5-1} = \sqrt{4} = 2$ [Find the value of the function when $x = 5$]

$f(10)$ $\Rightarrow \sqrt{x-1} = \sqrt{10-1} = \sqrt{9} = 3$ [Find the value of the function when $x = 10$]

$f(17)$ $\Rightarrow \sqrt{x-1} = \sqrt{17-1} = \sqrt{16} = 4$ [Find the value of the function when $x = 17$]

$f(26)$ $\Rightarrow \sqrt{x-1} = \sqrt{26-1} = \sqrt{25} = 5$ [Find the value of the function when $x = 26$]

The set that indicates the range of $f(x) \Rightarrow \{2, 3, 4, 5\}$

Question #64: What is the domain of $f(x) = \sqrt{121 - x^2}$?

Solution:

$\Rightarrow \sqrt{121 - x^2} \geq 0$ [To find the domain of the function, solve the given quadratic]

$\Rightarrow 121 - x^2 \geq 0$ [Square both sides]

$\Rightarrow x^2 - 121 \leq 0$ [Multiple both sides by -1 and flip the inequality sign]

$\Rightarrow (x - 11)(x + 11) \leq 0$ [Factor the binomial on the left side]

$\Rightarrow x - 11 \leq 0$ and $x + 11 \leq 0$ [Take each factor separately]

$\Rightarrow x \leq 11$ and $x \leq -11$ [Solve each factor for the value of x]

$\Rightarrow -11 \leq x \leq 11$ [Combine both values of x]

Question #65: What is the domain of $f(x) = \dfrac{x}{\sqrt{10 - x}}$?

Solution: All real numbers are in the domain of $f(x)$, except x values that give 0 in the denominator or negative values in the radical, both of which will make the function undefined.

The value inside the radical sign must be positive $\Rightarrow 10 - x > 0$

$\Rightarrow -x > -10$

$\Rightarrow x < 10$

PART 3.0: APPLICATIONS:

TOPICS COVERED:

- Percent Calculations

- Percent Changes

- Percent Discounts

- Percent Mark-Ups/Mark-Downs

- Percent Interests

- Percent Taxes & Commissions

- Ratios

- Proportions

EZ REFERENCE: -To review applications concepts, please refer to our EZ Review Applications.
-To practice medium-to-difficult level questions, please refer to our EZ Practice Advanced Workbook.

PRACTICE EXERCISE:

PERCENT CALCULATION:

Question #1: If $x > 0$, then $\dfrac{x}{20}$ is what percent of x?

Question #2: If $x > 0$, then $\dfrac{x}{15}$ is what percent of $\dfrac{x}{90}$?

Question #3: A man was planning to deposit a certain amount of money each month into a college fund for his children. He then decided not to make any contributions during June and July. To make the same annual contribution that he had originally planned, by what amount should he increase his monthly deposits?

Question #4: A certain flower shop sells only five types of bouquets, priced at $10, $12, $14, $15, and $17. On a certain day, the shop sells exactly the same number of each type of bouquets. What percent of the total sales proceeds came from the sale of the most expensive type of bouquet?

Question #5: In a certain company, 80 percent of its employees are under the age of 55 years, and the remaining employees are over the age of 55 years. If the total number of employees in the company is 925, what is the difference between the number of employees who are under the age of 55 years and the number of employees who are over the age of 55 year?

Question #6: In a certain toolbox that consists of only screws and nuts, there are twice as many screws as nuts. If 20 percent of the screws and 60 percent of the nuts are defective, what percent of the hardware in the box is not defective?

Question #7: In Town X, 12 percent of the population are minors, while in Town Y, 15 percent of the population are minors. If the population of Town Y is 20 percent more than the population of Town X, then the number of minors in Town Y is what percent of the number of minors in Town X?

Question #8: One class in a school is 20 percent boys. A second class, that is half the size of the first class, is 10 percent boys. What percent of both classes are boys?

Question #9: If 50 percent of the candidates are eliminated after each round of interview, what percent of the original number of candidates will be eliminated after four rounds?

Question #10: If 60 percent of the population of a certain town is employed, and 20 percent of those who are employed work for the local oil refinery, what percent of the population in the town do not work for the refinery?

Question #11: In a certain one-day art exhibition, an artist brings 240 paintings to sell. If he sell 25 percent of his paintings during the first hour and 60 percent of the remaining paintings during the second hour, how many of the paintings will not have been sold by the end of the second hour?

Question #12: In a certain math examination of 7,600 students, only 15 percent of the students were able to pass the basic level and move into the advanced level. Of these 15 percent, only 10 percent were able to pass the advanced level. How many of the students who passed the basic level did not pass the advanced level?

Question #13: There were 120 delegates in a conference room when a meeting started. During the first hour, 60 delegates left the room, while 72 delegates entered the room during the same time. What expression gives the number of delegates who were in the room after the first hour as a percentage of the number of delegates in the room who have been there since the beginning of the meeting?

Question #14:   After John gave 110 baseball cards to Monika and 165 to Susan, he still had 225 left. What percent of his cards did John give away?

Question #15:   John gave 20% of his baseball cards to Monika and 5% to Susan. If he still had 525 cards, how many did he have originally?

Question #16:   As a company policy, a gemologist must check 5 percent of its ruby and 10 percent of its sapphire for quality before shipping the gems. If a customer orders 120 rubies and 80 sapphires, what percent of all the gems must the gemologist check before shipping the order?

Question #17:   In a certain town, 80 percent of the registered voters are males and the rest are females. During a gubernatorial race, if 90 percent of the registered male voters and 50 percent of the registered female voters vote for Candidate *X*, what percent of the registered voters did not vote for Candidate *X*?

Question #18:   In a certain test, there are a total 240 questions. Jessica answered 75% of the first 180 questions correctly. What percent of the remaining questions did she need to answer correctly so that she answered 80% of all the questions on the test correctly?

Question #19:   In a certain club, 20 percent of the members are married. Among the members who are not married, 12 are males and 60 are females. What is the total number of members in the club?

Question #20:   During a certain art auction, Elizabeth won 90 percent of the first 150 bids and 60 percent of the remaining bids. If Elizabeth won 80 percent of all the bids, what was the total number of bids?

Question #21:   In a certain private school, 20 percent of the students live in the schools' boarding house and the rest live at home with their families. At the end of the school year, 60 percent of the students who live at home make it to the deans list. If 96 students who live at home are in the deans list, what is the total number of students in the school?

Question #22:   If 12*y* + 24 is 20 percent larger than *x*, what is the value of *x*?

PERCENT CHANGES:

Question #23:   In July, the value of a stock increased by 25%; and in August, it decreased by 20%. How did the value of the stock at the end of August compare with its value at the beginning of July?

Question #24:   The price of an item went up 20% since last year. If last year's price was *x*, what is this year's price of that item in terms of *x*?

Question #25:   The price of a gallon of gas was increased by 20%. How many gallons can be purchased for the amount of money that used to buy 60 gallons?

Question #26:   If the height of a certain tree increases 25 percent from *h* feet to 80 feet, then, in feet, what was the actual increase in the height of the tree?

Question #27:   If *x* is increased by 5% and *y* is decreased by 5%, the resulting numbers will be equal. What is the ratio of *x* to *y*?

Question #28:   If Muster's daily wages increases by 18 percent, he would earn $177 per day. However, if instead, his daily wages were to increase by 12 percent, how much would he earn per day?

Question #29:   In a certain school, if the enrollment increases by 15 percent over last year, this year's enrollment would be 8,280. However, if instead, the enrollment were to decrease by 20 percent from last year, what would be this year's total enrollment?

PERCENT DISCOUNT:

Question #30:   A certain store offers different discounts that range from 5 percent to 25 percent, inclusive. If an item is discounted to a price of $9.60, what could be the greatest possible original price?

PERCENT PROFIT:

Question #31:   A trader sells an item for a profit of 20 percent of the cost. What percent of the selling price is the profit?

Question #32:   A trader buys 120 bags of cement for $720. If 10 percent of the bags are spoiled, then at what price should he sell each of the remaining bags in order to make a profit of 15 percent?

Question #33:   A man bought 10 bushels of apples for a total cost of $80. If he lost two of the bushels, at what price would he have to sell each of the remaining bushels in order to earn a total profit of 25 percent of the total cost?

Question #34:   A store paid $60 to acquire a radio. At what price should it be offered for sale if the store offers customers a 10% discount but still wants to make a profit of 20% of the cost?

Question #35:   At a discount store everything is sold for 20% less than the marked price. If the store buys a radio for $80, what price should be marked on it if the store wants to make a 20% profit on the cost?

Question #36:   Last year a company's profit was 10 percent of its annual revenues. This year the company's revenue is 20 percent more than last year and it profited 15 percent of its annual revenue. The profit for this year was what percent of the profit for last year?

Question #37:   Last month Vivian saved 15 percent of her net earnings. This month, her net earnings are 10 percent less than last month's earnings and she saved 18 percent of her net savings. The amount she saved this month is what percent of the amount she saved last month?

PERCENT INTERESTS:

Question #38:   Jose borrowed $880 from a friend, interest free. If he pays back 2½ percent of the principal every quarter, and he has already paid $726, for how many more months does he have to pay in order to pay back his entire loan?

Question #39:   A certain local bank pays 6.5% a year fixed simple interest on a regular savings account and 7.25% a year on a money market account. If you have $1500 to invest for two years, how much more interest would you earn by putting the money in the money market account instead of the regular savings account?

Question #40:   A man invested $1,000 in a stock five years ago. The value of the stock increased by 20 percent during the first year, increased by 50 percent during the second year, remains unchanged during the third year, decreased by 20% during the fourth year, and decreased by 50% during the fifth year. What should be the value of the investment at the end of the fifth year?

Question #41:   An amount of money was invested at 7% a year. Five times that amount was invested at 9%. How much was invested at 9% if the total annual return was $910?

PERCENT TAXES & COMMISSION:

Question #42:   Tony is trying to buy a health insurance policy. If he buys it through an agent, he'll have to pay a sales tax of 7.5 percent. If he buys it directly from the company, he won't have to pay the sales tax, but he'll have to pay a fixed processing fee of $5.25. What is the least amount of money he can spend on buying the policy so that the purchase with the processing fee will not be more expensive than the purchase with the sales tax?

Question #43: John is paid a salary of $225 per week plus commission of 5% on all his sales over $500. What was the amount of his sales in a week in which he earned a total salary of $950?

RATIOS:

Question #44: If $\dfrac{x}{y} = \dfrac{2}{5}$, then what is the value of $\dfrac{5x}{2y}$?

Question #45: If $\dfrac{x}{y} = \dfrac{9}{2}$, then what is the value of $\dfrac{12x}{5y}$?

Question #46: If x and y are positive numbers, such that $\dfrac{5}{11}x = \dfrac{11}{5}y$, what is the ratio of x to y?

Question #47: If Kristen had 5 times as many watches as she actually has, she would have one-fifth as many watches as Sandra has. What is the ratio of the number of watches Kristen has to the number of watches Sandra has?

Question #48: In the following system of equations, if $z \neq 0$, then what is the ratio of x to z?
$x - y + z = 0$
$5x + y - 8z = 0$

Question #49: For positive integers a and b, $b^2 = a^3$ and $a^2 = 16$, what is the ratio of a to b?

Question #50: If a company's revenues for the month of December were 6 times the average (arithmetic mean) monthly revenues for the first eleven months (January through November), what is the ratio of the December revenues to the total revenues for the whole year?

Question #51: A candy jar contains three colors of candies, red, blue, and green in the ratio of 1:2:8. If the jar has 121 candies, how many more green candies are there than blue candies?

Question #52: The capacity of Tank A is seven times the capacity of Tank B. Together, Tank A and Tank B have twice the capacity of Tank C. What is the ratio of the capacity of Tank B to the capacity of Tank C?

Question #53: If $a = 2b$, $3b = 4c$, and $5c = 6d$, what is the ratio of a to d?

Question #54: If $a = 2b$, $5b = 7c$, and $9c = 10d$, what is the ratio of a to d?

PROPORTIONS:

Question #55: If at a production plant, 7 out of every 1,000 parts manufactured are defective and it runs a production cycle of 25,000 parts, how many of these parts would be defective?

Question #56: If 5 out of every 7 students in a school enroll for a preparation workshop, and there are 105 students in the school, how many students enroll in the preparation workshop?

Question #57: If in a small town, 7 out of every 9 new born babies are baby boys, and 72 births take place in a particular night, how many of the new born babies are baby boys?

Question #58: If 5 out of every 119 applications for a home loan are accepted, and there were 595 total applications in a day, how many applications were accepted?

Question #59: If 7 workers can complete a job in 72 hours, how many hours will it take 9 workers to finish the same job?

Question #60: If it takes a train 7 hours to cover a trip at the speed of 270 mph, how many hours will it take to cover the same trip at the speed of 126 mph?

PRACTICE EXERCISE – QUESTIONS & ANSWERS WITH EXPLANATIONS:

PERCENT CALCULATION:

Question #1:   If $x > 0$, then $\dfrac{x}{20}$ is what percent of x?

Solution: $\Rightarrow \dfrac{x}{20} = \dfrac{what}{100} \bullet x$ [Convert the statement into an equation]

             $\Rightarrow$ what $= \dfrac{100x}{20x} = 5\%$ [Solve for "*what*"]

Question #2:   If $x > 0$, then $\dfrac{x}{15}$ is what percent of $\dfrac{x}{90}$?

Solution: $\Rightarrow \dfrac{x}{15} = \dfrac{what}{100} \bullet \dfrac{x}{90}$ [Convert the statement into an equation]

             $\Rightarrow$ what $= \dfrac{100 \bullet 90 \bullet x}{15x} = 600\%$ [Solve for "*what*"]

Question #3:   A man was planning to deposit a certain amount of money each month into a college fund for his children. He then decided not to make any contributions during June and July. To make the same annual contribution that he had originally planned, by what amount should he increase his monthly deposits?

Solution:
Let the Original Monthly Contribution $\Rightarrow$ $100
Then the Annual Contribution $\Rightarrow$ $100 × 12 = $1,200
Since he is going to skip payments for 2 months, he would have to contribute $1,200 in 10 months:
New Monthly Contribution $\Rightarrow$ $1,200 ÷ 10 = $120
Increase in Monthly Contribution $\Rightarrow$ $120 – $100 = $20

Question #4:   A certain flower shop sells only five types of bouquets, priced at $10, $12, $14, $15, and $17. On a certain day, the shop sells exactly the same number of each type of bouquets. What percent of the total sales proceeds came from the sale of the most expensive type of bouquet?

Solution: Since the flower shop sells exactly the same number of each type of bouquets, let's assume they sell one of each type of bouquets.
Total Sales Proceeds $\Rightarrow$ $10 + $12 + $14 + $15 + $17 = $68
Percent of the total sales proceeds that came from the sale of the most expensive type of bouquet, which is the $17 bouquet $\Rightarrow \dfrac{17}{68} × 100 = 25\%$

Question #5:   In a certain company, 80 percent of its employees are under the age of 55 years, and the remaining employees are over the age of 55 years. If the total number of employees in the company is 925, what is the difference between the number of employees who are under the age of 55 years and the number of employees who are over the age of 55 year?

Solution:
No. of employees who are under 55 years old $\Rightarrow$ 80% of 925 = 0.80 × 925 = 740
No. of employees who are over 55 years old $\Rightarrow$ (100% – 80%) of 925 = 0.20 × 925 = 185
Difference between No. of employees under 55 years & the over 55 years $\Rightarrow$ 740 – 185 = 555

Question #6:   In a certain toolbox that consists of only screws and nuts, there are twice as many screws as nuts. If 20 percent of the screws and 60 percent of the nuts are defective, what percent of the hardware in the box is not defective?

Solution:
Let's assume that there are a total of 200 screws and 100 nuts in the box, with a total of 300 pieces.
Then, the No. of defective screws $\Rightarrow$ 20% of 200 = 40
And, the No. of defective nuts $\Rightarrow$ 60% of 100 = 60
Total No. of defective pieces $\Rightarrow$ 40 + 60 = 100
Total No. of non-defective pieces $\Rightarrow$ 300 – 100 = 200

Percent of non-defective pieces $\Rightarrow \dfrac{200}{300} \times 100 = 66\dfrac{2}{3}\%$

Question #7: In Town X, 12 percent of the population are minors, while in Town Y, 15 percent of the population are minors. If the population of Town Y is 20 percent more than the population of Town X, then the number of minors in Town Y is what percent of the number of minors in Town X?

Solution:
Let, the population of Town X $\Rightarrow 100$
Then, the population of Town Y $\Rightarrow 100 + (20\% \text{ of } 100) = 100 + 20 = 120$
No. of minors in Town X $\Rightarrow 12\% \text{ of } 100 = 0.12 \times 100 = 12$
No. of minors in Town Y $\Rightarrow 15\% \text{ of } 120 = 0.15 \times 120 = 18$

No. of minors in Town Y is what percent of the No. of minors in Town $X \Rightarrow \dfrac{18}{12} \times 100 = 150\%$

Question #8: One class in a school is 20 percent boys. A second class, that is half the size of the first class, is 10 percent boys. What percent of both classes are boys?

Solution:
Let, the Total No. of Students in First Class = 100 $\Rightarrow$ No of Boys in First Class = 20% of 100 = 20
Total No. of Students in Second Class = ½(100) = 50 $\Rightarrow$ No of Boys in First Class = 10% of 50 = 5
Total No. of Students in Both Classes = 150 $\Rightarrow$ No of Boys in Both Classes = 20 + 5 = 25
Let the percent of boys in both classes = n
EZ Problem Set-Up $\Rightarrow$ Total No. of Boys (25) is what percent of Total Students (150)

$\Rightarrow 25 = \dfrac{n}{100} \times 150$ [Set up the equation]

$\Rightarrow n = 16.67\%$ [Solve for n]

Question #9: If 50 percent of the candidates are eliminated after each round of interview, what percent of the original number of candidates will be eliminated after four rounds?

Solution:
Let the original No. of candidates $\Rightarrow 100$
No. of candidates eliminated after First Round $\Rightarrow 100 - (50\% \text{ of } 100) = 100 - 50 = 50$
No. of candidates eliminated after Second Round $\Rightarrow 50 - (50\% \text{ of } 50) = 50 - 25 = 25$
No. of candidates eliminated after Third Round $\Rightarrow 25 - (50\% \text{ of } 25) = 50 - 12.5 = 12.5$
No. of candidates eliminated after Fourth Round $\Rightarrow 12.5 - (50\% \text{ of } 12.5) = 12.5 - 6.25 = 6.25$
Total No. of candidates eliminated after 4 Rounds $\Rightarrow 50 + 25 + 12.5 + 6.25 = 93.75\%$

Question #10: If 60 percent of the population of a certain town is employed, and 20 percent of those who are employed work for the local oil refinery, what percent of the population in the town do not work for the refinery?

Solution:
Let's assume that the total population of the town $\Rightarrow 100$
Then, the No. of people who are employed $\Rightarrow 60\% \text{ of } 100 = 60$
And, the No. of employed people who work for the refinery $\Rightarrow 20\% \text{ of } 60 = 12$
Finally, the No. of people who do not work for the refinery $\Rightarrow 100 - 12 = 88$
Percent of people who do not work for the refinery $\Rightarrow 88\%$

Question #11: In a certain one-day art exhibition, an artist brings 240 paintings to sell. If he sell 25 percent of his paintings during the first hour and 60 percent of the remaining paintings during the second hour, how many of the paintings will not have been sold by the end of the second hour?

Solution:
Total No. of Paintings = 240
No. of Paintings sold during the First Hour $\Rightarrow 25\% \text{ of } 240 = 0.25 \times 240 = 60$
No. of Remaining Paintings after the First Hour $\Rightarrow 240 - 60 = 180$
No. of Paintings sold during the Second Hour $\Rightarrow 60\% \text{ of } 180 = 0.60 \times 180 = 108$
No. of Remaining Paintings after the Second Hour $\Rightarrow 180 - 108 = 72$

Question #12: In a certain math examination of 7,600 students, only 15 percent of the students were able to pass the basic level and move into the advanced level. Of these 15 percent, only 10 percent were able to pass the advanced level. How many of the students who passed the basic level did not pass the advanced level?

Solution:
No. of Students who took the Basic Level $\Rightarrow 7,600$

No. of Students who passed the Basic Level $\Rightarrow$ 15% of 7,600 = 0.15 × 7,600 = 1,140
No. of Students who took the Advanced Level $\Rightarrow$ 1,140
No. of Students who passed the Advanced Level $\Rightarrow$ 10% of 1,140 = 0.10 × 1,140 = 114
No. of students who passed the Basic Level but did not pass the Advanced Level $\Rightarrow$ 1140–114 = 1,026

Question #13: There were 120 delegates in a conference room when a meeting started. During the first hour, 60 delegates left the room, while 72 delegates entered the room during the same time. What expression gives the number of delegates who were in the room after the first hour as a percentage of the number of delegates in the room who have been there since the beginning of the meeting?

Solution: No. of Delegates in the room at the beginning $\Rightarrow$ 120
No. of Delegates in the room after the first hour $\Rightarrow$ 120 – 60 + 72 = 132
No. of Delegates in the room who have been there since the beginning of the meeting = 120
No. of Delegates in the room after the first hour is what percent of No. of Delegates in the room who have been there since the beginning of the meeting $\Rightarrow \dfrac{132}{120} \times 100 \Rightarrow 110\%$

Question #14: After John gave 110 baseball cards to Monika and 165 to Susan, he still had 225 left. What percent of his cards did John give away?

Solution: No. of cards John gave away to Monika $\Rightarrow$ 110
No. of cards John gave away to Susan $\Rightarrow$ 165
No. of cards John gave away to Monika & Susan $\Rightarrow$ 110 + 165 = 275
Total No of Cards John had at the beginning $\Rightarrow$ 275(gave away) + 225 (left over) = 500
Let the percent of cards that John gave away = x
EZ Problem Set-Up $\Rightarrow$ 275 (gave away) is what percent of 500 (total cards)?

$$\Rightarrow 275 = \frac{x}{100} \times 500 \qquad \text{[Set up the equation]}$$

$$\Rightarrow x = 275 \times \frac{100}{500} = 55\% \qquad \text{[Solve for } x\text{]}$$

Percent of his baseball cards that John gave away = 55%

Question #15: John gave 20% of his baseball cards to Monika and 5% to Susan. If he still had 525 cards, how many did he have originally?

Solution: Percent of cards John originally had before giving away anything $\Rightarrow$ 100%
Percent of cards John gave away to Monika $\Rightarrow$ 20%
Percent of cards John gave away to Susan $\Rightarrow$ 5%
Percent of cards John gave away to Monika & Susan $\Rightarrow$ 20% + 5% = 25%
Percent of cards John is left with after giving to Monika & Susan $\Rightarrow$ 100% – 25% = 75%
EZ Problem Set-Up $\Rightarrow$ 525 is 75% of what number?

$$\Rightarrow 525 = \frac{75}{100} x \qquad \text{[Set up the equation]}$$

$$\Rightarrow x = 525 \times \frac{100}{75} = 700 \qquad \text{[Solve for } x\text{]}$$

No. of baseball card that John originally had $\Rightarrow$ 700

Question #16: As a company policy, a gemologist must check 5 percent of its ruby and 10 percent of its sapphire for quality before shipping the gems. If a customer orders 120 rubies and 80 sapphires, what percent of all the gems must the gemologist check before shipping the order?

Solution: Total No. of gems ordered $\Rightarrow$ 120 + 80 = 200
5% of 120 Rubies $\Rightarrow$ 0.05 × 120 = 6
10% of 80 Sapphires $\Rightarrow$ 0.10 × 80 = 8
Total No. of gems for quality check $\Rightarrow$ 6 Rubies + 8 Sapphires = 14
EZ Problem Set-Up $\Rightarrow$ 14 is what percent of 200?

$$\Rightarrow 14 = \frac{x}{100} \times 200 \qquad \text{[Set up the equation]}$$

$$\Rightarrow x = 1,400 \div 200 = 7\% \qquad \text{[Solve for } x\text{]}$$

Question #17: In a certain town, 80 percent of the registered voters are males and the rest are females. During a gubernatorial race, if 90 percent of the registered male voters and 50 percent of the registered female voters vote for Candidate X, what percent of the registered voters did not vote for Candidate X?

Solution: Let the total No. of registered voters = n
No. of Registered Male Voters $\Rightarrow$ 80% of n = $0.80n$
No. of Registered Female Voters $\Rightarrow$ 20% of n = $0.20n$
No. of Registered Male Voters who vote for Candidate X $\Rightarrow$ 90% of $0.80n$ = $0.72n$
No. of Registered Female Voters who vote for Candidate X $\Rightarrow$ 50% of $0.20n$ = $0.10n$
No. of Registered Voters (male & female) who vote for Candidate X $\Rightarrow$ $0.72n + 0.10n = 0.82n$
No. of Registered Voters (male & female) who didn't vote for Candidate X $\Rightarrow$ $n - 0.82n = 0.18n$
Percent of registered voter who didn't vote for Candidate $X \Rightarrow$ 18%

Question #18: In a certain test, there are a total 240 questions. Jessica answered 75% of the first 180 questions correctly. What percent of the remaining questions did she need to answer correctly so that she answered 80% of all the questions on the test correctly?

Solution: Total No. of questions on the test $\Rightarrow$ 240
Percent of questions that needs to be answered correctly $\Rightarrow$ 80%
No. of questions that needs to be answered correctly $\Rightarrow$ 80% of 240 = 192
No. of questions that are already answered $\Rightarrow$ 180
Percent of questions that are already answered correctly $\Rightarrow$ 75%
No. of questions that are already answered correctly $\Rightarrow$ 75% of 180 = 135
Remaining No. of questions that needs to be answered $\Rightarrow$ 240 − 180 = 60
Remaining No. of questions that needs to be answered correctly $\Rightarrow$ 192 − 135 = 57

Percent of the remaining number of questions that needs to be answered $\Rightarrow \dfrac{57}{60} \times 100 = 95\%$

Question #19: In a certain club, 20 percent of the members are married. Among the members who are not married, 12 are males and 60 are females. What is the total number of members in the club?

Solution: Let the total No. of members $\Rightarrow x$
No. of Married Members $\Rightarrow$ 20% of x
No. of Unmarried Members $\Rightarrow$ 80% of x
No. of Unmarried Male Members $\Rightarrow$ 12
No. of Unmarried Female Members $\Rightarrow$ 60
EZ Problem Set-Up $\Rightarrow$ No. of Unmarried Members = No. of Unmarried Male Members + No. of Unmarried Female Members
      $\Rightarrow$ 80% of Total Members = 12 + 60 [Set up the equation]
      $\Rightarrow 0.80x = 72$ [Simplify the expression]
      $\Rightarrow x = 90$ [Divide both sides by 0.80]

Question #20: During a certain art auction, Elizabeth won 90 percent of the first 150 bids and 60 percent of the remaining bids. If Elizabeth won 80 percent of all the bids, what was the total number of bids?

Solution: Let the total No. of bids = x
EZ Problem Set-Up $\Rightarrow$ 90% of the first 150 bids + 60% of the remaining bids = 80% of all the bids
      $\Rightarrow (0.90)(150) + (0.60)(x - 150) = 0.80(x)$ [Set up the equation]
      $\Rightarrow 135 + 0.60x - 90 = 0.80x$ [Simplify the expression]
      $\Rightarrow 45 + 0.60x = 0.80x$ [Combine like-terms]
      $\Rightarrow 0.20x = 45$ [Subtract 0.60x from both sides]
      $\Rightarrow x = 225$ [Divide both sides by 0.20]

Question #21: In a certain private school, 20 percent of the students live in the schools' boarding house and the rest live at home with their families. At the end of the school year, 60 percent of the students who live at home make it to the deans list. If 96 students who live at home are in the deans list, what is the total number of students in the school?

Solution: Since 60% of the students live at home and 96 students who live at home make it to the deans list:

No. of students who live at home $\Rightarrow$ 60% of what is 96 $\Rightarrow \dfrac{96}{60} \times 100 = 160$

Since 160 students live at home, and 80 percent of all the students live at home:

Total No. of students in the school $\Rightarrow$ 80% of what is 160 $\Rightarrow \dfrac{160}{80} \times 100 = 200$

Question #22:   If $12y + 24$ is 20 percent larger than x, what is the value of x?
Solution: EZ Problem Set-Up $\Rightarrow 12y + 24$ is 20 percent larger than x

$\Rightarrow 12y + 24 = x + 20\%$ of x [Set up the equation]

$\Rightarrow 12y + 24 = 120\%$ of x [Combine the percents]

$\Rightarrow 12y + 24 = \dfrac{120}{100} x$ [Convert the percent into fraction]

$\Rightarrow 12y + 24 = \dfrac{6}{5} x$ [Reduce the fraction to lowest terms]

$\Rightarrow x = \dfrac{5}{6}(12y + 24)$ [Multiply both sides by 5/6]

$\Rightarrow x = 10y + 20$ [Apply distributive property]

PERCENT CHANGES:

Question #23:   In July, the value of a stock increased by 25%; and in August, it decreased by 20%. How did the value of the stock at the end of August compare with its value at the beginning of July?
Solution: Let's assume that the value of stock at the beginning of July = $100.
Then the value of stock at the end of July $\Rightarrow$ $100 + (25% of $100) = $100 + $25 = $125
And, the value of stock at the beginning of August = $125
Then, the value of stock at the end of August $\Rightarrow$ $125 – (20% of 125) = $125 - $25 = $100
The value of the stock at the end of August is the same as it was at the beginning of July.

Question #24:   The price of an item went up 20% since last year. If last year's price was x, what is this year's price of that item in terms of x?
Solution: Last year's price $\Rightarrow$ 100% of x
This year's price $\Rightarrow$ (100% of x) + (20% of x) = $x + 0.20x = 1.2x$

Question #25:   The price of a gallon of gas was increased by 20%. How many gallons can be purchased for the amount of money that used to buy 60 gallons?
Solution: Let the original price of 1 gallon $\Rightarrow$ $100
Amount of money needed to buy 60 gallons $\Rightarrow$ $100 × 60 = $6,000
New price of 1 gallon $\Rightarrow$ $100 + (20% of $100) = $120
No. of gallons that can be bought for $6,000 at the rate of $120 per gallon = $6,000 ÷ $120 = 50

Question #26:   If the height of a certain tree increases 25 percent from h feet to 80 feet, then, in feet, what was the actual increase in the height of the tree?
Solution: Let, the original height of the tree = h feet
EZ Problem Set-Up $\Rightarrow$ Original Height + Increase = New Height

$\Rightarrow h + (25\%$ of $h) = 80$ [Set up the equation]

$\Rightarrow h + 0.25h = 80$ [Convert the percent to decimal]

$\Rightarrow 1.25h = 80$ [Combine like terms]

$\Rightarrow h = 64$ [Divide both sides by 1.25]

Actual Increase $\Rightarrow$ New Height – Original Height = 80 – 64 = 16 feet

Question #27:   If x is increased by 5% and y is decreased by 5%, the resulting numbers will be equal. What is the ratio of x to y?
Solution: Value of x is increased by 5% $\Rightarrow x + 0.05x = 1.05x$
Value of y is decreased by 5% $\Rightarrow y - 0.05y = 0.95y$
The resulting numbers are equal $\Rightarrow 1.05x = 0.95y$

$$\Rightarrow \frac{x}{y} = \frac{0.95}{1.05} = \frac{19}{21}$$

Question #28: If Muster's daily wages increases by 18 percent, he would earn $177 per day. However, if instead, his daily wages were to increase by 12 percent, how much would he earn per day?

Solution: Let, Muster's current daily wages $\Rightarrow x$

EZ Problem Set-Up $\Rightarrow$ If Muster's daily wages increases by 18%, his daily wages $\Rightarrow$ $177

                 $\Rightarrow$ 118% of x = 177   [Set up the equation]

                 $\Rightarrow$ 1.18x = 177   [Convert the percent into decimal]

                 $\Rightarrow x$ = $150   [Divide both sides by 1.18]

Muster's current daily wages $\Rightarrow$ $150

If Muster's daily wages were to increase by 12%, his daily wages $\Rightarrow$ (100 + 12)% of $150

                                                                   $\Rightarrow$ 112% of $150

                                                                   $\Rightarrow$ $168

Question #29: In a certain school, if the enrollment increases by 15 percent over last year, this year's enrollment would be 8,280. However, if instead, the enrollment were to decrease by 20 percent from last year, what would be this year's total enrollment?

Solution: Let, last year's enrollment $\Rightarrow x$

EZ Problem Set-Up $\Rightarrow$ If the enrollment increases by 15%, the total enrollment = 8,280

                 $\Rightarrow$ 115% of x = 8,280   [Set up the equation]

                 $\Rightarrow$ 1.15x = 8,280   [Convert the percent into decimal]

                 $\Rightarrow x$ = 7,200   [Divide both sides by 1.15]

Last year's enrollment $\Rightarrow$ 7,200

If the enrollment were to decrease by 20%, total enrollment $\Rightarrow$ (100 – 20)% of 7,200

                                                                   $\Rightarrow$ 80% of 7,200

                                                                   $\Rightarrow$ 5,760

PERCENT DISCOUNT:

Question #30: A certain store offers different discounts that range from 5 percent to 25 percent, inclusive. If an item is discounted to a price of $9.60, what could be the highest possible original price?

Solution: Discount Percent $\Rightarrow$ 25%

Note: To get the highest possible original price, the percent of discount should also be the highest possible, which is 25%.

Sale Price $\Rightarrow$ $9.60

Let the original price $\Rightarrow p$

EZ Problem Set-Up $\Rightarrow$ (100% – 25%) of original price = $9.60

                 $\Rightarrow$ 75% of p = $9.60   [Set up the equation]

                 $\Rightarrow$ 0.75p = $9.60   [Convert the percent into decimal]

                 $\Rightarrow p$ = 12.80   [Divide both sides by 0.75]

PERCENT PROFIT:

Question #31: A trader sells an item for a profit of 20 percent of the cost. What percent of the selling price is the profit?

Solution: Let the cost of an item $\Rightarrow$ $100

Then, the selling price of item $\Rightarrow$ $100 + (20% of $100) = $120

Profit on sale $\Rightarrow$ $120 – $100 = $20

Profit as percent of cost price $\Rightarrow \dfrac{20}{120} \times 100 = 16\dfrac{2}{3}\%$

Question #32: A trader buys 120 bags of cement for $720. If 10 percent of the bags are spoiled, then at what price should he sell each of the remaining bags in order to make a profit of 15 percent?

Solution: Cost price of 120 bags of cement $\Rightarrow$ $720

No. of bags that are spoiled and can't be sold ⇒ 10% of 120 = 12
No. of bags that can be sold   ⇒ 120 − 12 = 108
Profit of 15% on $720   ⇒ $720 + (15% of $720) = $720 + $108 = $828
Selling Price per bag   ⇒ $828 ÷ 108 = $7.67

Question #33:   A man bought 10 bushels of apples for a total cost of $80. If he lost two of the bushels, at what price would he have to sell each of the remaining bushels in order to earn a total profit of 25 percent of the total cost?

Solution: The man bought 10 bushels of apples for $80, and then lost 2 bushels
Total Cost Price   ⇒ $80 for (10 − 2) bushels
Cost Price per Bushel   ⇒ $80 ÷ 8 = $10
The man wants to make an overall profit of 25% of what he paid to procure the 10 bushels of apples
Total Profit   ⇒ 25% of $80 = 0.25 × 80 = $20
To make a profit of $20, he must add that to his cost and that should be his sale price
Total Sale Price   ⇒ $80 + $20 = $100
Sale Price per Bushel   ⇒ $100 ÷ 8 = $12.50

Question #34:   A store paid $60 to acquire a radio. At what price should it be offered for sale if the store offers customers a 10% discount but still wants to make a profit of 20% of the cost?

Solution: Cost Price   ⇒ $60
Profit   ⇒ 20%
Price Realization⇒ $60 + (20% of $60) = $60 + $12 = $72
Discount   ⇒ 10%
EZ Problem Set-Up ⇒ 72 is 90% of Sale Price.
                         ⇒ $72 = 0.90x   [Set up the equation]
                         ⇒ x = $80   [Divide both sides by 0.90]
Sale Price ⇒ $80

Question #35:   At a discount store everything is sold for 20% less than the marked price. If the store buys a radio for $80, what price should be marked on it if the store wants to make a 20% profit on the cost?

Solution: Cost Price   ⇒ $80
Profit   ⇒ 20%
Price Realization ⇒ $80 + (20% of $80) = $80 + $16 = $96
Discount   ⇒ 20%
EZ Problem Set-Up ⇒ 96 is 80% of Sale Price.
                         ⇒ 96 = 0.80x   [Set up the equation]
                         ⇒ x = $120   [Divide both sides by 0.80]
Sale Price ⇒ $120

Question #36:   Last year a company's profit was 10 percent of its annual revenues. This year the company's revenue is 20 percent more than last year and it profited 15 percent of its annual revenue. The profit for this year was what percent of the profit for last year?

Solution: Let, the last years revenue   ⇒ $100
Then, last years profit   ⇒ 10% of $100 = 0.10 × $100 = $10
This years revenue   ⇒ 120% of $100 = 1.20 × $100 = $120
This years profit   ⇒ 15% of $120 = 0.15 × $120 = $18

Profit for this year (18) as a percent of profit for last year ($10) ⇒ $\frac{18}{10} \times 100 = 180\%$

Question #37:   Last month Vivian saved 15 percent of her net earnings. This month, her net earnings are 10 percent less than last month's earnings and she saved 18 percent of her net savings. The amount she saved this month is what percent of the amount she saved last month?

Solution: Let, last month's net earnings   ⇒ 100
Then, this month's net earnings   ⇒ 100 − (10% of 100) = 100 − 10 = $90
Last month's savings   ⇒ 15% of $100 = 0.15 × 100 = $15
This month's savings   ⇒ 18% of $90 = 0.18 × 90 = $16.2

This month's savings is what percent of last month's savings $\Rightarrow \dfrac{16.2}{15} \times 100 = 108\%$

PERCENT INTERESTS:

Question #38: Jose borrowed $880 from a friend, interest free. If he pays back 2½ percent of the principal every quarter, and he has already paid $726, for how many more months does he have to pay in order to pay back his entire loan?

Solution:
Total Amount of Loan $\Rightarrow$ $880
Quarterly Payments $\Rightarrow$ 2.5% of $880 = $22 every quarter
Amount already Paid Back $\Rightarrow$ $726
Balance Amount to be Paid $\Rightarrow$ $880 − $726 = $154
No. of Quarters to Pay Back $154 $\Rightarrow$ 154 ÷ 22 = 7 quarter = 21 months

Question #39: A certain local bank pays 6.5% a year fixed simple interest on a regular savings account and 7.25% a year on a money market account. If you have $1500 to invest for two years, how much more interest would you earn by putting the money in the money market account instead of the regular savings account?

Solution:
Annual Interest in RS Account $\Rightarrow P \times R \times T = \$1{,}500 \times 6.5\% \times 2 = 1500 \times 0.065 \times 2 = \$195$
Annual Interest in MM Account $\Rightarrow P \times R \times T = \$1{,}500 \times 7.25\% \times 2 = 1500 \times 0.0725 \times 2 = \$217.5$
Difference in Interest Earned $\Rightarrow \$217.5 - \$195 = \$22.50$

Question #40: A man invested $1,000 in a stock five years ago. The value of the stock increased by 20 percent during the first year, increased by 50 percent during the second year, remains unchanged during the third year, decreased by 20% during the fourth year, and decreased by 50% during the fifth year. What should be the value of the investment at the end of the fifth year?

Solution:
Simply express the percents in decimal and multiply to find the final value of the investment:
$\Rightarrow \$1{,}000\,(120\%)\,(150\%)\,(1)\,(80\%)\,(50\%) = \$1{,}000\,(1.20)\,(1.50)\,(1)\,(0.80)\,(0.50) = \$720$

Question #41: An amount of money was invested at 7% a year. Five times that amount was invested at 9%. How much was invested at 9% if the total annual return was $910?

Solution:
Let the amount invested at 7% $\Rightarrow x$
Annual return on the amount invested at 7% $\Rightarrow$ 7% of $x = 0.07x$
Then, the amount invested at 9% $\Rightarrow 5x$
Annual return on the amount invested at 9% $\Rightarrow$ 9% of $5x = 0.09(5x) = 0.45x$
EZ Problem Set-Up $\Rightarrow$ Total Annual Return on both Investments = Return on 7% Investment + Return on 9% Investment
                 $\Rightarrow 910 = 0.07x + 0.45x$ [Set up the equation]
                 $\Rightarrow 910 = 0.52x$ [Combine like-terms]
                 $\Rightarrow x = 1{,}750$ [Divide both sides by 0.52]
Amount invested at 7% $\Rightarrow$ $1,750
Amount invested at 9% $\Rightarrow 5 \times 1{,}750 = \$8{,}750$

PERCENT TAXES & COMMISSION:

Question #42: Tony is trying to buy a health insurance policy. If he buys it through an agent, he'll have to pay a sales tax of 7.5 percent. If he buys it directly from the company, he won't have to pay the sales tax, but he'll have to pay a fixed processing fee of $5.25. What is the least amount of money he can spend on buying the policy so that the purchase with the processing fee will not be more expensive than the purchase with the sales tax?

Solution:
Let the price of the policy $\Rightarrow \$p$
Additional Cost through Agent $\Rightarrow$ 7.5% of p
Additional Cost through Company $\Rightarrow$ $5.25
EZ Problem Set-Up $\Rightarrow$ Additional Cost through Agent = Additional Cost through Company
                 $\Rightarrow$ 7.5% of $p = \$5.25$ [Set up the equation]
                 $\Rightarrow 0.075p = \$5.25$ [Convert the decimal into percent]

$\Rightarrow p = \$70$ [Divide both sides by 0.075]

Note: The price of the policy, excluding the sales tax or the processing fee is the same whether the policy is bought through an agent or company.

Question #43: John is paid a salary of $225 per week plus commission of 5% on all his sales over $500. What was the amount of his sales in a week in which he earned a total salary of $950?

Solution: Fixed weekly salary = $225

Let the total sales for the week = x

Commission = 5% of $(x - 500)$

EZ Problem Set-Up $\Rightarrow$ Fixed Weekly Salary + Commission = Total Earnings

$\Rightarrow 225 + 0.05(x - 500) = 950$ [Set up the equation]

$\Rightarrow 225 + 0.05x - 25 = 950$ [Apply distributive property]

$\Rightarrow 200 + 0.05x = 950$ [Combine like-terms]

$\Rightarrow 0.05x = 750$ [Subtract 200 from both sides]

$\Rightarrow x = 15{,}000$ [Divide both sides by 0.05]

RATIOS:

Question #44: If $\dfrac{x}{y} = \dfrac{2}{5}$, then what is the value of $\dfrac{5x}{2y}$?

Solution: Solve the ratio $\Rightarrow \dfrac{x}{y} = \dfrac{2}{5}$ [Given]

$\Rightarrow 5x = 2y$ [Cross multiply]

Value of $\dfrac{5x}{2y}$ $\Rightarrow \dfrac{2y}{2y} = 1$ [Substitute $5x = 2y$]

Question #45: If $\dfrac{x}{y} = \dfrac{9}{2}$, then what is the value of $\dfrac{12x}{5y}$?

Solution: Solve the ratio $\Rightarrow \dfrac{x}{y} = \dfrac{9}{2}$ [Given]

$\Rightarrow 2x = 9y$ [Cross multiply]

$\Rightarrow 12x = 54y$ [Multiply both sides by 6]

Value of $\dfrac{12x}{5y}$ $\Rightarrow \dfrac{54y}{5y} = 10.8$ [Substitute $12x = 54y$]

Question #46: If x and y are positive numbers, such that $\dfrac{5}{11}x = \dfrac{11}{5}y$, what is the ratio of x to y?

Solution: $\Rightarrow \dfrac{5}{11}x = \dfrac{11}{5}y$ [Given]

$\Rightarrow 25x = 121y$ [Cross multiply]

$\Rightarrow \dfrac{x}{y} = \dfrac{121}{25}$ [Divide both sides by 25y]

Question #47: If Kristen had 5 times as many watches as she actually has, she would have one-fifth as many watches as Sandra has. What is the ratio of the number of watches Kristen has to the number of watches Sandra has?

Solution: Let the number of watches for Kristen = K & Let the number of watches for Sandra = S

EZ Problem Set-Up $\Rightarrow$ Kristen's five times as many watches = Sandra's one-fifth as many watches

$\Rightarrow 5K = \dfrac{1}{5}S$ [Set up the equation]

$\Rightarrow 25K = S$ [Cross multiply]

$$\Rightarrow \frac{K}{S} = \frac{1}{25} \qquad \text{[Divide both sides by } 25S\text{]}$$

Question #48: In the following system of equations, if $z \neq 0$, then what is the ratio of x to z?
$x - y + z = 0$
$5x + y - 8z = 0$

Solution: Solve the two given equations simultaneously:

$$
\begin{array}{ll}
\quad x \;-\; y \;+\; z \quad = 0 & \Rightarrow \text{Equation \#1]} \\
+\;\; 5x \;+\; y \;-\; 8z \quad = 0 & \Rightarrow \text{Equation \#2]} \\
\hline
\quad 6x \;+\; 0 \;-\; 7z \quad = 0 & \text{[Add the two equations]}
\end{array}
$$

$\Rightarrow 6x = 7z$ [Add $7z$ to both sides]

$$\Rightarrow \frac{x}{z} = \frac{7}{6} = 7:6 \qquad \text{[Divide both sides by } 6z\text{]}$$

Question #49: For positive integers a and b, $b^2 = a^3$ and $a^2 = 16$, what is the ratio of a to b?

Solution:

Solve for a	$\Rightarrow a^2 = 16$	[Given]
	$\Rightarrow a = 4$	[Square root both sides]
Solve for b	$\Rightarrow b^2 = a^3$	[Given]
	$\Rightarrow b^2 = 4^3$	[Substitute $a = 4$]
	$\Rightarrow b^2 = 64$	[Solve for the exponent]
	$\Rightarrow b = 8$	[Square root both sides]
Ratio of a to b	$\Rightarrow 4:8 = 1:2$	[Substitute $a = 4$ and $b = 8$]

Question #50: If a company's revenues for the month of December were 6 times the average (arithmetic mean) monthly revenues for the first eleven months (January through November), what is the ratio of the December revenues to the total revenues for the whole year?

Solution: Let, the average monthly sales for 11 months $\Rightarrow x$
Then, the total revenues for the 11 months $\Rightarrow 11x$
And, revenues for December $\Rightarrow 6x$
Total revenues for the year $\Rightarrow 11x + 6x = 17x$

$$\text{Ratio of December revenues to total revenues} \Rightarrow \frac{6x}{17x} = \frac{6}{17}$$

Question #51: A candy jar contains three colors of candies, red, blue, and green in the ratio of 1:2:8. If the jar has 121 candies, how many more green candies are there than blue candies?

Solution: Ratio of Red to Blue to Green $\Rightarrow$ 1:2:8
Total No. of Candies $\Rightarrow$ 121

No. of Red Candies $\Rightarrow \dfrac{1}{11} \times 121 = 1 \times 11 = 11$

No. of Blue Candies $\Rightarrow \dfrac{2}{11} \times 121 = 2 \times 11 = 22$

No. of Green Candies $\Rightarrow \dfrac{8}{11} \times 121 = 8 \times 11 = 88$

Difference between Green Candies and Blue Candies $\Rightarrow 88 - 22 = 66$

Question #52: The capacity of Tank A is seven times the capacity of Tank B. Together, Tank A and Tank B have twice the capacity of Tank C. What is the ratio of the capacity of Tank B to the capacity of Tank C?

Solution: Capacity of Tank A is seven times the capacity of Tank B $\Rightarrow A = 7B$ $\Rightarrow$ Equation #1
Tank A and Tank B have twice the capacity of Tank C $\Rightarrow A + B = 2C$ $\Rightarrow$ Equation #2
Substitute the value of A from Equation #1 into #2 $\Rightarrow 7B + B = 2C$ [Substitute $A = 7B$]

$$\Rightarrow 8B = 2C \qquad \text{[Combine like-terms]}$$

$$\Rightarrow \frac{8B}{8C} = \frac{2C}{8C} \qquad \text{[Divide both sides by } 8C\text{]}$$

$$\Rightarrow \frac{B}{C} = \frac{1}{4} \qquad \text{[Simplify the fractions]}$$

Question #53: If $a = 2b$, $3b = 4c$, and $5c = 6d$, what is the ratio of a to d?

Solution: Write down all the ratios and keep scaling up to cancel and equate:

$\Rightarrow a = 2b$ $\Rightarrow 3b = 4c$ $\Rightarrow 5c = 6d$

$\Rightarrow a = 2b$ $\Rightarrow 15b = 20c$ $\Rightarrow 20c = 24d$

                  [scale-up by 5]   [scale-up by 4]

                                   $\Rightarrow 15b = 20c = 24d$

$\Rightarrow a = 2b$ $\Rightarrow 15b = 24d$

                                   [equate b to d]

$\Rightarrow 15a = 30b$ $\Rightarrow 30b = 48d$

[scale-up by 15]   [scale-up by 2]

                $\Rightarrow 15a = 30b = 48d$

                $\Rightarrow 15a = 48d$

                [equate a to d]

$$\Rightarrow \frac{a}{d} = \frac{48}{15} = \frac{16}{5}$$

Question #54: If $a = 2b$, $5b = 7c$, and $9c = 10d$, what is the ratio of a to d?

Solution: Write down all the ratios and keep scaling up to cancel and equate:

$\Rightarrow a = 2b$ $\Rightarrow 5b = 7c$ $\Rightarrow 9c = 10d$

$\Rightarrow a = 2b$ $\Rightarrow 45b = 63c$ $\Rightarrow 63c = 70d$

                  [scale-up by 9]   [scale-up by 7]

                                   $\Rightarrow 45b = 63c = 70d$

$\Rightarrow a = 2b$ $\Rightarrow 45b = 70d$

                                   [equate b to d]

$\Rightarrow 45a = 90b$ $\Rightarrow 90b = 140d$

[scale-up by 45]   [scale-up by 2]

                $\Rightarrow 45a = 90b = 140d$

                $\Rightarrow 45a = 140d$

                [equate a to d]

$$\Rightarrow \frac{a}{d} = \frac{140}{45} = \frac{28}{9}$$

PROPORTIONS:

Question #55: If at a production plant, 7 out of every 1,000 parts manufactured are defective and it runs a production cycle of 25,000 parts, how many of these parts would be defective?

Solution: Let the number of defective parts = x

$\Rightarrow \dfrac{7}{1,000} = \dfrac{x}{25,000}$ [Set up the proportion]

$\Rightarrow 1,000x = 175,000$ [Cross multiply]

$\Rightarrow x = 175$ [Divide both sides by 1,000]

No. of defective parts $\Rightarrow 175$

Question #56: If 5 out of every 7 students in a school enroll for a preparation workshop, and there are 105 students in the school, how many students enroll in the preparation workshop?

Solution: Let the number of students enrolled in preparation workshop = x

$\Rightarrow \dfrac{5}{7} = \dfrac{x}{105}$ [Set up the proportion]

$\Rightarrow 7x = 525$ [Cross multiply]

$\Rightarrow x = 75$ [Divide both sides by 7]

No. of students enrolled in preparation workshop $\Rightarrow 75$

Question #57: If in a small town, 7 out of every 9 new born babies are baby boys, and 72 births take place in a particular night, how many of the new born babies are baby boys?

Solution: Let the number of new born babies who are baby boys = x

$\Rightarrow \dfrac{7}{9} = \dfrac{x}{72}$ [Set up the proportion]

$\Rightarrow 9x = 504$ [Cross multiply]

$\Rightarrow x = 56$ [Divide both sides by 9]

No. of new born babies who are baby boys $\Rightarrow$ 504

Question #58: If 5 out of every 119 applications for a home loan are accepted, and there were 595 total applications in a day, how many applications were accepted?

Solution: Let the number of applications that were accepted = x

$\Rightarrow \dfrac{5}{119} = \dfrac{x}{595}$ [Set up the proportion]

$\Rightarrow 119x = 2,975$ [Cross multiply]

$\Rightarrow x = 25$ [Divide both sides by 119]

No, of applicants who were accepted $\Rightarrow$ 25

Question #59: If 7 workers can complete a job in 72 hours, how many hours will it take 9 workers to finish the same job?

Solution: Let the number of hours it takes 9 workers to finish the same job = x

$\Rightarrow \dfrac{7\,workers}{9\,workers} \qquad \dfrac{72\,hrs}{x}$ [Set up the proportion]

$\Rightarrow \dfrac{7\,workers}{9\,workers} = \dfrac{x}{72\,hrs}$ [Since there is an inverse proportion, invert the second ratio]

$\Rightarrow 9x = 504$ [Cross multiply]

$\Rightarrow x = 56$ [Divide both sides by 9]

No. of hours in which 9 workers can complete the same job $\Rightarrow$ 56 hours

Question #60: If it takes a train 7 hours to cover a trip at the speed of 270 mph, how many hours will it take to cover the same trip at the speed of 126 mph?

Solution: Let the number of hours it will take to cover the same trip at the speed of 126 mph = x

$\Rightarrow \dfrac{7\,hrs}{x} \qquad \dfrac{270\,mph}{126\,mph}$ [Set up the proportion]

$\Rightarrow \dfrac{7\,hrs}{x} = \dfrac{126\,mph}{270\,mph}$ [Since there is an inverse proportion, invert the second ratio]

$\Rightarrow 126x = 1,890$ [Cross multiply]

$\Rightarrow x = 15$ [Divide both sides by 126]

No. of hours to cover the same trip at the speed of 126 mph $\Rightarrow$ 15 hours

THIS PAGE HAS BEEN INTENTIONALLY LEFT BLANK

PART 4.0: GEOMETRY:

TOPICS COVERED:

- Lines & Angles

- Polygons

- Triangles

- Quadrilaterals

- Circles

- Solid Geometry

- Coordinate Geometry

- Multiple Figures

EZ REFERENCE: -To review geometry concepts, please refer to our EZ Review Geometry.
-To practice medium-to-difficult level questions, please refer to our EZ Practice Advanced Workbook.

PRACTICE EXERCISE:

LINES & ANGLES:

Question #1:   In the figure given below, what is the value of $\dfrac{a+b}{a-b}$?

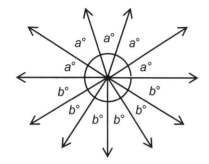

Question #2:   If the measures of two supplementary angles are in the ratio of 2:7, what is the measure of the bigger angle?

Question #3:   Angle A and angle B are complementary. The measure of angle B is 6 less than five times the measure of angle A. What is the measure of angle B?

Question #4:   Angle A and angle B are supplementary. The measure of angle B is 2 less than six times the measure of angle A. What is the measure of angle B?

Question #5:   In the figure given below, what is the value of y?

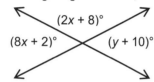

Question #6:   In the figure given below, if AB is parallel to CD, EG bisects angle BEF, and FG bisects angle EFD, what is the measure of angle EGF?

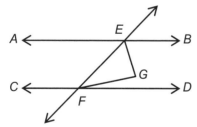

Question #7:   In the figure given below, $AB = 5$, $CD = 6$, and $AD = 15$. What is the distance from D to the midpoint of BC?

Question #8:   In the figure given below, $AC = 20$ and $AB = BC$. Point D (not shown) is on the line between B and C such that $BD = DC$. What is the distance from A to D?

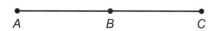

Question #9:   Points X, Y and Z lie on a line with Y between X and Z, and M and N are midpoints of XY and YZ, respectively. If XY:YZ = 5:1, what is XZ:MN?

Question #10:   Points P and Q are on a number line, such that P corresponds to 0.975 and Q corresponds to 0.987. If X is a point on the number line three-fourths of the distance from Q to P, and Y is a point on the number line two-thirds of the distance from P to Q, what is the ratio of XY to PQ?

POLYGONS:

Question #11:   What is the measure of 2 of the 8 angles of a regular octagon?

Question #12:   If the angles of a seven-sided polygon are in the ratio of 2:2:3:3:4:5:6, what is the difference in the degree measures between the largest and smallest angles?

TRIANGLES:

Question #13:   In the figure given below, in $\triangle ABC$, if AD bisects $\angle BAC$, then what is the measure of $\angle ADC$?

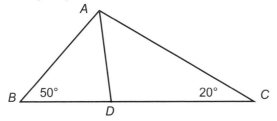

Question #14:   If the difference between the measures of two smaller angles of a right triangle is 52°, what is the measure in degrees, of the smallest angle?

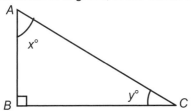

Question #15:   In the figure given below, in $\triangle ABC$, what is the value of EC?

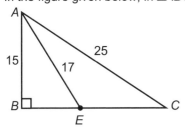

Question #16:   In the figure given below, in $\triangle ABC$, what is the value of AE?

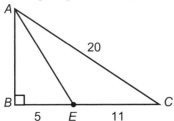

Question #17:   In the figure given below, what is the value of *x*?

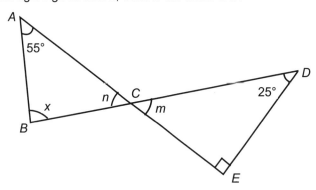

Question #18:   In the figure given below, in $\triangle ABC$, what is the value of *x*?

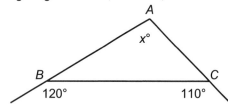

Question #19:   If the degree measure of the angles of a triangle are in the ratio of 1:2:6, what is the positive difference between the measure of the largest angle and the measure of the smallest angle?

Question #20:   In the figure given below, in $\triangle ABC$, what is the value of *x*?

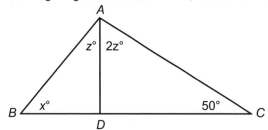

Question #21:   In $\triangle PQR$, the measure of $\angle Q$ is 6 more than twice the measure of measure of $\angle R$, and the measure of $\angle P$ is two less than five times the measure of $\angle R$. What is the measure of $\angle P$?

Question #22:   If the measure of the angles of a triangle are in the ratio of 1:2:3, and if the perimeter of the triangle is $60 + 20\sqrt{3}$ units, what is the length of the smallest side?

Question #23:   If the measure of the angles of a triangle are in the ratio of 1:1:2, and if the perimeter of the triangle is $10 + 5\sqrt{2}$ units, what is the length of the smallest side?

Question #24:   The lengths of the sides of a triangle are $(x - 2)$ units, $(2x + 8)$ units, and $(5x - 1)$ units. If the perimeter of the triangle is 69 units, what is the length of the shortest side?

Question #25:   In isosceles triangle *PQR*, each leg is 5 units less than twice the length of the base. If the perimeter of the triangle is 65 units, what is the length of a leg?

Question #26:   If the area of a triangle is 63 unit^2, and the length of the height minus the length of the base equals 5 units, then what is the length of the height?

QUADRILATERALS:

Question #27:   What is the area of rectangle whose length is 9 times its width, and its perimeter is 160 units?

Question #28:   What is the perimeter of rectangle whose length is 5 times its width, and its area is 125 unit^2?

Question #29:   A rectangular parking space is marked out by painting three of its sides white. If the length of the unpainted side is 11 units, and the sum of the lengths of the painted sides is 51 units, what is the area of the parking space in square feet?

Question #30:   The area of a certain rectangle is 125 unit^2. If the ratio of the length to the width of the rectangle is 5 to 1, what is the perimeter of the rectangle?

Question #31:   In rhombus *ABCD*, the two diagonals *AC* and *DB* intersect at point *O*. if the measure of one diagonal *AC* is 24 units and the measure of other diagonal *DB* is 18 units, what is the measure of a side of the rhombus?

Question #32:   In the figure given below, what is the area of trapezoid *ABCD*?

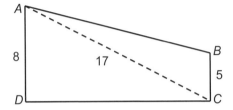

CIRCLES:

Question #33:   If the area of circle *X* is 64π unit^2 and the area of circle *Y* is 256π unit^2, what is the ratio of the radius of circle *X* to that of circle *Y*?

Question #34:   What is the diameter of a circle whose area is *A*?

SOLID GEOMETRY:

Question #35:   A rectangular tank is 10 units by 8 units by 2 units. What is the number of cubic unit of oil in the tank when it is 5/8 full?

Question #36:   A rectangle box with a square base contains 576 units^3. If the height of the box is 9 units, how many units are on each side of the base?

Question #37:   If the volume of a 2 × 6 × 8 rectangular solid is the same as the volume of a 1 × 8 × *n* rectangular solid, what is the value of *n*?

Question #38:   If the sum of the lengths of all the edges of a cube is 60 units, what is its volume?

Question #39:   A solid cube has a volume of 8 unit^3. What is the volume of the other cube whose sides are twice that of first cube?

Question #40:   The volume of a cube is "*v*" cubic units, and its surface area is "*a*" square units. If *v* = *a*, what is the length of each edge?

Question #41:   A cube whose edges are 3 inches is painted red on all sides. The cube is then cut into smaller cubes, all of which have edges that are 1 inch long. How many of the small cubes have no paint on them?

Question #42:   A cube whose edges are 4 inches is painted red on all sides. The cube is then cut into smaller cubes, all of which have edges that are 1 inch long. How many of the small cubes have no paint on them?

Question #43: A circular pipe has a diameter of 10 feet and a gallon of oil has a volume of 7.5 cubic feet. How many gallons of oil can fit into 50 feet of the pipe?

Question #44: Oil is poured into a cylindrical tank at the rate of 11 unit^3 per minute. How many minutes will it take to fill the tank if its radius is 5 units and its height is 14 units? (Use $\pi = \frac{22}{7}$)

COORDINATE GEOMETRY:

Question #45: If the slope of the line that contains the points $(k, 9)$ and $(1, 1)$ is ½, what is the value of k?

Question #46: If the figure given below, the coordinates of rectangle $ABCD$ are $A(-p, q)$, $B(-p, s)$, $C(r, -s)$, and $D(r, q)$, what is the area rectangle $ABCD$?

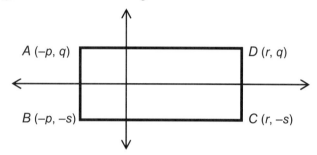

Question #47: If the coordinate of the parallelogram $ABCD$ are $A(-1, 7)$, $B(-2, 1)$, $C(7, 1)$, and $D(8, 7)$, what is the area and perimeter of the parallelogram?

Question #48: In the xy-coordinate plane points $P(1, 1)$, $Q(2, 8)$, and $R(6, 10)$ are three vertices of a parallelogram $PQRS$. What is the sum of the slopes of all the sides of the parallelogram?

Question #49: If the coordinate of the trapezoid $ABCD$ are $A(-5, 7)$, $B(-2, 1)$, $C(5, 1)$, and $D(8, 7)$, what is the area and perimeter of the trapezoid?

Question #50: If the coordinate of the $\triangle ABC$ are $A(0, 7)$, $B(-2, 1)$, and $C(5, 1)$, what is the area and perimeter of the triangle?

Question #51: If a circle passes through $A(0, 2)$ and $B(0, 12)$ with its center at the y-axis, what is the area and circumference of the circle?

Question #52: In a rectangular coordinate system, triangle ABC is drawn so that one side of the triangle connects two points on the y-axis, $B(0, -1)$ and $C(0, 5)$. If point A has coordinate $(a, 0)$ where $a > 0$, and the area of ABC is 24, then what is the value of a?

Question #53: In the figure given below, if the circle given below with center P is tangent to both axes and the distance from P to the origin is n, what is the area of the circle?

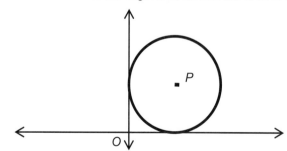

MULTIPLE FIGURES:

Question #54:   The figure below shows an aerial view of a piece of land. If all lines shown are straight lines and all angles shown are right angles, what is the perimeter of the piece of land?

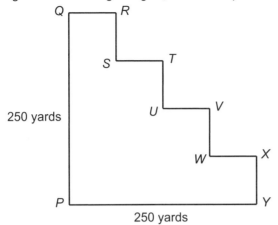

Question #55:   If a 6 by 8 rectangle is inscribed in a circle, what is the radius of the circle?

Question #56:   In the figure given below, if the area of the inscribed rectangular region is 50, then what is the area and circumference of the circle?

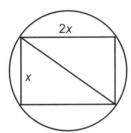

Question #57:   In the figure given below, the midpoints of the sides of square *ABCD* are connected to form square *EFGH*. What is the ratio of the area of square *ABCD* to the area of square *EFGH*?

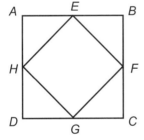

Question #58:   A rectangle has the same area as a circle of radius 10. If the length of the rectangle is 2, what is its width?

Question #59:   The perimeter of a rectangle is equal to the circumference of a circle of radius 5. If the length of the rectangle is 5, what is its width?

Question #60:   A triangle and a circle have equal areas. If the base of the triangle and the diameter of the circle each have length 10, what is the height of the triangle?

Question #61:   What is the length of each of the five equal sides of a regular pentagon if the perimeter of the pentagon is equal to the perimeter of a square whose area is 100?

Question #62: The length of a rectangle is 5 more than the side of a square, and the width of the rectangle is 5 less than the side of the square. If the area of the square is 75, what is the area of the rectangle?

Question #63: A triangle of height 5 and base 8 has an area exactly one-sixth that of a rectangle with width 10. What is the length of the rectangle?

Question #64: If the area of a smaller square is half the area of a larger square with area 1 square unit, then what is the ratio of the diagonal of the larger square to the diagonal of smaller square?

Question #65: What is the perimeter of rectangle X, which is 16 meters wide, and has the same area as rectangle Y, which is 52 meters by 24 meters?

Question #66: If the perimeter of square X and the diagonal of square Y have the same length, what is the ratio of the area of square X to the area of square Y?

Question #67: In the figure given below, the center of the circle is O, and PQ = OP. What is the measure of the marked angle?

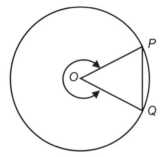

Question #68: In the figure given below, the center of the circle is O, ∠POQ = 120°, and OR with length 2.5 is perpendicular to PQ and it bisects PQ. What is the area of the circle?

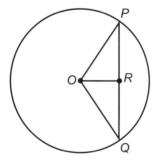

Question #69: If an arc AB with a length of 18π is ¾ of the circumference of a circle, what is the shortest distance between the endpoints of the arc?

Question #70: In a circle, a chord is 24 inches long and its shortest distance from the center of the circle is 9 inches. What is the radius of the circle?

Question #71: A is the center of a circle whose radius is 12, and B is the center of circle whose diameter is 12. If these two circles are tangent to one another, what is the area of the circle whose diameter is AB?

Question #72: In the figure given below, points A, B, and C are the centers of the three circles that are tangent to each other; and circle A has a radius of 15, circle B has a radius of 10, and circle C has a radius of 5. What is the perimeter of triangle ABC?

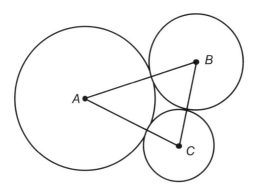

Question #73:   In the figure given below, *A*, *B*, and *C* are all squares tangent to each other with no overlap. If the area of square *A* is 25 and the area of square *B* is 49, what is the area of square *C*?

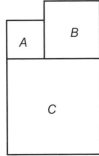

Question #74:   In the figure given below, what is the ratio of the area of Δ*EDC* to the area of square *ABCD*?

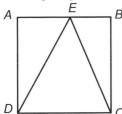

Question #75:   The length of a rectangle is twice its width. If the perimeter of the rectangle is the same as the perimeter of a square of side 6, what is the square of the length of the diagonal of the rectangle?

Question #76:   In the figure given below, *MNOP* and *OQRS* are squares. If the area of *OQRS* is 144, what is the area of *MNOP*?

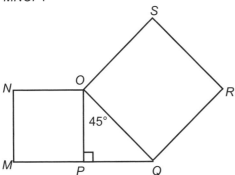

Question #77:   In the figure given below, square *A*, *B*, and *C* are connected at points *P*, *Q*, and *R*. If square *A* has area 81 and square *B* has area 144, what is the area of square *C*?

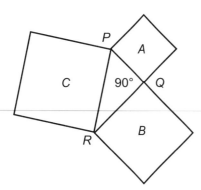

Question #78: In the figure given below, square *ABCD* has a side of 8. What is the sum of the length of the two arcs?

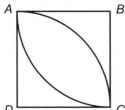

Question #79: A rectangular block with a volume of 250 unit³ was sliced into 2 identical cubes of equal volume. What is the difference, in square units, between the combined surface area of the 2 resulting cubes and the original surface area of the rectangular block?

Question #80: The height, *h*, of a cylinder is equal to the edge of a cube. If the cylinder and the cube have the same volume, what is the radius of the cylinder?

Question #81: Oil is poured from a full rectangular container with dimensions 5 units by 11 units by 14 units into a cylindrical container with a radius of 7 units. Assuming that the oil does not overflow or spill the container, how many inches high will the oil reach? (use π = 22/7)

Question #82: In the figure given below, each curved side is a semicircle with radius 5, and the two parallel sides each have length 20. What is the area of the shaded region?

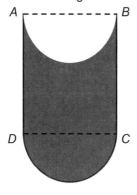

Question #83: In the figure given below, if the area of the square is 100, what is the area of the white region?

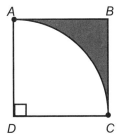

Question #84: In the figure given below, the two semi circles are tangent to one another and to the square. If the side of the square is 10, what is the area of the shaded region?

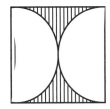

Question #85: In the figure given below, ABCD is a rectangle; and AE and BE are arcs of circle centered at D and C. What is the area of the shaded region?

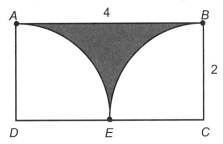

Question #86: In the figure given below, PQRS is a square whose sides are 15. AB, CD, EF, and GH are each 12, and are the diameters of the four semicircles. What is the area of the shaded region?

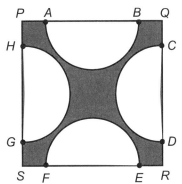

Question #87: The figure given below consists of two semicircles. If the big semicircle has a diameter of 24 and the small semicircle has a diameter of 12, what is the area of the shaded region?

Question #88: In the figure given below, if the circle with center *A* has an area of 256π, what is the area of the shaded region, i.e., the circle with center *B*?

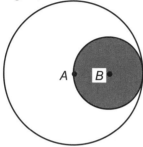

Question #89: In the figure given below, rectangle *ABCD* has an area of 128 and is composed of 8 equal squares. Find the area of the shaded region.

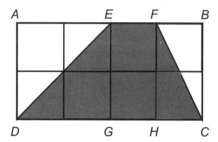

Question #90: In the figure given below, rectangle *ABCD* has an area of 128 and is composed of 8 equal squares. Find the area of the shaded region.

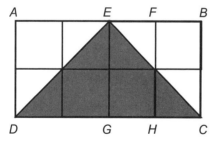

Question #91: In the figure given below, rectangle *ABCD* has an area of 128 and is composed of 8 equal squares. Find the area of the shaded region.

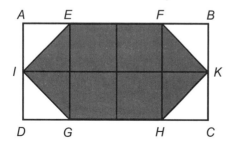

Question #92:   In the figure given below, rectangle *ABCD* has an area of 128 and is composed of 8 equal squares. Find the area of the shaded region.

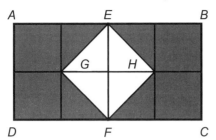

Question #93:   In the figure given below, the outside of a 10 by 15 units rectangular window has a 1-unit wide metallic lining, as shown by the shaded region. What fraction of the window's outside surface is covered by the lining?

Question #94:   In the figure given below, *ABCD* is a square with side 10; and *EG*, *EH*, *FG*, and *FH* are arcs of circle centered at *A*, *B*, *C*, and *D*. What is the area of the white region?

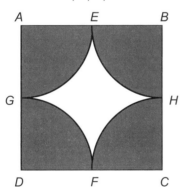

Question #95:   In the figure given below, *P*, *Q*, and *R*, which are the centers of the three circles, all lie on the same line. What is the ratio of the area of the entire white region to the area of the shaded region?

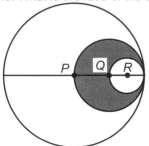

PRACTICE EXERCISE – QUESTIONS & ANSWERS WITH EXPLANATIONS:

LINES & ANGLES:

Question #1:   In the figure given below, what is the value of $\dfrac{a+b}{a-b}$?

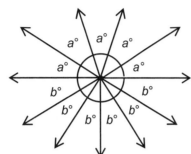

Solution: For the top part $\Rightarrow 5a = 180°$ [Sum of the angles of a straight line equal 180°]
                        $\Rightarrow a = 36°$ [Divide both sides by 5]
                For the top part $\Rightarrow 6b = 180°$ [Sum of the angles of a straight line equal 180°]
                        $\Rightarrow b = 30°$ [Divide both sides by 6]
                Value of $\dfrac{a+b}{a-b}$ $\Rightarrow \dfrac{36+30}{36-30} = \dfrac{66}{6} = 11$ [Substitute the values of a and b from above]

Question #2:   If the measures of two supplementary angles are in the ratio of 2:7, what is the measure of the bigger angle?

Solution: Let the measure of Smaller Angle = $2x$
                And, the measure of Bigger Angle = $7x$
                EZ Problem Set-Up $\Rightarrow$ Sum of pair of supplementary angles equal 180°:
                                $\Rightarrow 2x + 7x = 180°$ [Set up the equation]
                                $\Rightarrow 9x = 180°$ [Combine like-terms]
                                $\Rightarrow x = 20°$ [Divide both sides by 9]
                Measure of Smaller Angle $\Rightarrow 2x = 2 \times 20 = 40°$
                Measure of Bigger Angle $\Rightarrow 7x = 7 \times 20 = 140°$

Question #3:   Angle A and angle B are complementary. The measure of angle B is 6 less than five times the measure of angle A. What is the measure of angle B?

Solution: Let, the measure of $\angle A$ $\Rightarrow x$
                Then, the measure of $\angle B \Rightarrow 5x - 6$
                EZ Problem Set-Up $\Rightarrow$ Sum of complementary angles equal 90°
                                $\Rightarrow \angle A + \angle B = 90°$ [Set up the equation]
                                $\Rightarrow x + 5x - 6 = 90°$ [Substitute the values of the angles]
                                $\Rightarrow 6x - 6 = 90°$ [Combine like-terms]
                                $\Rightarrow 6x = 96°$ [Add 6 to both sides]
                                $\Rightarrow x = 16°$ [Divide both sides by 6]
                Measure of $\angle A \Rightarrow x = 16°$
                Measure of $\angle B \Rightarrow 5x - 6 = 5(16) - 6 = 80 - 6 = 74°$

Question #4:   Angle A and angle B are supplementary. The measure of angle B is 2 less than six times the measure of angle A. What is the measure of angle B?

Solution: Let, the measure of $\angle A \Rightarrow x$ Then, the measure of $\angle B \Rightarrow 6x - 2$
                EZ Problem Set-Up $\Rightarrow$ Sum of supplementary angles equal 180°
                                $\Rightarrow \angle A + \angle B = 180°$ [Set up the equation]
                                $\Rightarrow x + 6x - 2 = 180°$ [Substitute the values of the angles]
                                $\Rightarrow 7x - 2 = 180°$ [Combine like-terms]

$\Rightarrow 7x = 182°$ [Add 2 to both sides]

$\Rightarrow x = 26°$ [Divide both sides by 7]

Measure of $\angle A \Rightarrow x = 26°$

Measure of $\angle B \Rightarrow 6x - 2 = 6(26) - 2 = 156 - 2 = 154°$

Question #5:   In the figure given below, what is the value of y?

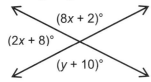

Solution: EZ Problem Set-Up $\Rightarrow$ Sum of the angles of a straight line equal 180°.

$\Rightarrow (8x + 2) + (2x + 8) = 180°$ [Set up the equation]

$\Rightarrow 10x + 10 = 180°$ [Combine like-terms]

$\Rightarrow 10x = 170$ [Subtract 10 from both sides]

$\Rightarrow x = 17°$ [Divide both sides by 10]

EZ Problem Set-Up $\Rightarrow$ Measures of vertical angles are equal to each other.

$\Rightarrow 8x + 2 = y + 10$ [Set up the equation]

$\Rightarrow 8(17) + 2 = y + 10$ [Substitute $x = 17°$]

$\Rightarrow 136 + 2 = y + 10$ [Apply distributive property]

$\Rightarrow 138 = y + 10$ [Combine like-terms]

$\Rightarrow y = 128$ [Subtract 10 from both sides]

Question #6:   In the figure given below, if AB is parallel to CD, EG bisects angle BEF, and FG bisects angle EFD, what is the measure of angle EGF?

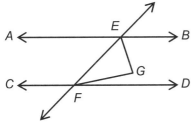

Solution: Measure of $\Rightarrow \angle BEF + \angle EFD = 180°$ [Same side interior angles are supplementary]

$\Rightarrow ½(\angle BEF + \angle EFD) = 90°$ [Divide both sides by 2]

$\Rightarrow \angle FEG + \angle EFG = 90°$ [Substitute $½\angle BEF = \angle FEG$ and $½\angle EFD = \angle EFG$]

In ΔEGF $\Rightarrow \angle FEG + \angle EFG + \angle EGF = 180°$ [Sum of angles in a triangle is 180°]

$\Rightarrow 90° + \angle EGF = 180°$ [Substitute $\angle FEG + \angle EFG = 90°$]

$\Rightarrow \angle EGF = 90°$ [Subtract 90° from both sides]

Question #7:   In the figure given below, $AB = 5$, $CD = 6$, and $AD = 15$. What is the distance from D to the midpoint of BC?

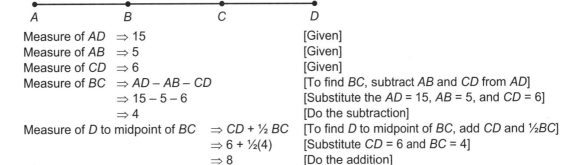

Solution: Measure of $AD \Rightarrow 15$ [Given]

Measure of $AB \Rightarrow 5$ [Given]

Measure of $CD \Rightarrow 6$ [Given]

Measure of $BC \Rightarrow AD - AB - CD$ [To find BC, subtract AB and CD from AD]

$\Rightarrow 15 - 5 - 6$ [Substitute the $AD = 15$, $AB = 5$, and $CD = 6$]

$\Rightarrow 4$ [Do the subtraction]

Measure of D to midpoint of $BC \Rightarrow CD + ½ BC$ [To find D to midpoint of BC, add CD and $½BC$]

$\Rightarrow 6 + ½(4)$ [Substitute $CD = 6$ and $BC = 4$]

$\Rightarrow 8$ [Do the addition]

Question #8: In the figure given below, $AC = 20$ and $AB = BC$. Point D (not shown) is on the line between B and C such that $BD = DC$. What is the distance from A to D?

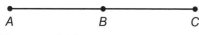

Solution:

Measure of AC	$\Rightarrow 20$	[Given]
Measure of AB or BC	$\Rightarrow \frac{1}{2}(AC)$	[Since $AB = BC$, so B is the midpoint of AC]
	$\Rightarrow \frac{1}{2}(20)$	[Substitute $AC = 20$]
	$\Rightarrow 10$	[Do the multiplication]
Measure of BD or DC	$\Rightarrow \frac{1}{2}(BC)$	[Since $BD = DC$, so D is the midpoint of BC]
	$\Rightarrow \frac{1}{2}(10) = 5$	[Substitute $BC = 10$]
Measure of AD	$\Rightarrow AB + BD$	[To find AD, add AB and BD]
	$\Rightarrow 10 + 5$	[Substitute $AB = 10$ and $BD = 5$]
	$\Rightarrow 15$	[Do the addition]

Question #9: Points X, Y and Z lie on a line with Y between X and Z, and M and N are midpoints of XY and YZ, respectively. If $XY{:}YZ = 5{:}1$, what is $XZ{:}MN$?

Solution: The best way to solve this problem is to sketch a figure. A good starting point would be to draw XY with a length of 5 units and YZ with a length of 1 unit. Then, place M in the center of XY, which will make XM & MY each with a length of 2.5 units. Next, place N in the center of YZ, which will make YN & NZ each with a length of 0.5 units. Make sure pick a number for XY and YZ, which has a ratio of 5:1. The figure should look like the following:

Ratio of XZ to $MN \Rightarrow 6{:}3 = 2{:}1$

Question #10: Points P and Q are on a number line, such that P corresponds to 0.975 and Q corresponds to 0.987. If X is a point on the number line three-fourths of the distance from Q to P, and Y is a point on the number line two-thirds of the distance from P to Q, what is the ratio of XY to PQ?

Solution: Since this is a ratio problem, eliminate the decimals; so, point P is at 975 and point Q is at 987.

Measure of PQ $\Rightarrow 987 - 975 = 12$ points
Measure of XQ $\Rightarrow \frac{3}{4}$ of $12 = 9$ points
Point X is a point on the number line three-fourths of the distance from Q to P $\Rightarrow X = 987 - 9 = 978$
Measure of PY $\Rightarrow 2/3$ of $12 = 8$ points
Point Y is a point on the number line two-thirds of the distance from P to Q $\Rightarrow Y = 975 + 8 = 983$
Measure of YQ $\Rightarrow PQ - PY = 12 - 8 = 4$ points
Measure of PX $\Rightarrow PQ - XQ = 12 - 9 = 3$ points
Measure of XY $\Rightarrow PY - PX$ or $XQ - YQ = 8 - 3$ or $9 - 4 = 5$ points

Ratio of XY to $PQ \Rightarrow 5{:}12$

POLYGONS:

Question #11: What is the measure of 2 of the 8 angles of a regular octagon?

Solution:

Sum of the Angles	$\Rightarrow (n - 2) \times 180°$	[Write the appropriate formula]
	$\Rightarrow (8 - 2) \times 180° = 6 \times 180° = 1{,}080°$	[Substitute the known values and simplify]
Each Interior Angle	$\Rightarrow$ Sum of Angles ÷ No. of Sides	[Write the appropriate formula]
	$\Rightarrow 1{,}080° \div 8 = 135°$	[Substitute the known values and simplify]
Two Interior Angles	$\Rightarrow 135° \times 2 = 270°$	[Multiply by 2]

Question #12: If the angles of a seven-sided polygon are in the ratio of 2:2:3:3:4:5:6, what is the difference in the degree measures between the largest and smallest angles?

Solution:

Sum of the Angles	$\Rightarrow (n - 2) \times 180°$	[Write the appropriate formula]
	$\Rightarrow (7 - 2) \times 180° = 5 \times 180° = 900°$	[Substitute the known values and simplify]

EZ Problem Set-Up ⇒ The angles of a seven-sided polygon are in the ratio of 2:2:3:3:4:5:6
                               ⇒ $2x + 2x + 3x + 3x + 4x + 5x + 6x = 900$ [Set up the equation]
                               ⇒ $25x = 900°$ [Combine like-terms]
                               ⇒ $x = 36°$ [Divide both sides by 25]
Degree Measure of the Smallest Angle   ⇒ $36° × 2 = 72°$
Degree Measure of the Largest Angle   ⇒ $36° × 6 = 216°$
Difference between the Degree Measure of the Largest and Smallest Angles ⇒ $216° − 72° = 144°$

TRIANGLES:

Question #13:   In the figure given below, in $\triangle ABC$, if AD bisects $\angle BAC$, then what is the measure of $\angle ADC$?

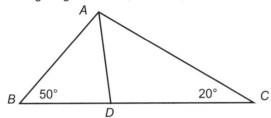

Solution: In $\triangle ABC$ ⇒ $\angle BAC + \angle ABC + \angle ACB = 180°$ [Sum of all interior angles of a triangle equals 180°]
                           ⇒ $\angle BAC + 50° + 20° = 180°$ [Substitute the values of the angles]
                           ⇒ $\angle BAC + 70° = 180°$ [Combine like-terms]
                           ⇒ $\angle BAC = 110°$ [Subtract 70° from both sides]
Measure of $\angle DAC$ ⇒ $\frac{1}{2}(\angle BAC)$ [AD bisect $\angle BAC$]
                         ⇒ $\frac{1}{2}(110°) = 55°$ [Substitute $\angle BAC = 110°$]
In $\triangle ADC$ ⇒ $\angle DAC + \angle ACD + \angle ADC = 180°$ [Sum of all interior angles of a triangle equals 180°]
                           ⇒ $55° + 20° + \angle ADC = 180°$ [Substitute the values of the angles]
                           ⇒ $75° + \angle ADC = 180°$ [Combine like-terms]
                           ⇒ $\angle ADC = 105°$ [Subtract 75° from both sides]

Question #14:   If the difference between the measures of two smaller angles of a right triangle is 52°, what is the measure in degrees, of the smallest angle?

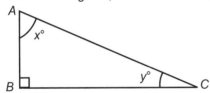

Solution: Draw a diagram, label it, and then write the equations.
Let, x = larger angle; y = smaller angle.
Sum of x and y is 90°   ⇒ $x + y = 90°$ ⇒ Equation #1
Difference between x and y is 52° ⇒ $x − y = 52°$ ⇒ Equation #2
Solve the two equations simultaneously:
⇒ $x \ + y = 90°$ [Rewrite Equation #1]
⇒ $\underline{x \ − y = 52°}$ [Rewrite Equation #2]
    $2x$ $= 142°$ [Add the two equations]
     x $= 71°$ [Divide both sides by 2]
Substitute the value of x in Equation #1:
⇒ $x + y = 90°$ [Rewrite Equation #1]
⇒ $71° + y = 90°$ [Substitute $x = 71°$]
⇒ $y = 19°$ [Subtract 71° from both sides]

Question #15:   In the figure given below, in $\triangle ABC$, what is the value of EC?

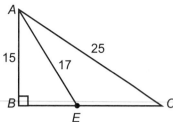

Solution: In $\triangle ABC$ $\Rightarrow AC^2 = AB^2 + BC^2$ [Apply Pythagorean Theorem]
                    $\Rightarrow 25^2 = 15^2 + BC^2$ [Substitute the values of the known sides]
                    $\Rightarrow BC^2 = 25^2 - 15^2$ [Subtract 15^2 from both sides]
                    $\Rightarrow BC^2 = 625 - 225$ [Solve the exponents]
                    $\Rightarrow BC^2 = 400$ [Do the subtraction]
                    $\Rightarrow BC = 20$ units   [Square root both sides]
           In $\triangle ABE$ $\Rightarrow AE^2 = AB^2 + BE^2$ [Apply Pythagorean Theorem]
                    $\Rightarrow 17^2 = 15^2 + BE^2$ [Substitute the values of the known sides]
                    $\Rightarrow BE^2 = 17^2 - 15^2$ [Subtract 15^2 from both sides]
                    $\Rightarrow BE^2 = 289 - 225$ [Solve the exponents]
                    $\Rightarrow BE^2 = 64$ [Do the subtraction]
                    $\Rightarrow BE = 8$ units   [Square root both sides]
     Measure of EC $\Rightarrow BC - BE$ [Measure of EC is the difference between BC and BE]
                    $\Rightarrow 20 - 8 = 12$ units   [Substitute the values and simplify]

Question #16:   In the figure given below, in $\triangle ABC$, what is the value of AE?

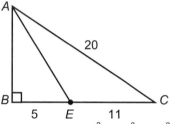

Solution: In $\triangle ABC$ $\Rightarrow AC^2 = AB^2 + BC^2$ [Apply Pythagorean Theorem]
                    $\Rightarrow 20^2 = AB^2 + (11 + 5)^2$ [Substitute the values of the known sides]
                    $\Rightarrow 20^2 = AB^2 + 16^2$ [Simplify within parentheses]
                    $\Rightarrow AB^2 = 20^2 - 16^2$ [Subtract 16^2 from both sides]
                    $\Rightarrow AB^2 = 400 - 256$ [Solve the exponents]
                    $\Rightarrow AB^2 = 144$ [Do the subtraction]
                    $\Rightarrow AB = 12$ units   [Square root both sides]
           In $\triangle ABE$ $\Rightarrow AE^2 = AB^2 + BE^2$ [Apply Pythagorean Theorem]
                    $\Rightarrow AE^2 = 12^2 + 5^2$ [Substitute the values of the known sides]
                    $\Rightarrow AE^2 = 144 + 25$ [Solve the exponents]
                    $\Rightarrow AE^2 = 169$ [Do the addition]
                    $\Rightarrow AE = 13$ units   [Square root both sides]

Question #17:   In the figure given below, what is the value of x?

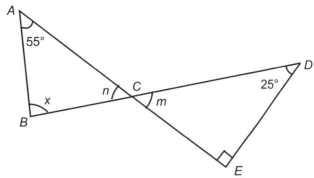

Solution: In ΔCDE   ⇒ 90° + 25° + m° = 180°   [Sum of all interior angles of a triangle equals 180°]
                              ⇒ 115° + m° = 180°   [Combine like-terms]
                              ⇒ m° = 65°   [Subtract 115° from both sides]
              Measure of ⇒ m° = n° = 65°   [Measure of vertical angles are equal to each other]
              In ΔABC   ⇒ 55° + 65° + x° = 180°   [Sum of all interior angles of a triangle equals 180°]
                              ⇒ 120° + x° = 180°   [Combine like-terms]
                              ⇒ x° = 60°   [Subtract 120° from both sides]

Question #18:   In the figure given below, in ΔABC, what is the value of x?

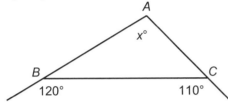

Solution: Measure of ∠ABC = 180° − 120° = 60°   [Sum of supplementary angles equal 180°]
              Measure of ∠ACB = 180° − 110° = 70°   [Sum of supplementary angles equal 180°]
              EZ Problems Set-Up ⇒ ∠ABC + ∠ACB + ∠BAC = 180°   [Sum of angles of a triangle equals 180°]
                              ⇒ 60° + 70° + ∠BAC = 180°   [Substitute the values of known angles]
                              ⇒ 130° + ∠BAC = 180°   [Combine like-terms]
                              ⇒ ∠BAC = x = 50°   [Subtract 130° from both sides]

Question #19:   If the degree measure of the angles of a triangle are in the ratio of 1:2:6, what is the positive difference between the measure of the largest angle and the measure of the smallest angle?

Solution: Measure of the Smallest Angle   ⇒ $\frac{1}{9}$ × 180° (sum of all angles) = 20°

              Measure of the Middle Angle   ⇒ $\frac{2}{9}$ × 180° (sum of all angles) = 40°

              Measure of the largest Angle   ⇒ $\frac{6}{9}$ × 180° (sum of all angles) = 120°

              Positive difference between the largest angle and the smallest angle ⇒ 120° − 20° = 100°

Question #20:   In the figure given below, if AD is perpendicular to BC in ΔABC, what is the value of x?

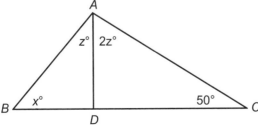

Solution: In ΔADC   ⇒ ∠ADC + ∠ACD + ∠DAC = 180°   [Sum of all interior angles of a triangle equals 180°]

$\Rightarrow 90° + 50° + 2z° = 180°$ [Substitute the values of the known angles]

$\Rightarrow 140° + 2z° = 180°$ [Combine like-terms]

$\Rightarrow 2z° = 40°$ [Subtract 140° from both sides]

$\Rightarrow z° = 20°$ [Divide both sides by 2]

In Δ ADB $\Rightarrow \angle ABD + \angle BAD + \angle ADB = 180°$ [Sum of all interior angles of a triangle equals 180°]

$\Rightarrow x° + z° + 90° = 180°$ [Substitute the values of the known angles]

$\Rightarrow x° + 20° + 90° = 180°$ [Substitute $z = 20°$]

$\Rightarrow x° + 110° = 180°$ [Combine like-terms]

$\Rightarrow x° = 70°$ [Subtract 110° from both sides]

Question #21: In Δ PQR, the measure of $\angle Q$ is 6 more than twice the measure of measure of $\angle R$, and the measure of $\angle P$ is two less than five times the measure of $\angle R$. What is the measure of $\angle P$?

Solution: In ΔPQR: Let the measure of $\angle R$ be x

$\angle Q$ is 6 more than twice the measure of $\angle R$ $\Rightarrow 2x + 6$

$\angle P$ is two less than five times the measure of $\angle R$ $\Rightarrow 5x - 2$

EZ Problem Set-Up $\Rightarrow$ Sum of the angles in a triangle = 180°

$\Rightarrow \angle P + \angle Q + \angle R = 180°$ [Set up the problem]

$\Rightarrow (5x - 2) + (2x + 6) + (x) = 180°$ [Substitute the values of the angles]

$\Rightarrow 8x + 4 = 180°$ [Combine like-terms]

$\Rightarrow 8x = 176°$ [Subtract 4° from both sides]

$\Rightarrow x = 22°$ [Divide both sides by 8]

Measure of: $\angle P \Rightarrow x = 22°$ [Substitute $x = 22°$]

$\angle Q \Rightarrow 2x + 6 = 2(22) + 6 = 44 + 6 = 50°$ [Substitute $x = 22°$]

$\angle R \Rightarrow 5x - 2 = 5(22) - 2 = 108°$ [Substitute $x = 22°$]

Question #22: If the measure of the angles of a triangle are in the ratio of 1:2:3, and if the perimeter of the triangle is $60 + 20\sqrt{3}$ units, what is the length of the smallest side?

Solution: Angles of triangle are in the ratio of 1:2:3 $\Rightarrow x + 2x + 3x = 180°$ [Sum of angles in triangle is 180°]

$\Rightarrow 6x = 180°$ [Combine like terms]

$\Rightarrow x = 30°$ [Divide both sides by 6]

The triangle is a 30°-60°-90° right triangle, and the sides are x, $2x$ and $x\sqrt{3}$.

Perimeter of the triangle $\Rightarrow S_1 + S_2 + S_3 = 60 + 20\sqrt{3}$ [Equate perimeter formula to given perimeter]

$\Rightarrow x + 2x + x\sqrt{3} = 60 + 20\sqrt{3}$ [Substitute the value of the sides]

$\Rightarrow 3x + x\sqrt{3} = 60 + 20\sqrt{3}$ [Combine like-terms]

$\Rightarrow x(3 + \sqrt{3}) = 20(3 + \sqrt{3})$ [Factor out the common terms on both sides]

$\Rightarrow x = 20$ units   [Cancel-out the common terms on both sides]

Question #23: If the measure of the angles of a triangle are in the ratio of 1:1:2, and if the perimeter of the triangle is $10 + 5\sqrt{2}$ units, what is the length of the smallest side?

Solution: Angles of triangle are in the ratio of 1:1:2 $\Rightarrow x + x + 2x = 180°$ [Sum of angles in triangle is 180°]

$\Rightarrow 4x = 180°$ [Combine like terms]

$\Rightarrow x = 45°$ [Divide both sides by 4]

The triangle is a 45°-45°-90° right triangle, and the sides are x, x and $x\sqrt{2}$.

Perimeter of the triangle $\Rightarrow S_1 + S_2 + S_3 = 10 + 5\sqrt{2}$ [Equate perimeter formula to given perimeter]

$\Rightarrow x + x + x\sqrt{2} = 10 + 5\sqrt{2}$ [Substitute the value of the sides]

$\Rightarrow 2x + x\sqrt{2} = 10 + 5\sqrt{2}$ [Combine like-terms]

$\Rightarrow x(2 + \sqrt{2}) = 5(2 + \sqrt{2})$ [Factor out the common terms on both sides]

$\Rightarrow x = 5$ units   [Cancel-out the common terms on both sides]

Question #24: The lengths of the sides of a triangle are $(x - 2)$ units, $(2x + 8)$ units, and $(5x - 1)$ units. If the perimeter of the triangle is 69 units, what is the length of the shortest side?

Solution: Perimeter of Triangle $\Rightarrow S_1 + S_2 + S_3 = 69$ [Equate perimeter formula to given perimeter]

$$\Rightarrow (x - 2) + (2x + 8) + (5x - 1) = 69 \qquad \text{[Substitute the values of the sides]}$$
$$\Rightarrow 8x + 5 = 69 \qquad \text{[Combine like-terms]}$$
$$\Rightarrow 8x = 64 \qquad \text{[Subtract 5 from both sides]}$$
$$\Rightarrow x = 8 \text{ units} \qquad \text{[Divide both sides by 8]}$$

Length of sides $\Rightarrow x - 2 \qquad \Rightarrow 8 - 2 = 6$ units $\qquad$ [Substitute $x = 8$]
$\Rightarrow 2x + 8 \qquad \Rightarrow 2(8) + 8 = 24$ units $\qquad$ [Substitute $x = 8$]
$\Rightarrow 5x - 1 \qquad \Rightarrow 5(8) - 1 = 39$ units $\qquad$ [Substitute $x = 8$]

Length of the shortest side $\Rightarrow$ 6 units

Question #25: In isosceles triangle PQR, each leg is 5 units less than twice the length of the base. If the perimeter of the triangle is 65 units, what is the length of a leg?

Solution: In ΔPQR: Let it the measure of the base, QR be x units

Measure of PQ is 5 units less than twice the length of the base $\Rightarrow 2x - 5$
Measure of PR is 5 units less than twice the length of the base $\Rightarrow 2x - 5$

Perimeter of $\Delta PQR \Rightarrow PQ + QR + PR = 65 \qquad$ [Equate perimeter formula to given perimeter]
$\Rightarrow x + 2x - 5 + 2x - 5 = 65 \qquad$ [Substitute the values of the sides]
$\Rightarrow 5x - 10 = 65 \qquad$ [Combine like-terms]
$\Rightarrow 5x = 75 \qquad$ [Add 10 to both sides]
$\Rightarrow x = 15 \text{ units} \qquad$ [Divide both sides by 5]

Length of Base $\Rightarrow x = 15$ units $\qquad$ [Substitute $x = 15$]
Length of Leg $\Rightarrow 2x - 5 = 2(15) - 5 = 30 - 5 = 25$ units $\qquad$ [Substitute $x = 15$]

Question #26: If the area of a triangle is 63 unit^2, and the length of the height minus the length of the base equals 5 units, then what is the length of the height?

Solution: Let, the height of the triangle $\Rightarrow H$ units $\quad$ And, the base of the triangle $\Rightarrow B$ units

Length of the height minus Length of the base is 5 $\Rightarrow H - B = 5$
$\Rightarrow H = B + 5$

Area of Triangle $\Rightarrow \frac{1}{2} \times$ Base $\times$ Height $\qquad$ [Write the appropriate formula]
$\Rightarrow \frac{1}{2} \times B \times (B + 5) = 63 \qquad$ [Substitute the values of the base and height]
$\Rightarrow B(B + 5) = 126 \qquad$ [Multiply both sides by 2]
$\Rightarrow B^2 + 5B = 126 \qquad$ [Apply distributive property]
$\Rightarrow B^2 + 5B - 126 = 0 \qquad$ [Subtract 126 from both sides]
$\Rightarrow (B - 9)(B + 14) = 0 \qquad$ [Factor the trinomial into two binomials]
$\Rightarrow B = +9 \text{ or } -14 \qquad$ [Solve for the positive value of B]

Height of Triangle $\Rightarrow H = B + 5 = 9 + 5 = 14$ units

QUADRILATERALS:

Question #27: What is the area of rectangle whose length is 9 times its width, and its perimeter is 160 units?

Solution: Let, the width of the rectangle $\qquad \Rightarrow W$ units
Then, the lengths of the rectangle $\Rightarrow 9W$ units
Perimeter of Rectangle $\quad \Rightarrow 2L + 2W = 160 \qquad$ [Equate the perimeter formula with the given perimeter]
$\Rightarrow 2(9W) + 2W = 160 \qquad$ [Substitute $L = 9W$]
$\Rightarrow 18W + 2W = 160 \qquad$ [Apply distributive property]
$\Rightarrow 20W = 160 \qquad$ [Combine like-terms]
Measure of *Width* $\quad \Rightarrow W = 8$ units $\qquad$ [Divide both sides by 20]
Measure of *Length* $\quad \Rightarrow L = 9W = 9 \times 8 = 72$ units $\quad$ [Substitute $W = 8$]
Area of Rectangle $\quad \Rightarrow LW \qquad$ [Write the appropriate formula]
$\Rightarrow 72 \times 8 = 576$ unit^2 $\qquad$ [Substitute the values and simplify]

Question #28: What is the perimeter of rectangle whose length is 5 times its width, and its area is 125 unit^2?

Solution: Let, the width of the rectangle $\qquad \Rightarrow W$ units
Then, the length of the rectangle $\Rightarrow 5W$ units
Area of Rectangle $\quad \Rightarrow LW = 125 \qquad$ [Equate the area formula with the given area]
$\Rightarrow W \times 5W = 125 \qquad$ [Substitute $L = 5W$]
$\Rightarrow 5W^2 = 125 \qquad$ [Apply distributive property]

$$\Rightarrow W^2 = 25 \qquad \text{[Divide both sides by 5]}$$

Measure of width $\Rightarrow W = 5$ units [Square root both sides]

Measure of length $\Rightarrow L = 5W = 5 \times 5 = 25$ units [Substitute $W = 5$]

Perimeter of Rectangle $\Rightarrow 2(L + W)$ [Write the appropriate formula]

$\Rightarrow 2(5 + 25) = 2(30) = 60$ units [Substitute the values and simplify]

Question #29: A rectangular parking space is marked out by painting three of its sides white. If the length of the unpainted side is 11 units, and the sum of the lengths of the painted sides is 51 units, what is the area of the parking space in square feet?

Solution: Measure of the unpainted side = 11 units

Since the lengths of painted sides = 51 units

Let the length of painted side = x

EZ Problem Set-Up $\Rightarrow$ 1 Painted Side (opposite the unpainted side) + 2 Painted Sides = 51

$\Rightarrow 11 + 2x = 51$ [Set up the equation]

$\Rightarrow 2x = 40$ [Subtract 11 from both sides]

$\Rightarrow x = 20$ units [Divide both sides by 2]

Area of Rectangle $\Rightarrow LW$ [Write the appropriate formula]

$\Rightarrow 20 \times 11 = 220$ unit^2 [Substitute the values and simplify]

Question #30: The area of a certain rectangle is 125 unit^2. If the ratio of the length to the width of the rectangle is 5 to 1, what is the perimeter of the rectangle?

Solution: Ratio of length to width is 5: 1 $\Rightarrow$ Let the width = W and length = $5W$

Area of Rectangle $\Rightarrow LW = 125$ [Equate the area formula with given area]

$\Rightarrow (5W)(W) = 125$ [Substitute $L = 5w$]

$\Rightarrow 5W^2 = 125$ [Apply distributive property]

$\Rightarrow W^2 = 25$ [Divide both sides by 5]

Measure of Width $\Rightarrow W = 5$ units [Square root both sides]

Measure of Length $\Rightarrow L = 5W = 5(5) = 25$ units [Substitute $W = 5$]

Perimeter of Rectangle $\Rightarrow 2(L + W)$ [Write the appropriate formula]

$\Rightarrow 2(25 + 5) = 2(30) = 60$ units [Substitute the values and simplify]

Question #31: In rhombus $ABCD$, the two diagonals AC and DB intersect at point O. if the measure of one diagonal AC is 24 units and the measure of other diagonal DB is 18 units, what is the measure of a side of the rhombus?

Solution: Measure of First Diagonal $\Rightarrow AC = 24$ units & Measure of $AO \Rightarrow \frac{1}{2}(24) = 12$ units

Measure of Second Diagonal $\Rightarrow BD = 18$ units & Measure of $BO \Rightarrow \frac{1}{2}(18) = 9$ units

Apply Pythagorean Theorem $\Rightarrow AB^2 = AO^2 + BO^2$ [Write the Pythagorean Theorem]

$\Rightarrow AB^2 = 12^2 + 9^2$ [Substitute the known values]

$\Rightarrow AB^2 = 144 + 81$ [Solve the exponents]

$\Rightarrow AB^2 = 225$ [Do the addition]

$\Rightarrow AB = 15$ units [Square root both sides]

Question #32: In the figure given below, what is the area of trapezoid $ABCD$?

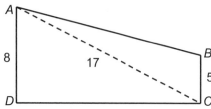

Solution: In $\triangle ADC$ $\Rightarrow AC^2 = AD^2 + DC^2$ [Apply Pythagorean Theorem]

$\Rightarrow 17^2 = 8^2 + DC^2$ [Substitute the values of the known sides]

$\Rightarrow 289 = 64 + DC^2$ [Solve the exponents]

$\Rightarrow DC^2 = 289 - 64$ [Subtract 64 from both sides]

$\Rightarrow DC^2 = 225$ [Do the subtraction]

$\Rightarrow DC = 15$ units [Square root both sides]

Area of Trapezoid $\Rightarrow \frac{1}{2}(b_1 + b_2)\,h$ [Write the appropriate formula]

$\Rightarrow \frac{1}{2}(AD + BC) \times (DC)$ [Write the names of the quantities]

$\Rightarrow \frac{1}{2}(8 + 5) \times 15$ [Substitute the values of the sides]

$\Rightarrow \frac{1}{2}(13) \times 15$ [Simplify]

$\Rightarrow 97.5$ unit^2 [Do the multiplication]

CIRCLES:

Question #33: If the area of circle X is 64π unit^2 and the area of circle Y is 256π unit^2, what is the ratio of the radius of circle X to that of circle Y?

Solution: Area of circle X $\Rightarrow \pi r^2 = 64\pi$ [Write the area of circle X]

$\Rightarrow r^2 = 64$ [Divide both sides by π]

$\Rightarrow r = 8$ units   [Square root both sides]

Area of circle Y $\Rightarrow \pi r^2 = 256\pi$ [Write the area of circle X]

$\Rightarrow r^2 = 256$ [Divide both sides by π]

$\Rightarrow r = 16$ units   [Square root both sides]

Ratio of Radius of circle X : Radius of circle $Y \Rightarrow 8:16 = 1:2$

Question #34: What is the diameter of a circle whose area is A?

Solution: $\Rightarrow A = \pi r^2$ [Write the formula of area of circle]

$\Rightarrow r^2 = \dfrac{A}{\pi}$ [Divide both sides by π]

$\Rightarrow r = \sqrt{\dfrac{A}{\pi}}$ [Square root both sides]

$\Rightarrow 2r = 2\sqrt{\dfrac{A}{\pi}}$ [Multiply both sides by 2]

$\Rightarrow d = 2\sqrt{\dfrac{A}{\pi}}$ [Substitute $2r = d$]

SOLID GEOMETRY:

Question #35: A rectangular tank is 10 units by 8 units by 2 units. What is the number of cubic unit of oil in the tank when it is 5/8 full?

Solution: V of Rectangular Tank $\Rightarrow LWH = 10 \times 8 \times 2 = 160$ units^3 [Apply appropriate formula and simplify]

V of 5/8 of the Tank $\Rightarrow \dfrac{5}{8} \times 160 = 100$ units^3 [Multiply the volume by 5/8]

Question #36: A rectangle box with a square base contains 576 units^3. If the height of the box is 9 units, how many units are on each side of the base?

Solution: Measure of *Length* = Measure of *Width*   [Base of the rectangular solid is a square]

Area of Base $\Rightarrow LW$ [Write the appropriate formula]

$\Rightarrow L^2$ [Substitute $W = L$]

Height of rectangular solid $\Rightarrow 9$ units   [Given]

EZ Problem Set-Up $\Rightarrow$ Volume of Rectangular Box = Area of Base × Height = 576 unit^3

$\Rightarrow L^2 H = 576$ [Set up the equation]

$\Rightarrow L^2 \times 9 = 576$ [Substitute $H = 9$]

$\Rightarrow L^2 = 64$ [Divide both sides by 9]

$\Rightarrow L = 8$ units   [Square root both sides]

Question #37: If the volume of a $2 \times 6 \times 8$ rectangular solid is the same as the volume of a $1 \times 8 \times n$ rectangular solid, what is the value of n?

Solution: Volume of $2 \times 6 \times 8$ Rectangular Solid $\Rightarrow 96$ unit^3

Volume of $1 \times 8 \times n$ Rectangular Solid $\Rightarrow 8n$ unit^3

EZ Problem Set-Up $\Rightarrow$ Volume of 2 × 6 × 8 Solid = Volume of 1 × 8 × n Solid
$\Rightarrow$ 96 = 8n [Set up the equation]
$\Rightarrow$ n = 12   [Divide both sides by 8]

Question #38: If the sum of the lengths of all the edges of a cube is 60 units, what is its volume?
Solution: Sum of lengths of all the edges of cube $\Rightarrow$ 60 units
Length of each leg of the cube $\Rightarrow$ Sum of Lengths of Edges ÷ No. of Edges
                                        $\Rightarrow$ 60 ÷ 12 = 5 units
Volume of Cube $\Rightarrow$ s^3 = $(5)^3$ = 125 unit^3 [Apply appropriate formula and simplify]

Question #39: A solid cube has a volume of 8 unit^3. What is the volume of the other cube whose sides are twice that of first cube?
Solution: Volume of first cube $\Rightarrow$ s^3 = 8 unit^3 [Write the appropriate formula]
                                        $\Rightarrow$ s = 2 units   [Substitute the known values]
Side of the other cube = twice the side of first cube = 2(2) = 4
Volume of the other cube $\Rightarrow$ s^3 = 4^3 = 64 unit^3 [Apply appropriate formula and simplify]

Question #40: The volume of a cube is "v" cubic units, and its surface area is "a" square units. If $v = a$, what is the length of each edge?
Solution: Let, the measure of the edge of cube $\Rightarrow$ s
Then, the Volume of the cube $\Rightarrow$ s^3
And, the Surface Area of the cube $\Rightarrow$ $6s^2$
EZ Problem Set-Up $\Rightarrow$ Volume = Surface Area
                    $\Rightarrow$ s^3 = $6s^2$ [Set up the equation]
                    $\Rightarrow$ s = 6 units   [Cube root both sides]
If the volume of a cube is equal to its surface area, the length of each edge = 6

Question #41: A cube whose edges are 3 inches is painted red on all sides. The cube is then cut into smaller cubes, all of which have edges that are 1 inch long. How many of the small cubes have no paint on them?
Solution: The best and probably the only way to answer this question is by good visualization skills. Imagine that the cube is cut in three slices form the top and three slices from the side, which will result in 27 identical cubes, each with an edge of 1 inch. All of the 9 cubes that are cut from the top and 9 cubes that are cut from the bottom are painted on at least one side. All of the 6 cubes cut from the middle layer of two sides and 2 cubes cut from the center of the middle payer of the other two sides are also painted on at least one side. All this adds up to 9 + 9 + 6 + 2 = 26 cubes that are painted on at least one side, which leaves only 27 − 26 = 1 cube, the core center one, which is not painted on any side.

Question #42: A cube whose edges are 4 inches is painted red on all sides. The cube is then cut into smaller cubes, all of which have edges that are 1 inch long. How many of the small cubes have no paint on them?
Solution: The best and probably the only way to answer this question is by good visualization skills. Imagine that the cube is cut in four slices form the top and four slices from the side, which will result in 64 identical cubes, each with an edge of 1 inch. All of the 16 cubes that are cut from the top and 16 cubes that are cut from the bottom are painted on at least one side. All of the 16 cubes cut from the two middle layers of two sides and 8 cubes cut from the center of the two middle layers of the other two sides are also painted on at least one side. All this adds up to 16 + 16 + 16 + 8 = 56 cubes that are painted on at least one side, which leaves only 64 − 56 = 8 cubes, the core center ones, which are not painted on any side.

Question #43: A circular pipe has a diameter of 10 feet and a gallon of oil has a volume of 7.5 cubic feet. How many gallons of oil can fit into 50 feet of the pipe?
Solution: Imagine the 50 feet of pipe as a circular cylinder on its side with a height of 50 feet and a diameter of 10 feet.
Height of Cylinder $\Rightarrow$ 50 feet
Radius of Cylinder $\Rightarrow$ 10 ÷ 2 = 5 feet
Volume of cylinder $\Rightarrow$ $\pi r^2 h$ = π × 5^2 × 50 = 1,250π feet^3 [Apply appropriate formula and simplify]
                       $\Rightarrow$ 1,250π ÷ 7.5 = 166.67π gallons   [Convert cubic feet to gallons]
No. of gallons of oil that can fit inside 50 feet of pipe $\Rightarrow$ 166.67π gallons

Question #44: Oil is poured into a cylindrical tank at the rate of 11 unit^3 per minute. How many minutes will it take to fill the tank if its radius is 5 units and its height is 14 units? (Use $\pi = \dfrac{22}{7}$)

Solution: Volume of Cylinder $\Rightarrow \pi r^2 h = \dfrac{22}{7}(5)^2(14) = 1100$ unit^3 [Apply appropriate formula and simplify]

Oil is poured into a cylindrical tank at the rate of 11 unit^3 per 1 minute

Time taken to pour 1,100 unit$^3 \Rightarrow \dfrac{1,100}{11} = 100$ minutes or $1\dfrac{2}{3}$ hours

COORDINATE GEOMETRY:

Question #45: If the slope of the line that contains the points $(k, 9)$ and $(1, 1)$ is ½, what is the value of k?

Solution: EZ Problem Set-Up $\Rightarrow$ Slope of the line that contains the points $(k, 9)$ and $(1, 1)$ = ½

$\Rightarrow$ Slope $= \dfrac{y_1 - y_2}{x_1 - x_2}$ [Set up the equation]

$\Rightarrow \dfrac{1}{2} = \dfrac{9-1}{k-1}$ [Substitute the given values]

$\Rightarrow 1(k-1) = 2(9-1)$ [Cross multiply]

$\Rightarrow k - 1 = 2(8)$ [Solve within parentheses]

$\Rightarrow k - 1 = 16$ [Simplify the right side]

$\Rightarrow k = 17$ [Add 1 to both sides]

Question #46: In the figure given below, the coordinates of rectangle $ABCD$ are $A(-p, q)$, $B(-p, s)$, $C(r, -s)$, and $D(r, q)$, what is the area of rectangle $ABCD$?

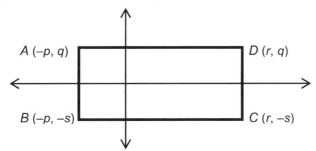

Solution: Length of Rectangle $ABCD$ $\Rightarrow BC = r - (-p) = (r + p)$ [B & C lie on the same horizontal line]

Width of Rectangle $ABCD$ $\Rightarrow AB = q - (-s) = (q + s)$ [A & B lie on the same vertical line]

Area of Rectangle $ABCD$ $\Rightarrow L \times W = (r + p)(q + s)$ [Substitute the known values]

Perimeter of Rectangle $ABCD$ $\Rightarrow 2(L + W) = 2[(r + p) + (q + s)] = 2(r + p + q + s)$

Question #47: If the coordinate of the parallelogram $ABCD$ are $A(-1, 7)$, $B(-2, 1)$, $C(7, 1)$, and $D(8, 7)$, what is the area and perimeter of the parallelogram?

Solution: Since the diagram is not provided in the question, let's get oriented by drawing the following diagram:

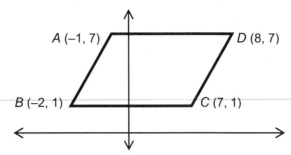

Length of Parallelogram *ABCD* $\Rightarrow BC = 7 - (-2) = 9$ [*B* & *C* lie on the same horizontal line]

Width of Parallelogram *ABCD* $\Rightarrow \sqrt{(x_1 - x_2)^2 + (y_1 - y_2)^2}$ [Use distance formula to find length]

$$\Rightarrow \sqrt{(-1--2)^2 + (7-1)^2} = \sqrt{(1)^2 + (6)^2} = \sqrt{1+36} = \sqrt{37}$$

Height of Parallelogram *ABCD* $\Rightarrow 7 - 1 = 6$ [*A* & *B* lie on the same vertical line]

Area of Parallelogram *ABCD* $\Rightarrow B \times H = 9 \times 6 = 54$

Perimeter of Parallelogram *ABCD* $\Rightarrow 2(L + W) = 2(9 + \sqrt{37}) = 18 + 2\sqrt{37}$

Question #48: In the *xy*-coordinate plane points *P*(1, 1), *Q*(2, 8), and *R*(6, 10) are three vertices of a parallelogram *PQRS*. What is the sum of the slopes of all the sides of the parallelogram?

Solution: Since the diagram is not provided in the question, let's get oriented by drawing the following diagram:

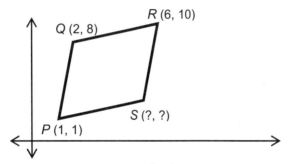

Slope of *PQ* $\Rightarrow \dfrac{y_1 - y_2}{x_1 - x_2} = \dfrac{8-1}{2-1} = 7$ [Simplify the expression]

Slope of *RS* $\Rightarrow$ Slope of *PQ* = 7   [Parallel sides have the same slope]

Slope of *QR* $\Rightarrow \dfrac{y_1 - y_2}{x_1 - x_2} = \dfrac{10-8}{6-2} = \frac{1}{2}$ [Simplify the expression]

Slope of *PS* $\Rightarrow$ Slope of *QR* = 0.5   [Parallel sides have the same slope]

Sum of slopes of all sides of parallelogram $\Rightarrow 7 + 7 + 0.5 + 0.5 = 15$

Question #49: If the coordinate of the trapezoid *ABCD* are *A*(–5, 7), *B*(–2, 1), *C*(5, 1), and *D*(8, 7), what is the area and perimeter of the trapezoid?

Solution: Since the diagram is not provided in the question, let's get oriented by drawing the following diagram:

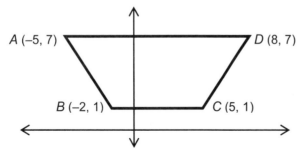

Base₁ of Trapezoid *ABCD* $\Rightarrow BC = 5 - (-2) = 7$ [*B* & *C* lie on the same horizontal line]

Base$_2$ of Trapezoid $ABCD$ $\Rightarrow AD = 8 - (-5) = 13$ [A & D lie on the same horizontal line]
Height of Trapezoid $ABCD$ $\Rightarrow 7 - 1 = 6$ [A & B lie on the same vertical line]
Area of Trapezoid $ABCD$ $\Rightarrow \frac{1}{2}(B_1 + B_2) \times H = \frac{1}{2}(7 + 13) \times 6 = \frac{1}{2}(20) \times 6 = 60$

Side$_1$ of Trapezoid $ABCD$ $\Rightarrow AB = \sqrt{(x_1 - x_2)^2 + (y_1 - y_2)^2}$ [Use distance formula to find length]

$$\Rightarrow \sqrt{(-5 - -2)^2 + (7 - 1)^2} = \sqrt{(-3)^2 + (6)^2} = \sqrt{9 + 36} = \sqrt{45} = 3\sqrt{5}$$

Side$_2$ of Trapezoid $ABCD$ $\Rightarrow DC = \sqrt{(x_1 - x_2)^2 + (y_1 - y_2)^2}$ [Use distance formula to find length]

$$\Rightarrow \sqrt{(8 - 5)^2 + (7 - 1)^2} = \sqrt{(3)^2 + (6)^2} = \sqrt{9 + 36} = \sqrt{45} = 3\sqrt{5}$$

Perimeter of Trapezoid $ABCD \Rightarrow B_1 + B_2 + S_1 + S_2 = 7 + 13 + 3\sqrt{5} + 3\sqrt{5} = 20 + 6\sqrt{5}$

Question #50: If the coordinate of the $\triangle ABC$ are $A(0, 7)$, $B(-2, 1)$, and $C(5, 1)$, what is the area and perimeter of the triangle?

Solution: Since the diagram is not provided in the question, let's get oriented by drawing the following diagram:

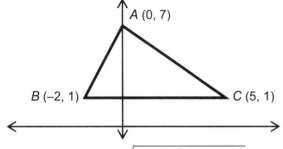

Length of AB $\Rightarrow \sqrt{(x_1 - x_2)^2 + (y_1 - y_2)^2}$ [Use distance formula to find length]

$$\Rightarrow \sqrt{(-2 - 0)^2 + (1 - 7)^2} = \sqrt{(-2)^2 + (-6)^2} = \sqrt{4 + 36} = \sqrt{40} = 2\sqrt{10}$$

Length of BC $\Rightarrow 5 - (-2) = 7$ [B and C lie on the same horizontal line]
Length of AC $\Rightarrow \sqrt{(x_1 - x_2)^2 + (y_1 - y_2)^2}$ [Use distance formula to find length]

$$\Rightarrow \sqrt{(5 - 0)^2 + (1 - 7)^2} = \sqrt{(5)^2 + (-6)^2} = \sqrt{25 + 36} = \sqrt{61}$$

Height of $\triangle ABC$ $\Rightarrow 7 - 1 = 6$ [A and B lie on the same vertical line]
Area of $\triangle ABC$ $\Rightarrow \frac{1}{2} \times B \times H = \frac{1}{2} \times 7 \times 6 = 21$ [Apply appropriate formula and simplify]
Perimeter of $\triangle ABC$ $\Rightarrow S_1 + S_2 + S_3 = 7 + 2\sqrt{10} + \sqrt{61}$ [Apply appropriate formula and simplify]

Question #51: If a circle passes through $A(0, 12)$ and $B(0, 2)$ with its center at the y-axis, what is the area and circumference of the circle?

Solution: Since the diagram is not provided in the question, let's get oriented by drawing the following diagram:

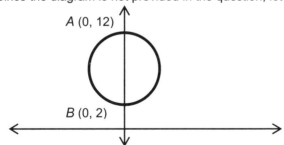

Diameter of Circle $\Rightarrow 12 - 2 = 10$ [A and B lie on the same vertical line]
Radius of Circle $\Rightarrow \frac{1}{2}(10) = 5$ [Find the radius]
Area of Circle $\Rightarrow \pi r^2 = \pi \times (5)^2 = 25\pi$ [Apply appropriate formula and simplify]
Circumference of Circle $\Rightarrow 2\pi r = 2\pi(5) = 10\pi$ [Apply appropriate formula and simplify]

Question #52: In a rectangular coordinate system, triangle *ABC* is drawn so that one side of the triangle connects two points on the *y*-axis, *B*(–1, 0) and *C*(5, 0). If point *A* has coordinate (0, *a*) where *a* > 0, and the area of *ABC* is 24, then what is the value of *a*?

Solution: The first thing to do is to construct the following figure based on the information given in the question, and label everything that's given.

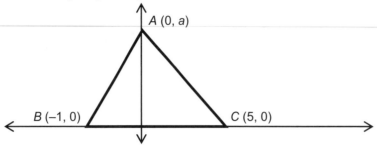

Length of Base   ⇒ *BC* = 6 units   [*B* and *C* lie on the same horizontal line]
Lengths of Height   ⇒ *a*   [*A* and *B* lie on the same vertical line]
Area of Δ*ABC*   ⇒ ½ × *b* × *h* = 24   [Set the formula of area equal to the given area]
                  ⇒ ½ (6) (*a*) = 24   [Substitute the known values]
                  ⇒ 3(*a*) = 24   [Simplify both sides]
                  ⇒ *a* = 8   [Divide both sides by 3]
Height of the triangle ⇒ *a* = 8

Question #53: In the figure given below, if the circle given below with center *P* is tangent to both axes and the distance from *P* to the origin is *n*, what is the area of the circle?

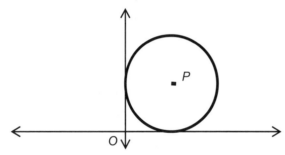

Solution: Since we know that the distance from the center of the circle, *P*, to the origin *O*, is *n*, we can make a 45°-45°-90° triangle by connecting the center of the circle, *P*, with the origin, *O*, and with the *x*-axis at *Q*.

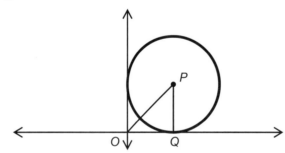

Apply Pythagorean Theorem ⇒ $OQ^2 + PQ^2 = OP^2$ [Write the Pythagorean Theorem]
                      ⇒ $r^2 + r^2 = n^2$ [Substitute the known values]
                      ⇒ $2r^2 = n^2$ [Combine like-terms]
                      ⇒ $r^2 = \dfrac{n^2}{2}$ [Divide both sides by 2]
                      ⇒ $r = \dfrac{n}{\sqrt{2}}$ [Square root both sides]

$$\text{Area of Circle} \Rightarrow \pi r^2 = \pi\left(\frac{n}{\sqrt{2}}\right)^2 = \frac{n^2\pi}{2}$$ [Apply appropriate formula and simplify]

MULTIPLE FIGURES:

Question #54: The figure below shows an aerial view of a piece of land. If all lines shown are straight lines and all angles shown are right angles, what is the perimeter of the piece of land?

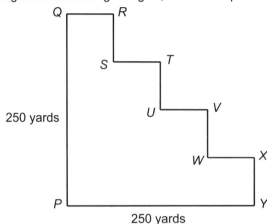

Solution: Length of PY $\Rightarrow QR + ST + UV + WX$
                 Length of PQ $\Rightarrow RS + TU + VW + XY$
                 Perimeter of the Figure $\Rightarrow PY + PQ + (QR + ST + UV + WX) + (RS + TU + VW + XY)$
                 $\Rightarrow 2PY + 2PQ = 2(250) + 2(250) = 500 + 500 = 1,000$ units

Question #55: If a 6 by 8 rectangle is inscribed in a circle, what is the radius of the circle?
Solution: (Diagonal of Rectangle)^2 $\Rightarrow$ (Length)^2 + (Width)^2 [Apply Pythagorean Theorem]
                 (Diagonal of Rectangle)^2 $\Rightarrow (6)^2 + (8)^2$ [Substitute the known values]
                 (Diagonal of Rectangle)^2 $\Rightarrow 36 + 64$ [Solve the exponents]
                 (Diagonal of Rectangle)^2 $\Rightarrow 100$ [Do the addition]
                 Diagonal of Rectangle $\Rightarrow 10$ [Square root both sides]
                 Diameter of Circle $\Rightarrow 10$ [Diameter of circle is same as diagonal of rectangle]
                 Radius of Circle = ½(10) $\Rightarrow 5$ [Radius of circle is half of diameter]

Question #56: In the figure given below, if the area of the inscribed rectangular region is 50, then what is the area and circumference of the circle?

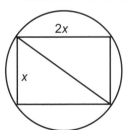

Solution: Area of Rectangle $\Rightarrow LW = 50$ [Write the appropriate formula]
                 $\Rightarrow x(2x) = 50$ [Substitute the known values]
                 $\Rightarrow x^2 = 25$ [Simplify the expression]
                 $\Rightarrow x = 5$ [Square root both sides]
                 Apply Pythagorean Theorem $\Rightarrow length^2 + width^2 = diagonal^2$ [Write the Pythagorean Theorem]
                 $\Rightarrow (x)^2 + (2x)^2 = d^2$ [Substitute the known values]
                 $\Rightarrow (5)^2 + (10)^2 = d^2$ [Substitute x = 5]
                 $\Rightarrow 25 + 100 = d^2$ [Solve the exponents]

$$\Rightarrow 125 = d^2 \qquad \text{[Combine like-terms]}$$
$$\Rightarrow d = 5\sqrt{5} \qquad \text{[Square root both sides]}$$

Diameter of the Circle $\Rightarrow$ Diagonal of Rectangle = $5\sqrt{5}$ [Diameter of circle is diagonal of rectangle]

Radius of the Circle $\Rightarrow \frac{1}{2}d = \dfrac{5\sqrt{5}}{2}$ [Radius of circle is half of diameter]

Area of Circle $\Rightarrow \pi r^2 = \pi\left(\dfrac{5\sqrt{5}}{2}\right)^2 = \dfrac{125}{4}\pi$ [Apply appropriate formula and simplify]

Circumference of Circle $\Rightarrow 2\pi r = 2\pi\left(\dfrac{5\sqrt{5}}{2}\right) = 5\sqrt{5}\pi$ [Apply appropriate formula and simplify]

Question #57: In the figure given below, the midpoints of the sides of square *ABCD* are connected to form square *EFGH*. What is the ratio of the area of square *ABCD* to the area of square *EFGH*?

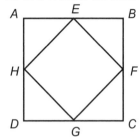

Solution: Let side of Square *ABCD* $\Rightarrow 2$ [Assumption]
Area of Square *ABCD* $\Rightarrow s^2 = 2^2 = 4$ [Apply appropriate formula and simplify]
Length of *AE* or *AH* $\Rightarrow \frac{1}{2}$ of *AB* = 1   [Point *E* is the midpoint of *AB*]
Apply Pythagorean Theorem $\Rightarrow EH^2 = AE^2 + AH^2$ [Write the Pythagorean Theorem]
$\Rightarrow EH^2 = 1^2 + 1^2$ [Substitute *AE* = *AH* = 1]
$\Rightarrow EH^2 = 2$ [Combine like-terms]
$\Rightarrow EH = \sqrt{2}$ [Square root both sides]
Area of Square *EFGH* $\Rightarrow s^2 = \left(\sqrt{2}\right)^2 = 2$ [Apply appropriate formula and simplify]

Ratio of Area of Square *ABCD* to the Area of Square *EFGH* $\Rightarrow$ 4:2 = 2:1 = 2

Question #58: A rectangle has the same area as a circle of radius 10. If the length of the rectangle is 2, what is its width?
Solution: Radius of Circle $\Rightarrow 10$ [Given]
Area of Circle $\Rightarrow \pi r^2 = \pi(10^2) = 100\pi$ [Apply appropriate formula and simplify]
Length of Rectangle $\Rightarrow 2$ [Given]
Let, Width of Rectangle $\Rightarrow W$ [Assumption]
Area of Rectangle $\Rightarrow LW = 2W$ [Apply appropriate formula and simplify]
EZ Problem Set-Up $\Rightarrow$ Area of Rectangle = Area of Circle
$\Rightarrow 2W = 100\pi$ [Set up the equation]
$\Rightarrow W = 50\pi$ [Divide both sides by 2]

Question #59: The perimeter of a rectangle is equal to the circumference of a circle of radius 5. If the length of the rectangle is 5, what is its width?
Solution: Radius of Circle $\Rightarrow 5$ [Given]
Circumference of Circle $\Rightarrow 2\pi r = 2\pi(5) = 10\pi$ [Apply appropriate formula and simplify]
Length of Rectangle $\Rightarrow 5$ [Given]
Let, Width of Rectangle $\Rightarrow W$ [Assumption]
Perimeter of Rectangle $\Rightarrow 2(L + W) = 2(5 + W)$ [Apply appropriate formula and simplify]
EZ Problem Set-Up $\Rightarrow$ Perimeter of Rectangle = Circumference of Circle
$\Rightarrow 2(5 + W) = 10\pi$ [Set up the equation]

$\Rightarrow 5 + W = 5\pi$ [Divide both sides by 2]

$\Rightarrow W = 5\pi - 5$ [Subtract 5 from both sides]

Question #60: A triangle and a circle have equal areas. If the base of the triangle and the diameter of the circle each have length 10, what is the height of the triangle?

Solution:

Base of Triangle	$\Rightarrow 10$	[Given]
Diameter of Circle	$\Rightarrow 10$	[Given]
Radius of Circle	$\Rightarrow \frac{1}{2}(10) = 5$	[Radius is half of diameter]
Area of Circle	$\Rightarrow \pi r^2 = \pi(5)^2 = 25\pi$	[Apply appropriate formula and simplify]
EZ problem Set-Up	$\Rightarrow$ Area of Triangle = Area of Circle	
	$\Rightarrow \frac{1}{2} \times b \times h = 25\pi$	[Set up the equation]
	$\Rightarrow \frac{1}{2} \times 10 \times h = 25\pi$	[Substitute the known values]
	$\Rightarrow 5h = 25\pi$	[Simplify the expression on the left side]
	$\Rightarrow h = 5\pi$	[Divide both sides by 5]

Question #61: What is the length of each of the five equal sides of a regular pentagon if the perimeter of the pentagon is equal to the perimeter of a square whose area is 100?

Solution:

Area of Square	$\Rightarrow s^2 = 100$	[Equate the area formula with the given area]
	$\Rightarrow s = 10$	[Square root both sides]
Perimeter of Square	$\Rightarrow 4s = 4 \times 10 = 40$	[Apply appropriate formula and simplify]
Let, Side of Pentagon	$\Rightarrow n$	[Assumption]
Perimeter of Pentagon	$\Rightarrow 5n$	[Write the appropriate formula]
EZ Problem Set-Up	$\Rightarrow$ Perimeter of Pentagon = Perimeter of Square	
	$\Rightarrow 5n = 40$	[Set up the equation]
	$\Rightarrow n = 8$	[Divide both sides by 5]

Question #62: The length of a rectangle is 5 more than the side of a square, and the width of the rectangle is 5 less than the side of the square. If the area of the square is 75, what is the area of the rectangle?

Solution:

Let, Side of Square	$\Rightarrow n$	[Assumption]
Area of Square	$\Rightarrow n^2 = 75$	[Given]
Length of Rectangle	$\Rightarrow L = (n + 5)$	[Length of rectangle is 5 more than side of square]
Width of Rectangle	$\Rightarrow W = (n - 5)$	[Width of rectangle is 5 less than side of square]
Area of Rectangle	$\Rightarrow LW$	[Write the appropriate formula]
	$\Rightarrow (n + 5)(n - 5)$	[Substitute $L = (n + 5)$ and $W = (n - 5)$]
	$\Rightarrow n^2 - 5^2$	[Factor: $(a + b)(a + b) = a^2 - b^2$]
	$\Rightarrow 75 - 25$	[Substitute $n^2 = 75$]
	$\Rightarrow 50$	[Do the subtraction]

Question #63: A triangle of height 5 and base 8 has an area exactly one-sixth that of a rectangle with width 10. What is the length of the rectangle?

Solution:

Area of Triangle	$\Rightarrow \frac{1}{2} \times B \times H = \frac{1}{2}(5)(8) = 20$	[Apply appropriate formula and simplify]
Area of Rectangle	$\Rightarrow LW = 10L$	[Apply appropriate formula and simplify]
EZ Problem Set Up	$\Rightarrow$ Area of Triangle = 1/6(Area of Rectangle)	
	$\Rightarrow 20 = \frac{1}{6}(10L)$	[Set up the equation]
	$\Rightarrow 120 = 10L$	[Multiply both sides by 6]
	$\Rightarrow L = 12$	[Divide both sides by 10]

Question #64: If the area of a smaller square is half the area of a larger square with area 1 square unit, then what is the ratio of the diagonal of the larger square to the diagonal of smaller square?

Solution:

Area of Larger Square	$\Rightarrow s^2 = 1 \text{ unit}^2$	[Given]
Side of Larger Square	$\Rightarrow s = 1$	[Square root both sides]
Diagonal of Larger Square	$\Rightarrow d = \sqrt{2}$	[Diagonal of square is side times $\sqrt{2}$]
Area of Smaller Square	$\Rightarrow s^2 = \frac{1}{2} \text{ unit}^2$	[Area of smaller square = ½ area of larger square]

Side of Smaller Square $\Rightarrow s = \sqrt{\dfrac{1}{2}}$ [Square root both sides]

Diagonal of Smaller Square $\Rightarrow d = \sqrt{\dfrac{1}{2}} \times \sqrt{2} = 1$ [Diagonal of square is side times $\sqrt{2}$]

Ratio of diagonal of the larger square to the diagonal of smaller square $\Rightarrow \sqrt{2}:1$

Question #65: What is the perimeter of rectangle X, which is 16 meters wide, and has the same area as rectangle Y, which is 52 meters by 24 meters?

Solution:
In Rectangle X: Length $= L$ [Assumption]
                   Width $= 16$ [Given]
                   Area $= LW = 16L$ [Apply appropriate formula and simplify]
In Rectangle Y: Length $= 52$ [Given]
                   Width $= 24$ [Given]
                   Area $= LW = 52 \times 24 = 1{,}248$ [Apply appropriate formula and simplify]
EZ Problem Set-Up $\Rightarrow$ Area of Rectangle X = Area of Rectangle Y
$\Rightarrow 16L = 1{,}248$ [Set up the equation]
$\Rightarrow L = 78$ [Divide both sides by 16]
Perimeter of Rectangle $X \Rightarrow 2(L + W) = 2(78 + 16) = 2(94) = 188$

Question #66: If the perimeter of square X and the diagonal of square Y have the same length, what is the ratio of the area of square X to the area of square Y?

Solution:
Let, Diagonal of Square Y $\Rightarrow n$ [Assumption]

Then, Side of Square Y $\Rightarrow \dfrac{n}{\sqrt{2}}$ [The side of square is side divided by $\sqrt{2}$]

Area of Square Y $\Rightarrow s^2 = \left(\dfrac{n}{\sqrt{2}}\right)^2 = \dfrac{n^2}{2}$ [Apply appropriate formula and simplify]

Perimeter of Square X $\Rightarrow n$ [Perimeter of Square X is the diagonal of square Y]
$\Rightarrow 4s = n$ [Equate the perimeter formula with the perimeter]

$\Rightarrow s = \dfrac{n}{4}$ [Divide both sides by 4]

Area of Square X $\Rightarrow s^2 = \left(\dfrac{n}{4}\right)^2 = \dfrac{n^2}{16}$ [Apply appropriate formula and simplify]

Ratio of Area of Square X to Area of Square $Y \Rightarrow \dfrac{n^2}{16} : \dfrac{n^2}{2} = \dfrac{\frac{1}{16}}{\frac{1}{2}} = \dfrac{1}{16} \div \dfrac{1}{2} = \dfrac{1}{16} \times \dfrac{2}{2} = \dfrac{2}{16} = \dfrac{1}{8}$

Question #67: In the figure given below, the center of the circle is O, and $PQ = OP$. What is the measure of the marked angle?

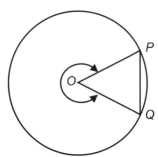

Solution:
In $\triangle OPQ$ $\Rightarrow OP = OQ$ [Radius of the same circle are equal]
$\Rightarrow OP = PQ$ [Given]
$\Rightarrow OP = OQ = PQ$ [If $a = b$ and $b = c$, then $a = b = c$]

Measure of ∠POQ ⇒ ∠OPQ = ∠OQP = 60°   [ΔOPQ, it means ΔOPQ is an equilateral triangle]
Measure of Marked Angle ⇒ 360° − 60° = 300°   [Angle around a circle is 360°]

Question #68: In the figure given below, the center of the circle is O, ∠POQ = 120°, and OR with length 2.5 is perpendicular to PQ and it bisects PQ. What is the area of the circle?

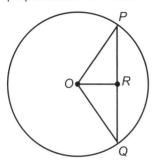

Solution: Measure of ∠POR   ⇒ 120°
Note: OR is perpendicular bisector of PQ and it bisects ∠POQ
Measure of ∠QOR   ⇒ ½∠POR = ½(120°) = 60°
ΔPOR and ΔQOR are 30°-60°-90° triangles, whose sides are in the ratio of x, $\sqrt{3}\,x$, and $2x$.
In ΔPOR   ⇒ Side opposite 30° angle = $OR = x$ ⇒ 2.5
            ⇒ Side opposite 90° angle = $OP = 2x$ ⇒ 2 × 2.5 = 5
Radius of Circle O ⇒ $OP = 5$
Area of the Circle O ⇒ $\pi r^2 = \pi(5)^2 = 25\pi$

Question #69: If an arc AB with a length of 18π is ¾ of the circumference of a circle, what is the shortest distance between the endpoints of the arc?
Solution: Let's first draw a diagram that can help us facilitate the solution to the problem.

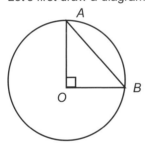

Major Arc AB represents ⇒ ¾ of 360° = or 270°
Minor Arc AB represents ⇒ ¼ of 360° = or 90°
¾ of the Circumference of Circle ⇒ 18π
Total Circumference of Circle ⇒ $18\pi × 4/3 = 24\pi$
Circumference of Circle ⇒ $2\pi r = 24\pi$ [Equate the circumference formula with the actual value]
                 ⇒ $r = 12$ [Divide both sides by 2π]
OA and OB are both radii of the same circle and are therefore equal. Since $AO = OB = 12$, triangle AOB is an isosceles right triangle.
Note: The shortest distance between A and B is AB, which is the hypotenuse of the isosceles right triangle AOB
Apply Pythagorean Theorem ⇒ $AB^2 = AO^2 + OB^2$ [Write the Pythagorean Theorem]
                      ⇒ $AB^2 = 12^2 + 12^2$ [Substitute the known values]
                      ⇒ $AB^2 = 144 + 144$ [Solve the exponents]
                      ⇒ $AB^2 = 288$ [Do the addition]
                      ⇒ $AB = 12\sqrt{2}$ [Square root both sides]

Question #70: In a circle, a chord is 24 inches long and its shortest distance from the center of the circle is 9 inches. What is the radius of the circle?
Solution: Let's first draw a diagram to get a better understanding of the problem:

First, draw a circle, then a chord, which is 16 inches long. Next, since the shortest distance form the center of the circle to the chord is 9, this must be the perpendicular distance from the center to the chord, so draw a perpendicular from the center to the chord. Finally, connect the center of the circle to the endpoint of the chord so there is a right triangle.

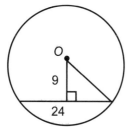

We have a right triangle whose one leg is 9 and the other leg is half of 24, or 12, and the hypotenuse in the radius of the circle.

Apply Pythagorean Theorem $\Rightarrow a^2 + b^2 = c^2$ [Write the Pythagorean Theorem]
                                  $\Rightarrow 9^2 + 12^2 = c^2$ [Substitute the known values]
                                  $\Rightarrow 81 + 144 = c^2$ [Solve the exponents]
                                  $\Rightarrow 225 = c^2$ [Do the addition]
                                  $\Rightarrow c = 15$ [Square root both sides]
Radius of the circle = 15 inches

Question #71: A is the center of a circle whose radius is 12, and B is the center of circle whose diameter is 12. If these two circles are tangent to one another, what is the area of the circle whose diameter is AB?

Solution: First thing to do is to draw the following diagram.

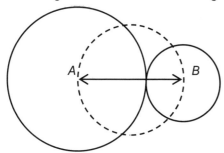

Radius of Big Circle $\Rightarrow 12$ [Given]
Radius of Small Circle $\Rightarrow \frac{1}{2}(d) = \frac{1}{2}(12) = 6$ [Radius is half of diameter]
Diameter of New Circle (AB) $\Rightarrow 12 + 6 = 18$ [d of new circle = r of big circle + r of small circle]
Radius of New Circle (AB) $\Rightarrow \frac{1}{2}(d) = \frac{1}{2}(18) = 9$ [Radius is half of diameter]
Area of New Circle (AB) $\Rightarrow \pi r^2 = \pi (9)^2 = 81\pi$ [Apply appropriate formula and simplify]

Question #72:   In the figure given below, points A, B, and C are the centers of the three circles that are tangent to each other; and circle A has a radius of 15, circle B has a radius of 10, and circle C has a radius of 5. What is the perimeter of triangle ABC?

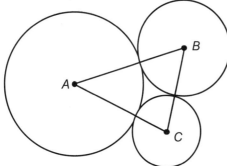

Solution: Length of AB = Radius of Circle A + Radius of Circle B $\Rightarrow 15 + 10 = 25$
                Length of BC = Radius of Circle B + Radius of Circle C $\Rightarrow 10 + 5 = 15$

Length of AC = Radius of Circle A + Radius of Circle C $\Rightarrow$ 15 + 5 = 20
Perimeter of ΔABC $\Rightarrow$ $AB + BC + AC$ = 25 + 15 + 20 = 60

Question #73: In the figure given below, A, B, and C are all squares tangent to each other with no overlap. If the area of square A is 25 and the area of square B is 49, what is the area of square C?

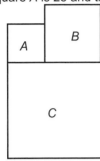

Solution:

Area of Square A	$\Rightarrow s^2 = 25$	[Equate the area formula with the given area]
Side of Square A	$\Rightarrow s = 5$	[Square root both sides]
Area of Square B	$\Rightarrow s^2 = 49$	[Equate the area formula with the given area]
Side of Square B	$\Rightarrow s = 7$	[Square root both sides]
Side of Square C	$\Rightarrow$ Side of Square A + Side of Square B	
	$\Rightarrow$ 5 + 7 = 12	[Substitute the known values]
Area of Square C	$\Rightarrow s^2 = 12^2 = 144$	[Apply appropriate formula and simplify]

Question #74: In the figure given below, what is the ratio of the area of ΔEDC to the area of square $ABCD$?

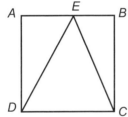

Solution:

In Square $ABCD$:	Let each side	$\Rightarrow s = 10$	[Assumption]
	Then, Area	$\Rightarrow s^2 = 10^2 = 100$	[Solve the exponent]
In ΔEDC:	Base	$\Rightarrow DC = 10$	[Base of triangle is same as side of square]
	Height	$\Rightarrow AD = 10$	[Height of triangle is same as side of square]
	Area	$\Rightarrow \frac{1}{2}bh = \frac{1}{2}(10)(10) = 50$	[Simplify the expression]

Ratio of Area of Square ΔEDC to the Area of Square $ABCD$ = 50:100 = 1:2 = $\frac{1}{2}$

Question #75: The length of a rectangle is twice its width. If the perimeter of the rectangle is the same as the perimeter of a square of side 6, what is the square of the length of the diagonal of the rectangle?

Solution:

Side of Square	$\Rightarrow$ 6	[Given]
Perimeter of Square	$\Rightarrow 4s = 4 \times 6 = 24$	[Apply appropriate formula and simplify]
Let, the Width of Rectangle	$\Rightarrow W$	[Assumption]
Then, the Length of Rectangle	$\Rightarrow 2W$	[Length of rectangle is twice its width]
EZ Problem Set-Up	$\Rightarrow$ Perimeter of Rectangle = Perimeter of Square = 24	
	$\Rightarrow 2(L + W) = 24$	[Set up the equation]
	$\Rightarrow L + W = 12$	[Divide both sides by 2]
	$\Rightarrow 2W + W = 12$	[Substitute $L = 2W$]
	$\Rightarrow 3W = 12$	[Combine like-terms]
	$\Rightarrow W = 4$	[Divide both sides by 3]
Width of Rectangle	$\Rightarrow W = 4$	[From above]
Length of Rectangle	$\Rightarrow L = 2 \times 4 = 8$	[Length of rectangle is twice its width]
Apply Pythagorean Theorem	$\Rightarrow D^2 = L^2 + W^2$	[Write the Pythagorean Theorem]
	$\Rightarrow D^2 = 4^2 + 8^2$	[Substitute the known values]
	$\Rightarrow D^2 = 16 + 64$	[Solve the exponent]

$\Rightarrow D^2 = 80$ [Do the addition]

Question #76: In the figure given below, MNOP and OQRS are squares. If the area of OQRS is 144, what is the area of MNOP?

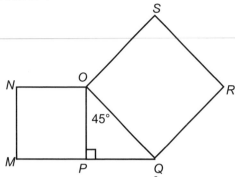

Solution: Area of Square OQRS $\Rightarrow s^2 = 144$ [Equate the area formula with the given area]
                                $\Rightarrow s = 12$ [Square root both sides]
Side of Square OQRS = Hypotenuse of Right Triangle OPQ = OQ = 12
Let OP = PQ = x
In 45°-45°-90° ΔOPQ $\Rightarrow OP^2 + PQ^2 = OQ^2$ [Apply Pythagorean Theorem]
                                $\Rightarrow x^2 + x^2 = 12^2$ [Substitute the known values]
                                $\Rightarrow 2x^2 = 144$ [Combine like-terms]
                                $\Rightarrow x^2 = 72$ [Divide both sides by 2]
Area of Square MNOP $\Rightarrow OP^2 = x^2$ [Write the appropriate formula]
                                $\Rightarrow 72$ [Substitute $x^2 = 72$]

Question #77: In the figure given below, square A, B, and C are connected at points P, Q, and R. If square A has area 81 and square B has area 144, what is the area of square C?

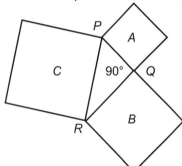

Solution: Area of Square A = 81 $\Rightarrow s^2 = 81$ [Equate the area formula with the given area]
                                $\Rightarrow s = PQ = 9$ [Square root both sides]
Area of Square B = 144 $\Rightarrow s^2 = 144$ [Equate the area formula with the given area]
                                $\Rightarrow s = RQ = 12$ [Square root both sides]
In right triangle PQR $\Rightarrow PR^2 = PQ^2 + RQ^2$ [Apply Pythagorean Theorem]
                                $\Rightarrow PR^2 = 9^2 + 12^2$ [Substitute the known values]
                                $\Rightarrow PR^2 = 81 + 144$ [Solve the exponents]
                                $\Rightarrow PR^2 = 225$ [Do the addition]
                                $\Rightarrow PR = 15$ [Square root both sides]
Side of Square C $\Rightarrow PR = 15$ [PR is the side of square C]
Area of Square C $\Rightarrow s^2 = 15^2 = 225$ [Apply appropriate formula and simplify]

Question #78: In the figure given below, square ABCD has a side of 8. What is the sum of the length of the two arcs?

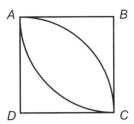

Solution: If the arc is completely drawn with point D as the center, it will be a full circle with a radius (DC) that is equal to the side of the square, and since the central angle $\angle D$ is 90°, the length of one arc will be a quarter of the circumference of the circle.

Circumference $\Rightarrow 2\pi r = 2(8)\pi = 16\pi$ [Simplify the expression]
Length of one arc $\Rightarrow \frac{1}{4}(16\pi) = 4\pi$ [Length of one arc is ¼ of the circumference]
Length of both arcs $\Rightarrow 2(4\pi) = 8\pi$ [Multiply by 2]

Question #79:   A rectangular block with a volume of 250 unit^3 was sliced into 2 identical cubes of equal volume. What is the difference, in square units, between the combined surface area of the 2 resulting cubes and the original surface area of the rectangular block?

Solution: Volume of Rectangular Block $\Rightarrow$ 250 unit^3 [Given]
Volume of Cubical Block $\Rightarrow$ 250 ÷ 2 = 125   [Volume of cube is half of rectangle block]
                                                          $\Rightarrow s^3 = 125$ [Equate the volume formula with the value]
                                                          $\Rightarrow s = 5$ [Cube root both sides]
Surface Area of Cubical Block $\Rightarrow 6s^2 = 6(5)^2 = 6(25) = 150$ unit^2 [Do the multiplication]
Surface Area of 2Cubical Blocks $\Rightarrow$ 150 × 2 = 300 unit^2 [Multiply by 2 to double the SA]
Since the edge of the cube is 5, the dimensions of the rectangular solids are 5 by 5 by 10
SA of Rectangular Block $\Rightarrow 2[(lw) + (wh) + (hw)]$ [Write the appropriate formula and solve]
                      $\Rightarrow 2[(5 × 5) + (5 × 10) + (5 × 10)] = 2[25 + 50 + 50] = 2[125] = 250$ unit^2
Difference between the combined surface area of the two cubes & surface area of rectangular block:
SA of 2 Cubes – SA of Rectangular Block $\Rightarrow$ 300 – 250 = 50 unit^2

Question #80:   The height, h, of a cylinder is equal to the edge of a cube. If the cylinder and the cube have the same volume, what is the radius of the cylinder?

Solution: The height of the Cylinder = Edge of the Cube = h
EZ Problem Set-Up $\Rightarrow$ Volume of Cylinder = Volume of Cube
                        $\Rightarrow \pi r^2 h = h^3$ [Set up the equation]
                        $\Rightarrow \pi r^2 = h^2$ [Divide both sides by h]
                        $\Rightarrow r^2 = \dfrac{h^2}{\pi}$ [Divide both sides by π]
                        $\Rightarrow r = \dfrac{h}{\sqrt{\pi}}$ [Square root both sides]

Question #81:   Oil is poured from a full rectangular container with dimensions 5 units by 11 units by 14 units into a cylindrical container with a radius of 7 units. Assuming that the oil does not overflow or spill the container, how many inches high will the oil reach? (use $\pi = 22/7$)

Solution: Volume of Rectangular Container $\Rightarrow LWH = 5 × 11 × 14 = 770$ unit^3 [Do the multiplication]
EZ Problem Set-Up $\Rightarrow$ Volume of Cylindrical Container = Volume of Rectangular Container
                        $\Rightarrow \pi r^2 h = 770$ [Set up the equation]
                        $\Rightarrow \dfrac{22}{7}(7)^2 h = 770$ [Substitute the values]
                        $\Rightarrow \dfrac{22}{7}(49)h = 770$ [Solve the exponent]
                        $\Rightarrow 154h = 770$ [Simplify the left side]
                        $\Rightarrow h = 5$ units   [Divide both sides by 154]
Note: After the oil is poured, the volume of the oil in the cylinder will still be the same volume as the rectangular container.

Question #82: In the figure given below, each curved side is a semicircle with radius 5, and the two parallel sides each have length 20. What is the area of the shaded region?

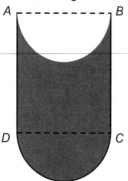

Solution:
Length of rectangle $ABCD$ = BC ⇒ 20   [Given]
Width of rectangle $ABCD$ = AB ⇒ $2(r) = 2(5) = 10$ [Diameter of semicircle]
Area of rectangle $ABCD$ ⇒ $L \times W = 20 \times 10 = 200$ [Apply appropriate formula and simplify]
Note: Area of the shaded region is the same as the area of rectangle $ABCD$, because the bottom shaded semicircle together with the top shaded region makes a perfect rectangle $ABCD$.

Question #83: In the figure given below, if the area of the square is 100, what is the area of the white region?

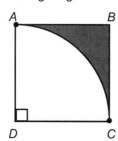

Solution:
Area of Square   ⇒ $s^2 = 100$ [Equate the area formula with the given value]
                          ⇒ $s = 10$ [Square root both sides]
Radius of Circle   ⇒ 10   [Side of square = Radius of extended circle(arc)]
Area of Circle   ⇒ $\pi r^2 = \pi(10)^2 = 100\pi$ [Apply appropriate formula and simplify]
Area of White Region   ⇒ ¼ (Area of Circle)   [Area of white region is ¼ the extended circle]
                          ⇒ ¼$(100\pi) = 25\pi$ [Substitute the values and simplify]

Question #84: In the figure given below, the two semi circles are tangent to one another and to the square. If the side of the square is 10, what is the area of the shaded region?

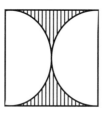

Solution:
Area of Square   ⇒ $s^2 = 10^2 = 100$
Radius of 2 Semicircles   ⇒ ½ of Side of Square = ½ of 10 = 5
Area of 2 Semicircles   ⇒ $\pi r^2 = \pi (5)^2 = 25\pi$
Area of Shaded Region   ⇒ Area of Square – Area of 2 Semicircles = $100 - 25\pi$

Question #85: In the figure given below, $ABCD$ is a rectangle; and AE and BE are arcs of circle centered at D and C. What is the area of the shaded region?

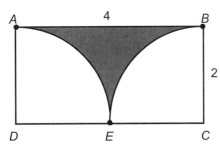

Solution: Area of Rectangle *ABCD* $\Rightarrow LW = 4 \times 2 = 8$
Area of 2 White Quarter Circles $\Rightarrow \frac{1}{2}(\pi r^2) = \frac{1}{2}(\pi)(2)^2 = 2\pi$
Area of Shaded Region $\Rightarrow$ Area of Rectangle – Area of 2 White Quarter Circles $= 8 - 2\pi$

Question #86: In the figure given below, *PQRS* is a square whose sides are 15. *AB*, *CD*, *EF*, and *GH* are each 12, and are the diameters of the four semicircles. What is the area of the shaded region?

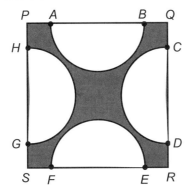

Solution: Area of Square *PQRS* $\Rightarrow s^2 = 15^2 = 225$
Area of 1 Semi-Circle $\Rightarrow \frac{1}{2}(\pi r^2) = \frac{1}{2}(\pi)(6)^2 = \frac{1}{2}(\pi)(36) = 18\pi$
Area of 4 Semi-Circle $\Rightarrow 18\pi \times 4 = 72\pi$
Area of Shaded Region $\Rightarrow$ Area of Square *ABCD* – Area of 4 Semi-Circles $= 225 - 72\pi$

Question #87: The figure given below consists of two semicircles. If the big semicircle has a diameter of 24 and the small semicircle has a diameter of 12, what is the area of the shaded region?

Solution: Diameter of Big Semicircle $\Rightarrow 24$
Radius of Big Semicircle $\Rightarrow \frac{1}{2}(d) = \frac{1}{2}(24) = 12$
Area of Big Semicircle $\Rightarrow \frac{1}{2}(\pi r^2) = \frac{1}{2}(\pi)(12)^2 = \frac{1}{2}(144\pi) = 72\pi$
Diameter of Small Semicircle $\Rightarrow \frac{1}{2}(24) = 12$
Radius of Small Semicircle $\Rightarrow \frac{1}{2}(d) = \frac{1}{2}(12) = 6$
Area of Small Semicircle $\Rightarrow \frac{1}{2}(\pi r^2) = \frac{1}{2}(\pi)(6)^2 = \frac{1}{2}(36\pi) = 18\pi$
Area of Shaded Region $\Rightarrow$ Area of Big Semicircle – Area of Small Semicircles $= 72\pi - 18\pi = 54\pi$

Question #88: In the figure given below, if the circle with center *A* has an area of 256π, what is the area of the shaded region, i.e., the circle with center *B*?

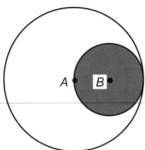

Solution: Area of Circle A $\Rightarrow \pi r^2 = 256\pi$
                                             $\Rightarrow r^2 = 256$
                                             $\Rightarrow r = 16$
Diameter of Circle B $\Rightarrow$ Radius of Circle A = 16
Radius of Circle B $\Rightarrow \frac{1}{2}(16) = 8$
Area of Circle B $\Rightarrow \pi r^2 = \pi(8)^2 = 64\pi$

Question #89:   In the figure given below, rectangle $ABCD$ has an area of 128 and is composed of 8 equal squares. Find the area of the shaded region.

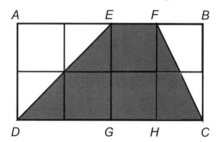

Solution: Area of Rectangle $ABCD \Rightarrow$ 128
Area of Each Square $\Rightarrow$ 128 ÷ 8 = 16
Side of Square $\Rightarrow \sqrt{16} = 4$
Area of ΔEGD $= \frac{1}{2}bh$ $= \frac{1}{2} \times 8 \times 8 \Rightarrow$ 32
$+$ Area of ΔEHC $= \frac{1}{2}bh$ $= \frac{1}{2} \times 4 \times 8 \Rightarrow +16$
$+$ Area of Rectangle $EFHG$ $= LW$ $= 4 \times 8$ $\Rightarrow \underline{+32}$
Total Shaded Area $\Rightarrow \underline{\;80\;}$

Question #90:   In the figure given below, rectangle $ABCD$ has an area of 128 and is composed of 8 equal squares. Find the area of the shaded region.

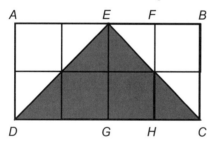

Solution: Area of Rectangle $ABCD \Rightarrow$ 128
Area of Each Square $\Rightarrow$ 128 ÷ 8 = 16
Side of Square $\Rightarrow \sqrt{16} = 4$
Area of Rectangle $ABCD = l \times w$ $= 16 \times 8$ $\Rightarrow$ 128
$-$ Area of ΔAED $= \frac{1}{2}bh$ $= \frac{1}{2} \times 8 \times 8 \Rightarrow -32$
$-$ Area of ΔBEC $= \frac{1}{2}bh$ $= \frac{1}{2} \times 8 \times 8 \Rightarrow \underline{-32}$
Total Shaded Area $\Rightarrow \underline{\;64\;}$

Question #91:   In the figure given below, rectangle *ABCD* has an area of 128 and is composed of 8 equal squares. Find the area of the shaded region.

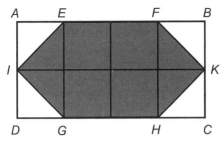

Solution: Area of Rectangle *ABCD* ⇒ 128
Area of Each Square   ⇒ 128 ÷ 8 = 16
Side of Square   ⇒ $\sqrt{16}$ = 4
Area of Square *EFGH*   = s^2 = 8^2 ⇒ 64
+ Area of Δ*IEG*   = ½ *bh* = ½ × 8 × 4 ⇒ +16
+ Area of Δ*KFH*   = ½ *bh* = ½ × 8 × 4 ⇒ +16
Total Shaded Area   ⇒ 96

Question #92:   In the figure given below, rectangle *ABCD* has an area of 128 and is composed of 8 equal squares. Find the area of the shaded region.

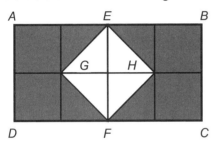

Solution: Area of Rectangle *ABCD* ⇒ 128
Area of Each Square   ⇒ 128 ÷ 8 = 16
Side of Square   ⇒ $\sqrt{16}$ = 4
Diagonal of Each Square ⇒ $c^2 = a^2 + b^2$
                       ⇒ $c^2 = 4^2 + 4^2 = 16 + 16 = 32$
                       ⇒ $c = \sqrt{32} = \sqrt{16 \times 2} = 4\sqrt{2}$
Area of Rectangle *ABCD*   = *LW*   =   16 × 8   ⇒ 128
– Area of Square *EGFH*   = s^2 = $\left(4\sqrt{2}\right)^2$ ⇒ –32
Total Shaded Area   ⇒ 96

Question #93:   In the figure given below, the outside of a 10 by 15 units rectangular window has a 1-unit wide metallic lining, as shown by the shaded region. What fraction of the window's outside surface is covered by the lining?

Solution: Area of Whole Window $\Rightarrow LW = 10 \times 15 = 150$ unit^2
                 Area of White Region $\Rightarrow LW = (10 - 1 - 1 - 1) \times (15 - 1 - 1 - 1) = 7 \times 12 = 84$ unit^2
                 Area of Shaded Region $\Rightarrow$ Area of the Whole Window − Area of White Region = $150 - 84 = 66$ unit^2

                 Fraction of Shaded Region $\Rightarrow \dfrac{66}{150} = \dfrac{11}{25}$

Question #94:   In the figure given below, $ABCD$ is a square with side 10; and EG, EH, FG, and FH are arcs of circle centered at A, B, C, and D. What is the area of the white region?

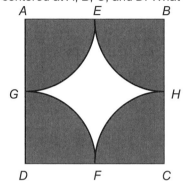

Solution: Area of Square $ABCD$ $\Rightarrow s^2 = 10^2 = 100$
                 Area of 4 Shaded Quarter Circles $\Rightarrow \pi r^2 = (\pi)(5)^2 = 25\pi$
                 Area of White Region $\Rightarrow$ Area of Square − Area of 4 Shaded Quarter Circles $\Rightarrow 100 - 25\pi$

Question #95:   In the figure given below, P, Q, and R, which are the centers of the three circles, all lie on the same line. What is the ratio of the area of the entire white region to the area of the shaded region?

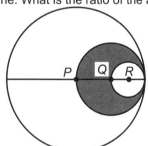

Solution: Let, the Radius of Circle P $\Rightarrow 8$ [Assumption]
                 Area of Circle P $\Rightarrow \pi r^2 = \pi(8)^2 = 64\pi$ [Apply appropriate formula and simplify]
                 Radius of Circle Q $\Rightarrow ½ \times 8 = 4$ [½(Radius of Circle P)]
                 Area of Circle Q $\Rightarrow \pi r^2 = \pi(4)^2 = 16\pi$ [Apply appropriate formula and simplify]
                 Radius of Circle R $\Rightarrow ½ \times 4 = 2$ [½(Radius of Circle Q)]
                 Area of Circle R $\Rightarrow \pi r^2 = \pi(2)^2 = 4\pi$ [Apply appropriate formula and simplify]
                 Area of White Region $\Rightarrow$ Area of Circle R + (Area of Circle P − Area of Circle Q)
                                          $\Rightarrow 4\pi + (64\pi - 16\pi) = 4\pi + 48\pi = 52\pi$
                 Area of Shaded Region $\Rightarrow$ Area of Circle Q − Area of Circle R = $16\pi - 4\pi = 12\pi$
                 Ratio of Area of White Region to Area of Shaded Region $\Rightarrow 52\pi{:}12\pi = 13{:}3$

PART 5.0: WORD PROBLEMS:

TOPICS COVERED:

- Arithmetic Word Problems

- Algebraic Word Problems

- Numeral Problems

- Literal Expressions

- Age & Weight Problems

- Work Problems

- Motion Problems

- Mixture Problems

- Measurements

EZ REFERENCE: -To review word problem concepts, please refer to our EZ Review Word Problems.
-To practice medium-to-difficult level questions, please refer to our EZ Practice Advanced Workbook.

PRACTICE EXERCISE:

ARITHMETIC PROBLEMS:

Question #1:   A local manufacturer rents a building to make widgets for a fixed cost of $150,000 per year. The variable cost of producing one widget is $10. In a certain year, the manufacturer produces and sells 50,000 widgets and makes a net profit of $225,000, after paying the fixed cost to rent the building. If every widget got sold for the same price, what was the selling price, in dollars, of each widget?

Question #2:   Walking at a constant rate, it takes Newton 60 minutes to walk from home to the nearest newspaper stand, and quarter of that time to walk from the newspaper stand to the playground. It takes him a third of the time it takes him to walk from the playground to the school than it does for him to walk from the newspaper stand to the playground. How many minutes longer does it take Newton to walk from the newspaper stand to the playground than it takes him to walk from the playground to the school?

Question #3:   If a certain 6 feet by 9 feet sheet of wood lamination that weighs 1.25 pounds and is 0.15 inches thick costs $120 for 150 sheets, how much will a stack of lamination sheets 8 feet thick cost?

Question #4:   A person needs $2.52 in postage to mail a letter. If he has 10 each of 55-cent stamps, 20-cent stamps, 10-cent stamps, 5-cent stamps, and 1-cent stamps, what is the minimum number of stamps he can use to put the exact postage on the letter?

Question #5:   John runs from Monday to Friday. On Monday, he runs n miles. On Tuesday, he ran twice as much as Monday. On Wednesday, he ran 12 miles more than twice as much as Tuesday. On Thursday, he ran 2 miles fewer than half as much Wednesday. On Friday, he ran half as much as Thursday plus an additional 7 miles. What is the average number of miles he ran per day over the 5-day period?

Question #6:   A dressmaker requires 1 yard of material for 1 coat, 2 yards of material for 4 shirts, and 4 yards of material for 1 coat and 2 pants. How many yards of material is required to make 2 coats, 2 shirts, and 2 pants?

ALGEBRAIC PROBLEMS:

Question #7:   Nikki has half as many cards as Tasha. If Tasha gives away 7 of her cards, she would still have 1 more card than Nikki. How many cards do Nikki and Tasha have altogether?

Question #8:   In a certain school bus, after leaving the school, there are equal number of boys and girls. At the first stop, 6 girls get off the bus and nobody gets on. After the first stop, there are twice as many boys as girls on the bus. How many boys are on the bus? (Note: don't consider the driver.)

Question #9:   In a bookstore, each ball pen costs $2 and each fountain pen costs $7 each. At these prices, a mixed bunch of 25 pens containing ball pen and fountain pen costs $75. How many fountain pens are in the bunch?

Question #10:   Mary finishes the first half of a test in one-third the time it takes her to finish the second half. If the whole test takes her an hour, how many minutes does she spend on the first half of the test?

Question #11:   In a farm, if 98 chickens and rabbits are put together, they have a total of 220 legs. How many chickens are there?

Question #12:   A jeweler received two shipments of rings. In the first shipment, 2 percent of the rings were made in platinum and the rest in gold. In the second shipment, which was twice as large as the first one, 1.5 percent of the rings were made in platinum and the rest in gold. If the jeweler received a total of 250 platinum rings, how many rings were in the second shipment?

Question #13:   In a certain fraction, the numerator is 20 less than the denominator. If the fraction is equal to $\dfrac{2}{7}$, what is the numerator of this fraction?

Question #14:   In certain classroom, there are 8 more girls than boys. If there are 20 students in the class, how many are girls?

Question #15:   In a class, 20 children were sharing equally the cost of a birthday gift for their teacher. When 4 of the children decided not to contribute, each of the other children had to pay $1.50 more. How much, in dollars, did the gift cost?

Question #16:   John has $100 more than Tony does. After John spends $20 on buying books, he has five times as much as Tony. How much money does Tony have?

Question #17:   If the cost of a apples priced at 12 cents each is equal to the cost of $a - 8$ oranges priced at 18 cents each, then what is the value of a?

Question #18:   If w number of watches sold per day varies with the price p per watch according to the relationship given by the equation $w = 925 - 15p$, what would be the total daily sales proceed from sale of 100 watches?

Question #19:   An auto repair shop charges $125 for alignment, balancing, and regular oil, but $150 for alignment, balancing, and premium oil. If the premium oil costs six times as mush as the regular oil, what is the cost of just the alignment and balancing?

Question #20:   In a course of seven successive days, a certain player wins twice as many board games each day as on the previous day. If in the seven-day period, the player wins a total of 625 games, how many games does the player win on the fifth day?

Question #21:   A certain manufacturing company produces items for which the production cost is comprised of annual fixed costs totaling $190,000 and variable costs averaging $9 per unit. If the company sets the selling price per item to $19, how many units must be produced and sold to earn an annual profit of $725,000?

Question #22:   If n is an integer, and the average (arithmetic mean) of 5, 6, and n is less than 10, what is the greatest possible value of n?

Question #23:   If John saved more than $90 by purchasing a printer at a 15 percent discount, what is the smallest integer amount that could be the original price of the printer?

Question #24:   How many positive integers n are there that satisfy the inequality $-2 < 2n + 5 < 17$?

Question #25:   A fundraiser collected exactly $999 from a retirement community. If each person in the community contributed at least $18, what is the greatest number of members that could be in the community?

Question #26:   If $2 < m < 7$ and $1 < n < 8$, what is the possible range of values for mn?

Question #27:   As per company policy, at least five-sixth of the 70 board of directors must vote in favor of a resolution for it to pass. What is the greatest number of directors who could vote against the resolution and still have it pass?

Question #28:   If $8x + 17 > 15 + 7x$, and x is a negative integer, then what is the value of x?

NUMERAL PROBLEMS:

Question #29:   When the number n is multiplied by 8, the result is the same as when 8 is added to n. What is the value of $7n$?

Question #30: If there is a magic number, such that, if you add 6 to the number or multiply the number by 6, the result would be the same, what is that magic number?

Question #31: If five times n is equal to n decreased by 20, then what is the value of n?

Question #32: If the product of 8, 10, and x is equal to the product of 1, 10, and y, such that $xy \neq 0$, what is the value of $\dfrac{x}{y}$?

Question #33: If 2 less than 6 times a certain number is 8 more than the number, what is the number?

Question #34: If $\dfrac{3}{4}$ of a number is 7 more than $\dfrac{1}{6}$ of the number, what is $\dfrac{5}{6}$ of the number?

Question #35: A certain number n is first increased by 10, then the result is multiplied by 10, then the result is decreased by 10, and then the result is divided by 10. What is the final result, in terms of n?

Question #36: What number when divided by 19 has a quotient of 7 and a remainder of 11?

Question #37: If the sum of 12, 17, and x is 51, then what is the product of 6 and $(x + 5)$?

Question #38: If the only possible values of m are -7, 0, and 1, and the only possible values of n are -5, 0, and 2, what is the greatest possible value of $2m + n^2$?

Question #39: What positive number, when squared, is equal to the cube of the positive square root of 25?

Question #40: The result obtained when x is multiplied by y is equal to ten times the result obtained when y is subtracted from x. If y equals 5, what does x equal?

Question #41: What is the value of the second of the three consecutive integers if the sum of the first and third is 24?

Question #42: There are three consecutive odd integers, such that seven times the middle integer is 85 more than the sum of the smallest and largest integers. What is the value of the largest of the three integers?

Question #43: If $n + 2$ is the largest of five consecutive integers, what is the sum of the five integers?

Question #44: How many integers in the set of all integers from 1 to 100, inclusive, are not the square of an odd integer?

Question #45: How many distinct integers between 100 and 150, inclusive, can be evenly divisible by neither 2 nor 5?

Question #46: One positive integer is one-third of another integer. If the product of the two integers is 12, what is their sum?

Question #47: If n is an odd integer, what is the sum of the smallest odd integer greater than $5n + 6$ and the largest odd integer less than $2n + 7$?

Question #48: If $m = 2^3 \times 3^2 \times 6$, and n is a positive integer, what is the greatest number of values for n such that $\dfrac{m}{24n}$ is an integer?

Question #49: If x, y, and z are integers with $x < y < z$, and $y = 100$, what is the greatest value of $x + y - z$?

Question #50: How many positive integers less than 100 are NOT equal to squares of integers?

Question #51: How many distinct integers between 1 and 60 consist of the digit 2, the digit 5, or the digit 2 and 5?

Question #52: If x, y, and z are distinct positive integers such that $0 < x < y < z < 22$, where x is even, y is odd, and z is prime, what is the greatest possible value of $x + y + z$?

Question #53: If $x + y + z = -15$, and x, y, and z are each different negative integers, what is the smallest possible value of z?

Question #54: If m and n are positive integers, and $(17^m)^n = 17^{17}$, what is the average (arithmetic mean) of m and n?

Question #55: Each of the 20 students in the students club contributed either a nickel or a quarter to the Alumni Fund. If the total amount collected was $2.20, how many students contributed a quarter?

LITERAL EXPRESSIONS:

Question #56: A certain union is divided into r regions. Each region has g groups. Each group has m members. How many members are there in the entire union?

Question #57: A certain shipment contains t trucks. Each truck contains c containers. Each container contains p pallets. Each pallet contains b boxes. Each box contains 100 matchsticks. How many matchsticks are contained in half of the shipment?

Question #58: A certain worker can plant x trees in $\dfrac{1}{y}$ hours. At this rate, how many trees can the worker plant in y hours?

Question #59: In a certain oil refinery, the level of oil in a tank increases at the rate of i inches in m minutes. At this rate, how many feet will the level increase in h hours?

Question #60: At the rate of y yards per s seconds, how many yards does a skater travel in m minutes?

Question #61: What is the number of seconds in h hours, m minutes, and s seconds?

Question #62: How many quarters are equivalent to n nickels and d dimes?

Question #63: A jar contains r red marbles and b blue marbles. If 2 red marbles are added and 7 blue marbles are removed, then in terms of r and b, what fraction of the remaining marbles is red?

Question #64: The cost to rent a boat for a day is n dollars. If a group of 25 people decide to share the cost equally, but only 15 of them were actually able to contribute, then, in terms of n, how many more dollars does each person has to pay?

Question #65: Peter has x more marbles than Sam has, and together they have a total of y marbles. How many marbles does Sam have?

Question #66: If a shopkeeper buys 100 identical radios for a total cost of r dollars, and then sells each radio for a price that was 20 percent above the original cost per radio, then, in terms of r, what was the selling price of each radio?

Question #67: In a certain party, 1/8 of the guests wore a red coat and 1/9 of the remaining guests wore a blue coat. If there were B guests who wore a blue coat, then, in terms of B, how many guests wore a red coat?

Question #68: If a student scores an average (arithmetic mean) of x points per test for t tests and then scores y points in the next test, what is the student's average score for the $t + 1$ tests?

Question #69: If the sum of two numbers that differ by 7 is n, then, in terms of n, what is the value of the greater of the two numbers?

Question #70: If $n > 0$ and r is n percent of s, then, in terms of n, s is what percent of r?

Question #71: There are *a* applications that needs to be processed. After *b* of the applications has been processed, what percent of the applications are still not processed?

Question #72: A truck travels *n* miles per hour for 5 hours and then travels ¼*n* miles per hour every hour thereafter. How many miles will the truck cover in 15 hours?

Question #73: At a certain bookstore, one-sixth of the books sold in a day were math books and one-half of the remaining books sold were English books. If *n* of the books sold were English books, then in terms of *n*, how many of the books sold were math books?

Question #74: There are two cylindrical tanks, one big, and the other small. The volume of the bigger tank is *x* gallons and the volume of smaller tank is *y* gallons. The bigger tank is filled to its maximum capacity with oil, and the smaller tank is completely empty. If just enough oil is poured from the bigger tank to completely fill the smaller tank, what fraction of the bigger tank is now filled with oil?

Question #75: In a certain company, there are *n* employees, and their average (arithmetic mean) salary is *m*. If there is only one manager in the company, and his salary is 8 times the average salary of all the other employees, then the manager's salary is what fraction of the total salary of all the employees in the company?

AGE & WEIGHT PROBLEMS:

Question #76: If in 25 years, Monika will be six times as old as she was 10 years ago, how old is Monika now?

Question #77: Mary is six times as old as Tom, but in 20 years, Mary will be only twice as old as Tom. How old is Mary now?

Question #78: If ½*x* years ago, Monika was 16, and ½*x* years from now she will be 2*x* years old, how old will she be 4*x* years from now?

Question #79: In 1975, Monika was 4 times as old as Susan, but in 1985 Monika was only twice as old as Susan was. How old was Susan in 1990?

Question #80: If the son is 27 years younger than his mother and one-seventh the age of his father, and the father is 9 years older than his mother; how old is the son?

WORK PROBLEMS:

Question #81: John earns $9.80 per hour on days other than weekends and one and a half times that rate on weekends. Last week he worked a total of 60 hours, including 8 hours on the weekend. What were his earnings for the week?

Question #82: Photocopier *A* can make copies at a constant rate of 175 copies every 25 seconds working at its highest speed, and Photocopier *B* can make copies at a constant rate of 100 copies every 20 seconds working at its highest speed. If both photocopiers run simultaneously at their highest speed, how many seconds will it take them to make a total of 240 copies?

Question #83: A certain test is two hours long and has 120 questions. If a student completes 60 questions in 50 minutes, how many seconds does he have on an average for completing each of the remaining questions?

Question #84: Jose can paint the first half of a house in two-fifths the time it takes him to paint the second half of the house. If it takes him 21 hours to paint the entire house, how many hours did he spend painting the first half of the house?

Question #85: A certain job can be completed by four machines, working individually, in 2, 4, 6, and 8 hours, respectively. What is the greatest part of the job that can be done in one hour by two of the machines working together at their respective rates?

Question #86: If John can do one coat of paint for all his walls in 6 hours, and George can do one coat of paint for the same walls in 8 hours, how many hours will it take John and George to do two coats of paint for the same walls if they work together at these rates?

Question #87: Working alone, a man can fence his yard in 12 hours, his older son can do it in 18 hours, and his younger son can do it in 24 hours. What is the ratio of the time it takes the man to fence the yard alone, working alone at his rate, to the time it takes the two sons to fence the yard, working together at their individual rates?

Question #88: Henry and Jacob, working together, can finish a job in 6 hours. If Jacob can do the job by himself in 15 hours, what percent of the job does Henry do?

Question #89: If six workers working at the same rate can do two-fifths of a job in 50 minutes, how many minutes would it take one worker working at the same rate to do one-tenths of the job?

Question #90: In a certain landscaping company, there are 16 workers, but exactly 5 of them actively work on the field at any given point in time. For an 8-hour workday, if each worker work exactly the same amount of time on the field, how many minutes does each worker work on the field?

MOTION PROBLEMS:

Question #91: Robin is on a road trip driving from Morgantown to Yorktown. After driving for one and a half hours at an average speed of 80 miles per hour and taking a break, she still has 50 miles left to travel. What is her total driving distance between Morgantown and Yorktown?

Question #92: A man drove 750 miles at an average speed of 50 miles per hour. How many miles per hour faster would he have to drive in order for the trip to take 5 hours less?

Question #93: Two cars travel away from each other in opposite directions at 16 miles per hour and 56 miles per hour respectively. If the first car travels for 30 minutes and the second car for 15 minutes, how many miles apart will they be at the end of their trips?

Question #94: A family is on a 90-mile trip. If they travel at an average speed of 75 miles per hour for the first 20 miles, and then at 25 miles per hour for the remainder of the trip, how many minutes longer will it take them than if they travel at 50 miles per hour for the entire trip?

Question #95: For a certain trip, a car averages 60 miles per hour for the first 7 hours of the trip, and averages 80 miles per hour for each additional hour of the same trip. If the average speed for the entire trip is 75 miles per hour, how many hours long is the entire trip?

Question #96: Anita walks from her home to her school in 50 minutes, and walks back along the same route to return home from school. If her average speed on the trip back home is twice as fast as her average speed on the trip to school, how many hours does she spend walking on the round trip?

Question #97: A man runs from his home to his work at an average speed of 6 miles per hour, and then walks back home along the same route at an average of 3 miles per hour. If his whole journey took one hour, how many mile is his home from his work?

Question #98: Two bikers are 20 miles apart and start biking towards each other along the same route. The first biker travels at a constant rate of 6 miles per hour and the second biker travels at a constant rate of 5 miles per hour. If the second biker starts his trip 24 minutes after the first biker, how far from his original starting point would he have traveled before the two bikers meet?

MIXTURE PROBLEMS:

Question #99: If 10 gallons of apple juice that cost $5.00 per gallon is mixed with 15 gallons of grape juice that cost $7.00 per gallon, what is the cost per gallon of the resulting mixture?

Question #100: A tank contains 10,000 gallons of a solution that is 9 percent calcium chloride by volume. If 2,000 gallons of water evaporates form the tank, what % of the remaining solution will be calcium chloride?

PRACTICE EXERCISE – QUESTIONS & ANSWERS WITH EXPLANATIONS:

ARITHMETIC PROBLEMS:

Question #1: A local manufacturer rents a building to make widgets for a fixed cost of $150,000 per year. The variable cost of producing one widget is $10. In a certain year, the manufacturer produces and sells 50,000 widgets and makes a net profit of $225,000, after paying the fixed cost to rent the building. If every widget got sold for the same price, what was the selling price, in dollars, of each widget?

Solution:

Fixed Cost to rent the building	$\Rightarrow$ $150,000
Variable Cost	$\Rightarrow$ $10 per unit
Total No. of widgets produced	$\Rightarrow$ 50,000
Total Variable Cost = 10 × 50,000	$\Rightarrow$ 500,000
Total Cost = Fixed Cost + Variable Cost	$\Rightarrow$ $150,000 + $500,000 = $650,000
Net Profit	$\Rightarrow$ $225,000
Total Revenues = Total Cost + Net Profit	$\Rightarrow$ $650,000 + $225,000 = $875,000
Sale Price per widget	$\Rightarrow$ $875,000 ÷ 50,000 = $17.5

Question #2: Walking at a constant rate, it takes Newton 60 minutes to walk from home to the nearest newspaper stand, and quarter of that time to walk from the newspaper stand to the playground. It takes him a third of the time it takes him to walk from the playground to the school than it does for him to walk from the newspaper stand to the playground. How many minutes longer does it take Newton to walk from the newspaper stand to the playground than it takes him to walk from the playground to the school?

Solution:

Time for Walking from Home to the Newspaper Stand	$\Rightarrow$ 60 minutes
Time for Walking from the Newspaper Stand to the Playground	$\Rightarrow$ ¼(60) = 15 minutes
Time for Walking from the Playground to the School	$\Rightarrow$ 1/3(15) = 5 minutes
Difference between the Walk to the Playground & Walk to the School	$\Rightarrow$ 15 – 5 = 10 minutes

Question #3: If a certain 6 feet by 9 feet sheet of wood lamination that weighs 1.25 pounds and is 0.15 inches thick costs $120 for 150 sheets, how much will a stack of lamination sheets 8 feet thick cost?

Solution: No. of sheets in a 8 feet or 8 × 12 = 96 inch thick stack $\Rightarrow \dfrac{total\ thickness}{thickness\ per\ sheet} = \dfrac{96}{0.15} = 640$

Cost of 150 Sheets $\Rightarrow$ $120

Cost of 1 Sheet $\Rightarrow \dfrac{120}{150}$

Cost of 640 Sheets $\Rightarrow \dfrac{120}{150} × 640 = \$512$

Cost of 8 feet thick stack or 640 lamination sheets = $512

Note: The size and weight of the lamination sheet is irrelevant in this case.

Question #4: A person needs $2.52 in postage to mail a letter. If he has 10 each of 55-cent stamps, 20-cent stamps, 10-cent stamps, 5-cent stamps, and 1-cent stamps, what is the minimum number of stamps he can use to put the exact postage on the letter?

Solution: In order to use the minimum number of stamps, you should use the maximum number of the largest possible cent value of stamps.

Total Postage Needed	$\Rightarrow$ $2.52
Use 4 55-cent stamps	$\Rightarrow$ –$2.20
Remaining Postage Needed	$\Rightarrow$ $0.32
Use 1 20-cent stamp	$\Rightarrow$ –$0.20
Remaining Postage Needed	$\Rightarrow$ $0.12
Use 1 10-cent stamp	$\Rightarrow$ –$0.10
Remaining Postage Needed	$\Rightarrow$ $0.02
Use 2 1-cent stamps	$\Rightarrow$ –$0.02
Remaining Postage	$\Rightarrow$ $0.00
Total No. of stamps used	$\Rightarrow$ 4(55-cent) + 1(20-cent) + 1(10-cent) + 2(1-cent) = 8

This is the combination that uses the least number of stamps. There are other possibilities, but they all will need more number of stamps.

Question #5: John runs from Monday to Friday. On Monday, he runs n miles. On Tuesday, he ran twice as much as Monday. On Wednesday, he ran 12 miles more than twice as much as Tuesday. On Thursday, he ran 2 miles fewer than half as much Wednesday. On Friday, he ran half as much as Thursday plus an additional 7 miles. What is the average number of miles he ran per day over the 5-day period?

Solution: Let's translate one sentence at a time:

Monday $\Rightarrow$ he ran n miles
            $\Rightarrow n$ miles

Tuesday $\Rightarrow$ he ran twice as much as he did on Monday
            $\Rightarrow 2(\text{Mon}) = 2(n) = 2n$ miles

Wednesday $\Rightarrow$ he ran 12 miles more than twice as much as he did on Tuesday
            $\Rightarrow 2(\text{Tue}) + 12 = 2(2n) + 12 = 4n + 12$

Thursday $\Rightarrow$ he ran 2 fewer than half as much as he did on Wednesday
            $\Rightarrow \frac{1}{2}(\text{Wed}) - 2 = \frac{1}{2}(4n + 12) - 2 = 2n + 6 - 2 = 2n + 4$

Friday $\Rightarrow$ he ran half as much as he did on Thursday plus an additional 7 miles
            $\Rightarrow \frac{1}{2}(\text{Thurs}) = \frac{1}{2}(2n + 4) + 7 = n + 2 + 7 = n + 9$

Total Miles ran over the 5-day Period $\Rightarrow (n) + (2n) + (4n + 12) + (2n + 4) + (n + 9) = 10n + 25$ miles

Average No. of Miles $\Rightarrow \dfrac{10n + 25}{5} = 2n + 5$

Question #6: A dressmaker requires 1 yard of material for 1 coat, 2 yards of material for 4 shirts, and 4 yards of material for 1 coat and 2 pants. How many yards of material is required to make 2 coats, 2 shirts, and 2 pants?

Solution:
Amount of Material required to make 1 Coat $\Rightarrow$ 1 yard
Amount of Material required to make 4 Shirts $\Rightarrow$ 2 yards
Amount of Material required to make 1 Shirt $\Rightarrow 2 \div 4 = 0.5$ yards
Amount of material required to make 1 Coat & 2 Pants $\Rightarrow$ 4 yards
Amount of Material required to make 2 Pants $\Rightarrow$ 4 yards – Material Required to make 1 Coat
                                          $\Rightarrow$ 4 yards – 1 yard = 3 yards
Amount of Material required to make 1 Pant $\Rightarrow 3 \div 2 = 1.5$ yards
Amount of Material required to make 1 Coat + 1 Shirt + 1 Pant $\Rightarrow$ 1 + 0.5 + 1.5 = 3 yards
Amount of Material required to make 2 Coats + 2 Shirts + 2 Pants $\Rightarrow 2 \times 3 = 6$ yards

ALGEBRAIC PROBLEMS:

Question #7: Nikki has half as many cards as Tasha. If Tasha gives away 7 of her cards, she would still have 1 more card than Nikki. How many cards do Nikki and Tasha have altogether?

Solution:
Nikki has half as many cards as Tasha $\Rightarrow N = \frac{1}{2}T$ $\Rightarrow$ Equation #1
When Tasha gives away 7 cards, she'll have 1 more than Nikki $\Rightarrow N + 1 = T - 7$ $\Rightarrow$ Equation #2
Substitute the value of N from Equation #1 into #2 $\Rightarrow \frac{1}{2}T + 1 = T - 7$ [Substitute $N = \frac{1}{2}T$]
                                              $\Rightarrow \frac{1}{2}T - T + 1 = -7$ [Subtract T from both sides]
                                                $\Rightarrow \frac{1}{2}T - T = -8$ [Subtract 1 from both sides]
                                                $\Rightarrow -\frac{1}{2}T = -8$ [Combine like-terms]
                                                $\Rightarrow T = 16$ [Multiply both sides by –2]
Substitute the value of T into Equation #1 $\Rightarrow N = \frac{1}{2}T$ [Rewrite Equation #1]
                                                $\Rightarrow N = \frac{1}{2}(16)$ [Substitute $T = 16$]
                                                $\Rightarrow N = 8$ [Apply distributive property]
No. of cards that Nikki and Tasha, together have $\Rightarrow$ 8 + 16 = 24 cards

Question #8: In a certain school bus, after leaving the school, there are equal number of boys and girls. At the first stop, 6 girls get off the bus and nobody gets on. After the first stop, there are twice as many boys as girls on the bus. How many boys are on the bus? (Note: don't consider the driver)

Solution: Organize the data in a grid:
          Boys   Girls

Let Original be x x
At First Stop 0 -6
After First Stop x $x - 6$
EZ Problem Set-Up $\Rightarrow$ After the first stop, there are twice as many boys as girls on the bus

      $\Rightarrow x = 2(x - 6)$ [Set up the equation]
      $\Rightarrow x = 2x - 12$ [Apply distributive property]
      $\Rightarrow -x = -12$ [Subtract $2x$ from both sides]
      $\Rightarrow x = 12$ [Multiply both sides by -1]
No. of boys on the bus $\Rightarrow$ 12 boys

Question #9: In a bookstore, each ball pen costs $2 and each fountain pen costs $7 each. At these prices, a mixed bunch of 25 pens containing ball pen and fountain pen costs $75. How many fountain pens are in the bunch?

Solution: Let, No. of Ball Pen $\Rightarrow B$
And, No. of Fountain Pen $\Rightarrow F$
Each ball pen costs $2 and each fountain pen costs $7 each $\Rightarrow B + F = 25$ $\Rightarrow$ Equation #1
25 pens containing ball pen and fountain pen costs $75 $\Rightarrow 2B + 7F = 75$ $\Rightarrow$ Equation #2
Solve Equation #1 and #2 simultaneously:

$-2B$ $+$ $(-2F)$ $= -50$ [Multiply equation #1 by -2]
$\underline{\;\;2B\;\;\;\; +\;\;\;\;\;\; 7F\;\;\;\;\; = 75\;\;\;}$ [Let equation #2 remain as it is]
      $5F$ $= 25$ [Add equation #1 and #2]
       F $= 5$ [Divide both sides by 5]
$\Rightarrow B + F = 25$ [Rewrite Equation #1]
$\Rightarrow B + 5 = 25$ [Substitute $F = 5$]
$\Rightarrow B = 20$ [Subtract 5 from both sides]
Hence, $B = 20$ and $F = 5$.

Question #10: Mary finishes the first half of a test in one-third the time it takes her to finish the second half. If the whole test takes her an hour, how many minutes does she spend on the first half of the test?

Solution: Let, the time spent on Second Half of the Test $\Rightarrow n$

Then, the time spent on First Half of the Test $\Rightarrow \dfrac{1}{3} n$

Total Time spent to finish the Whole Test $\Rightarrow$ 1 hour = 60 minutes
EZ Problem Set-Up $\Rightarrow$ Time on First Half + Time on Second Half = Total Time on Whole Test

      $\Rightarrow n + \dfrac{1}{3} n = 60$ [Set up the equation]

      $\Rightarrow \dfrac{3}{3} n + \dfrac{1}{3} n = 60$ [Scale-Up all the fractions to their LCD]

      $\Rightarrow \dfrac{4}{3} n = 60$ [Combine like-terms]

      $\Rightarrow n = 60 \times \dfrac{3}{4} = 45$ [Multiply both sides by 3/4]

Time spent on Second Half of the test $\Rightarrow n = 45$ minutes

Time spent on First Half of the test $\Rightarrow \dfrac{1}{3} n = \dfrac{1}{3} \times 45 = 15$ minutes

Question #11: In a farm, if 98 chickens and rabbits are put together, they have a total of 220 legs. How many chickens are there?

Solution: Let, the No. of chickens $\Rightarrow c$
And, the No. of rabbits $\Rightarrow r$
There are 98 chickens and rabbits $\Rightarrow c + r = 98$ $\Rightarrow$ Equation #1
There are a total of 220 legs $\Rightarrow 2c + 4r = 220$ $\Rightarrow$ Equation #2
(Note: chickens have 2 legs & rabbits have 4 legs)
Multiply equation #1 by (-2) $\Rightarrow -2c - 2r = -196$ $\Rightarrow$ Equation #3
Add Equation #2 and Equation #3 $2c +\;\; 4r\;\; =\;\; 220$ [Rewrite Equation #2]

$$-2c - \quad 2r \quad = -196 \quad \text{[Rewrite Equation \#3]}$$
$$2r \quad = \quad 24 \quad \text{[Add both equations]}$$
$$r \quad = \quad 12 \quad \text{[Divide both sides by 2]}$$

Substitute the value of r in Equation #1 $\Rightarrow c + r = 98$ [Rewrite Equation #1]

$$\Rightarrow c + 12 = 98 \quad \text{[Substitute } r = 12]$$
$$\Rightarrow c = 86 \quad \text{[Subtract 12 from both sides]}$$

No. of chickens $\Rightarrow 86$
No. of rabbits $\Rightarrow 12$

Question #12: A jeweler received two shipments of rings. In the first shipment, 2 percent of the rings were made in platinum and the rest in gold. In the second shipment, which was twice as large as the first one, 1.5 percent of the rings were made in platinum and the rest in gold. If the jeweler received a total of 250 platinum rings, how many rings were in the second shipment?

Solution: Let the total No. of rings in the first shipment $\Rightarrow n$
Then the total No. of rings in the second shipment $\Rightarrow 2n$
No. of platinum rings in the first shipment $\Rightarrow$ 2% of $n = (0.02)n$
No. of platinum rings in the second shipment $\Rightarrow$ 1.5% of $2n = (0.015)2n$
Total No. of platinum rings in both shipments $\Rightarrow 250$
EZ Problem Set-Up $\Rightarrow$ No. of platinum rings in the first shipment + No. of platinum rings in the second shipment = Total No. of platinum rings in both shipments:

$$\Rightarrow (0.02)n + (0.015)2n = 250 \quad \text{[Set up the equation]}$$
$$\Rightarrow (0.02)n + (0.03)n = 250 \quad \text{[Apply distributive property]}$$
$$\Rightarrow (0.05)n = 250 \quad \text{[Combine like-terms]}$$
$$\Rightarrow n = 250 \div 0.05 = 5,000 \quad \text{[Divide both sides by 0.05]}$$

No. of rings in the first shipment $\Rightarrow n = 5,000$
No. of rings in the second shipment $\Rightarrow 2n = 2(5,000) = 10,000$

Question #13: In a certain fraction, the numerator is 20 less than the denominator. If the fraction is equal to $\frac{2}{7}$, what is the numerator of this fraction?

Solution: Let the denominator of the fraction be x

EZ Problem Set-Up $\Rightarrow$ If the numerator is 20 less than the denominator, the value of the fraction is $\frac{2}{7}$:

$$\Rightarrow \frac{x - 20}{x} = \frac{2}{7} \quad \text{[Set up the equation]}$$
$$\Rightarrow 7(x - 20) = 2x \quad \text{[Cross-multiply]}$$
$$\Rightarrow 7x - 140 = 2x \quad \text{[Apply distributive property]}$$
$$\Rightarrow 5x - 140 = 0 \quad \text{[Subtract } 2x \text{ from both sides]}$$
$$\Rightarrow 5x = 140 \quad \text{[Add 140 to both sides]}$$
$$\Rightarrow x = 28 \quad \text{[Divide both sides by 5]}$$

Denominator of the fraction $\Rightarrow x = 28$
Numerator of the fraction $\Rightarrow x - 20 = 8$

Question #14: In certain classroom, there are 8 more girls than boys. If there are 20 students in the class, how many are girls?

Solution: Let, the No. of boys in the class $\Rightarrow n$
Then, the No. of girls in the class $\Rightarrow n + 8$
Total Students in the class $\Rightarrow 20$
EZ Problem Set-Up $\Rightarrow$ No. of Boys + No. of Girls + Total No. of students

$$\Rightarrow n + (n + 8) = 20 \quad \text{[Set up the equation]}$$
$$\Rightarrow 2n + 8 = 20 \quad \text{[Combine like-terms]}$$
$$\Rightarrow 2n = 12 \quad \text{[Subtract 8 from both sides]}$$
$$\Rightarrow n = 6 \quad \text{[Divide both sides by 2]}$$

No. of boys in the class $\Rightarrow n = 6$
No. of girls in the class $\Rightarrow n + 8 = 6 + 8 = 14$

Question #15: In a class, 20 children were sharing equally the cost of a birthday gift for their teacher. When 4 of the children decided not to contribute, each of the other children had to pay $1.50 more. How much, in dollars, did the gift cost?

Solution: Let, the amount, in dollars, that each of the 20 children were originally going to contribute $\Rightarrow n$

Then, the cost of the gift $\Rightarrow 20n$

Now, when 4 of the children backed out, the amount that each of the 16 remaining children had to pay $\Rightarrow (n + 1.50)$

EZ Problem Set-Up $\Rightarrow$ Cost of the gift = Amount that each of the 16 remaining children paid

$\Rightarrow 20n = 16(n + 1.5)$ [Set up the equation]
$\Rightarrow 20n = 16n + 24$ [Apply distributive property]
$\Rightarrow 4n = 24$ [Subtract 16n from both sides]
$\Rightarrow n = 6$ [Divide both sides by 4]

Total Cost of the Gift $\Rightarrow 20n = 20 \times 6 = \$120$

Alternately: This problem can also be solved by simple logic:

Additional amount that the 16 remaining children had to contribute $\Rightarrow 16 \times 1.5 = \$24$
Contribution per Child $\Rightarrow 24 \div 4 = \$6$
Total Cost $\Rightarrow 20 \times 6 = \$120$

Question #16: John has $100 more than Tony does. After John spends $20 on buying books, he has five times as much as Tony. How much money does Tony have?

Solution: John has $100 more than Tony $\Rightarrow J = T + 100$ $\Rightarrow$ Equation #1
After spending $20, John has 5 times of Tony $\Rightarrow J - 20 = 5T$
     $\Rightarrow J = 5T + 20$ $\Rightarrow$ Equation #2

EZ Problem Set-Up $\Rightarrow$ Equate Equation #1 and Equation #2

$\Rightarrow 5T + 20 = T + 100$ [Set up the equation]
$\Rightarrow 4T + 20 = 100$ [Subtract T from both sides]
$\Rightarrow 4T = 80$ [Subtract 20 from both sides]
$\Rightarrow T = 20$ [Divide both sides by 4]

Amount of money that Tony has $\Rightarrow \$20$

Question #17: If the cost of a apples priced at 12 cents each is equal to the cost of $a - 8$ oranges priced at 18 cents each, then what is the value of a?

Solution: Cost of a apples $\Rightarrow 12a$
Cost of $a - 8$ oranges $\Rightarrow 18(a - 8)$

EZ Problem Set-Up $\Rightarrow$ Cost of a apples = Cost of $a - 8$ oranges

$\Rightarrow 12a = 18(a - 8)$ [Set up the equation]
$\Rightarrow 12a = 18a - 144$ [Apply distributive property]
$\Rightarrow -6a = -144$ [Subtract both sides by 18a]
$\Rightarrow a = 24$ [Divide both sides by -6]

Question #18: If w number of watches sold per day varies with the price p per watch according to the relationship given by the equation $w = 925 - 15p$, what would be the total daily sales proceed from sale of 100 watches?

Solution: EZ Problem Set-Up $\Rightarrow$ Solve the given equation by substituting 100 for w and solving for p

$\Rightarrow w = 925 - 15p$ [Set up the equation]
$\Rightarrow 100 = 925 - 15p$ [Substitute w = 100]
$\Rightarrow -15p = -825$ [Subtract 925 from both sides]
$\Rightarrow p = 55$ [Divide both sides by -15]

Total daily sales proceeds $\Rightarrow$ (No. of watches sold) × (price per watch) = $wp = 100 \times 55 = \$5,500$

Question #19: An auto repair shop charges $125 for alignment, balancing, and regular oil, but $150 for alignment, balancing, and premium oil. If the premium oil costs six times as mush as the regular oil, what is the cost of just the alignment and balancing?

Solution: Charges $125 for alignment, balancing, & regular oil $\Rightarrow A + B + R = \$125$ $\Rightarrow$ Equation #1
Charges $150 for alignment, balancing, & premium oil $\Rightarrow A + B + P = \$150$ $\Rightarrow$ Equation #2

Premium oil costs six times as mush as the regular oil $\Rightarrow P = 6R$ $\Rightarrow$ Equation #3
Substitute the value of P from Equation #3 into #2 $\Rightarrow A + B + 6R = \$150$ $\Rightarrow$ Equation #4
Subtract Equation #1 from Equation #4 $\Rightarrow$ $A \quad + B + \quad 6R \ = \$150$ [Rewrite Equation #4]

$$\Rightarrow \underline{-(A \quad + B + \quad R \quad = \$125)} \text{ [Rewrite Equation #1]}$$

$$\Rightarrow \qquad\qquad\qquad 5R \ = \$25 \quad \text{[Subtract the two equations]}$$

$$\Rightarrow \qquad\qquad\qquad\quad R \ = \$5 \quad \text{[Divide both sides by 5]}$$

Substitute the value of R in Equation #1 $\Rightarrow A + B + R = \$125$ [Rewrite Equation #1]

$$\Rightarrow A + B + \$5 = \$125 \quad \text{[Substitute } R = \$5]$$

$$\Rightarrow A + B = \$120 \quad \text{[Subtract \$5 from both sides]}$$

Cost of just the alignment and balancing $\Rightarrow \$120$

Question #20: In a course of seven successive days, a certain player wins twice as many board games each day as on the previous day. If in the seven-day period, the player wins a total of 625 games, how many games does the player win on the fifth day?

Solution: Let the number of games won on the first day be x; then, the number of games won on the second day will be $2x$, on the third day will be $4x$, on the fourth day will be $8x$, on the fifth day will be $16x$, on the sixth day will be $32x$, and on the seventh day will be $62x$.
EZ Problem Set-Up $\Rightarrow$ No. of games won in the seven-day period = 625

$$\Rightarrow x + 2x + 4x + 8x + 16x + 32x + 62x = 625 \quad \text{[Set up the equation]}$$

$$\Rightarrow 125x = 625 \quad \text{[Combine like-terms]}$$

$$\Rightarrow x = 5 \quad \text{[Divide both sides by 125]}$$

No. of games won on the fifth day $\Rightarrow 16x = 16 \times 5 = 80$.

Question #21: A certain manufacturing company produces items for which the production cost is comprised of annual fixed costs totaling \$190,000 and variable costs averaging \$9 per unit. If the company sets the selling price per item to \$19, how many units must be produced and sold to earn an annual profit of \$725,000?

Solution: Let the number of items sold be x
Profit $\Rightarrow \$725,000$
Selling Price $\Rightarrow \$19$ per item
Revenue $\Rightarrow$ (Selling Price) × (No of Items Sold) = $19x$
Cost $\Rightarrow$ Fixed Cost + Variable Cost = $\$190,000 + 9x$
EZ Problem Set-Up $\Rightarrow$ Profit = Revenue − Cost

$$\Rightarrow 725,000 = 19x - (190,000 + 9x) \quad \text{[Set up the equation]}$$

$$\Rightarrow 725,000 = 10x - 190,000 \quad \text{[Simplify the right side]}$$

$$\Rightarrow 10x = 915,000 \quad \text{[Isolate } x \text{ on left side]}$$

$$\Rightarrow x = 91,500 \quad \text{[Divide both sides by 10]}$$

Question #22: If n is an integer, and the average (arithmetic mean) of 5, 6, and n is less than 10, what is the greatest possible value of n?

Solution: EZ Problem Set-Up $\Rightarrow$ Average of 5, 6, and n is less than 10

$$\Rightarrow \frac{5 + 6 + n}{3} < 10 \quad \text{[Set up the inequality]}$$

$$\Rightarrow 5 + 6 + n < 30 \quad \text{[Multiply both sides by 3]}$$

$$\Rightarrow 11 + n < 30 \quad \text{[Combine like-terms]}$$

$$\Rightarrow n < 19 \quad \text{[Subtract 11 from both sides]}$$

Since n is an integer, the most it can be is $\Rightarrow 18$

Question #23: If John saved more than \$90 by purchasing a printer at a 15 percent discount, what is the smallest integer amount that could be the original price of the printer?

Solution: Let the original price of the printer = x
EZ Problem Set-Up $\Rightarrow$ 15 percent of the original price must be greater than \$90

$$\Rightarrow 15\% \text{ of } x > 90 \quad \text{[Set up the inequality]}$$

$$\Rightarrow 0.15x > 90 \quad \text{[Convert the words into an inequality]}$$

$$\Rightarrow x > 600 \quad \text{[Divide both sides by 0.15]}$$

If the original price of the printer were $600, John would have saved exactly $90. Now, in order to save more than $90 by buying a printer at a 15 percent discount, the smallest integer amount that could be the original price of the printer should be more than $600, which is $601.

Question #24: How many positive integers n are there that satisfy the inequality $-2 < 2n + 5 < 17$?

Solution:
$\Rightarrow -2 < 2n + 5 < 17$ [Write the inequality]
$\Rightarrow -7 < 2n < 12$ [Subtract 5 from all sides]
$\Rightarrow -\dfrac{7}{2} < n < 6$ [Divide all sides by 2]

No. of positive integers n that satisfies the given inequality $\Rightarrow$ 5 (1, 2, 3, 4, and 5)

Question #25: A fundraiser collected exactly $999 from a retirement community. If each person in the community contributed at least $18, what is the greatest number of members that could be in the community?

Solution: Let the No. of people in the retirement community = n
EZ Problem Set-Up $\Rightarrow$ In order to find the greatest possible number of people in the retirement community, each person must contribute the minimum possible amount, which is $18.
$\Rightarrow 18n \le 999$ [Set up the inequality]
$\Rightarrow n \le 55.5$ [Divide both sides by 18]
Since n represents the number of people in the retirement community, it must be a positive integer; hence, the greatest possible value of n, or the number of people in the retirement community is 55.

Question #26: If $2 < m < 7$ and $1 < n < 8$, what is the possible range of values for mn?

Solution: In order to find the possible range of values for mn, find the smallest possible value of mn by multiplying the smallest possible value of m with the smallest possible value of n; likewise, find the largest possible value of mn by multiplying the largest possible value of m with the largest possible value of n.
$\Rightarrow (2)(1) < mn < (7)(8)$
$\Rightarrow 2 < mn < 56$

Question #27: As per company policy, at least five-sixth of the 70 board of directors must vote in favor of a resolution for it to pass. What is the greatest number of directors who could vote against the resolution and still have it pass?

Solution: Since at least $\dfrac{5}{6}$ of the board of directors must vote in favor of the resolution for it to pass, then no more than $1 - \dfrac{5}{6}$, or $\dfrac{1}{6}$ of the directors could vote against it.

$\Rightarrow \dfrac{1}{6}$ of 70 = 11.67

Greatest number of directors who could vote against the resolution and still have it pass $\Rightarrow$ 11

Question #28: If $8x + 17 > 15 + 7x$, and x is a negative integer, then what is the value of x?

Solution:
$\Rightarrow 8x + 17 > 15 + 7x$ [Solve the inequality]
$\Rightarrow x + 17 > 15$ [Subtract 7x from both sides]
$\Rightarrow x > -2$ [Subtract 17 from both sides]
Since x is a negative integer, the only negative integer that is greater than -2 is $-1 \Rightarrow x = -1$

NUMERAL PROBLEMS:

Question #29: When the number n is multiplied by 8, the result is the same as when 8 is added to n. What is the value of $7n$?

Solution: EZ Problem Set-Up $\Rightarrow$ When n is multiplied by 8, the result is the same as when 8 is added to n
$\Rightarrow n \times 8 = n + 8$ [Set up the equation]
$\Rightarrow 8n = n + 8$ [Combine terms]
$\Rightarrow 7n = 8$ [Subtract n from both sides]

$$\Rightarrow n = \frac{8}{7} \qquad \text{[Divide both sides by 7]}$$

Value of $7n$ $\qquad \Rightarrow 7 \times \frac{8}{7} = 8$

Question #30: If there is a magic number, such that, if you add 6 to the number or multiply the number by 6, the result would be the same, what is that magic number?

Solution: Let, the magic number = n

EZ Problem Set-Up $\Rightarrow$ Adding 6 to n = Multiplying n by 6

$\Rightarrow n + 6 = n \times 6$ $\qquad$ [Set up the equation]

$\Rightarrow n + 6 = 6n$ $\qquad$ [Apply distributive property]

$\Rightarrow 5n = 6$ $\qquad$ [Subtract n from both sides]

$\Rightarrow n = 1.2$ $\qquad$ [Divide both sides by 5]

Question #31: If five times n is equal to n decreased by 20, then what is the value of n?

Solution: EZ problem Set-Up $\Rightarrow$ Five times n is equal to n decreased by 20

$\Rightarrow 5n = n - 20$ $\qquad$ [Set up the equation]

$\Rightarrow 4n = -20$ $\qquad$ [Subtract n from both sides]

$\Rightarrow n = -5$ $\qquad$ [Divide both sides by 4]

Question #32: If the product of 8, 10, and x is equal to the product of 1, 10, and y, such that $xy \neq 0$, what is the value of $\frac{x}{y}$?

Solution: EZ problem Set-Up $\Rightarrow$ Product of 8, 10, and x is equal to the product of 1, 10, and y

$\Rightarrow (8)(10)(x) = (1)(10)(y)$ $\qquad$ [Set up the equation]

$\Rightarrow 80x = 10y$ $\qquad$ [Apply distributive property]

$\Rightarrow \frac{x}{y} = \frac{1}{8}$ $\qquad$ [Divide both sides by 80y]

Question #33: If 2 less than 6 times a certain number is 8 more than the number, what is the number?

Solution: Let the value of the original number = x

EZ problem Set-Up $\Rightarrow$ 2 less than 6 times a certain number is 8 more than the number

$\Rightarrow 6x - 2 = x + 8$ $\qquad$ [Set up the equation]

$\Rightarrow 5x - 2 = 8$ $\qquad$ [Subtract x from both sides]

$\Rightarrow 5x = 10$ $\qquad$ [Add 2 to both sides]

$\Rightarrow x = 2$ $\qquad$ [Divide both sides by 5]

Question #34: If $\frac{3}{4}$ of a number is 7 more than $\frac{1}{6}$ of the number, what is $\frac{5}{6}$ of the number?

Solution: Let the value of that number = x

EZ problem Set-Up $\Rightarrow \frac{3}{4}$ of a number is 7 more than $\frac{1}{6}$ of the number

$\Rightarrow \frac{3}{4}x = 7 + \frac{1}{6}x$ $\qquad$ [Set up the equation]

$\Rightarrow \frac{3}{4}x - \frac{1}{6}x = 7$ $\qquad$ [Subtract 1/6x from both sides]

$\Rightarrow \frac{9}{12}x - \frac{2}{12}x = 7$ $\qquad$ [Scale-Up the fractions to their LCD, which is 12]

$\Rightarrow \frac{7}{12}x = 7$ $\qquad$ [Combine like-terms]

$\Rightarrow x = 12$ $\qquad$ [Multiply both sides by 12/7]

Value of $\frac{5}{6}x$ $\qquad \Rightarrow \frac{5}{6} \times 12 = 10$ $\qquad$ [Multiply both sides by 5/6]

Question #35: A certain number n is first increased by 10, then the result is multiplied by 10, then the result is decreased by 10, and then the result is divided by 10. What is the final result, in terms of n?

Solution: EZ Problem Set-Up $\Rightarrow$ Just keep following the directions as given in the problem

$\Rightarrow n$ [Write a certain number n]

$\Rightarrow n + 10$ [Increase the number by 10]

$\Rightarrow 10(n + 10) = 10n + 100$ [Multiply the result by 10]

$\Rightarrow (10n + 100) - 10 = 10n + 90$ [Decrease the result by 10]

$\Rightarrow (10n + 90) \div 10 = n + 9$ [Divide the result by 10]

Question #36: What number when divided by 19 has a quotient of 7 and a remainder of 11?

Solution: Divisor = 19   Quotient = 7   Remainder = 11

EZ Problem Set-Up $\Rightarrow$ Dividend = (Divisor × Quotient) + Remainder

$\Rightarrow$ Dividend = (19 × 7) + 11   [Substitute the known values]

$\Rightarrow$ Dividend = 133 + 11   [Do the multiplication]

$\Rightarrow$ Dividend = 144   [Do the addition]

Question #37: If the sum of 12, 17, and x is 51, then what is the product of 6 and $(x + 5)$?

Solution: Sum $\Rightarrow 12 + 17 + x = 51$

$\Rightarrow 29 + x = 51$

$\Rightarrow x = 22$

Product $\Rightarrow 6(x + 5) = 6(22 + 5) = 6(27) = 162$

Question #38: If the only possible values of m are –7, 0, and 1, and the only possible values of n are –5, 0, and 2, what is the greatest possible value of $2m + n^2$?

Solution: Possible Values of m $\Rightarrow -7, 0, 1$

Possible Values of n $\Rightarrow -5, 0, 2$

Greatest Possible value of $2m + n^2$ $\Rightarrow$ Pick a value for m, which is the largest positive number

$\Rightarrow$ Pick a value for n, which has the largest absolute value

$\Rightarrow 2(1) + (-5)^2 = 2 + 25 = 27$

Question #39: What positive number, when squared, is equal to the cube of the positive square root of 25?

Solution: Let, the value of the positive number = n

EZ Problem Set-Up $\Rightarrow$ Square of n is equal to the cube of the positive square root of 25

$\Rightarrow n^2 = \left(\sqrt{25}\right)^3$ [Set up the equation]

$\Rightarrow n^2 = (5)^3$ [Square root the right side]

$\Rightarrow n^2 = 125$ [Cube the right side]

$\Rightarrow n = 5\sqrt{5}$ [Square root both sides]

Question #40: The result obtained when x is multiplied by y is equal to ten times the result obtained when y is subtracted from x. If y equals 5, what does x equal?

Solution: EZ Problem Set-Up $\Rightarrow x$ times y is equal to ten times of y minus x

$\Rightarrow xy = 10(x - y)$ [Set up the equation]

$\Rightarrow x(5) = 10(x - 5)$ [Substitute $y = 5$]

$\Rightarrow 5x = 10x - 50$ [Apply distributive property]

$\Rightarrow 0 = 5x - 50$ [Subtract 5x from both sides]

$\Rightarrow 5x = 50$ [Add 50 to both sides]

Value of x $\Rightarrow x = 10$ [Divide both sides by 5]

Question #41: What is the value of the second of the three consecutive integers if the sum of the first and third is 24?

Solution: Let the value of first integer $\Rightarrow n$

Then, the value of second integer $\Rightarrow n + 1$

And, the value of third integer $\Rightarrow n + 2$

EZ Problem Set-Up $\Rightarrow$ In a set of three consecutive integers, the sum of the first and third is 24

$\Rightarrow n + (n + 2) = 24$ [Set up the equation]

$$\Rightarrow 2n + 2 = 24 \qquad \text{[Combine like-terms]}$$
$$\Rightarrow 2n = 22 \qquad \text{[Subtract 2 from both sides]}$$
$$\Rightarrow n = 11 \qquad \text{[Divide both sides by 2]}$$

Value of the first (smallest) integer $\Rightarrow n = 11$
Value of the second (middle) integer $\Rightarrow n + 1 = 11 + 1 = 12$
Value of the third (biggest) integer $\Rightarrow n + 2 = 11 + 1 = 13$

Question #42: There are three consecutive odd integers, such that seven times the middle integer is 85 more than the sum of the smallest and largest integers. What is the value of the largest of the three integers?

Solution: Let, the value of first odd integer $\qquad \Rightarrow n$
Then, the value of second odd integer $\Rightarrow n + 2$
And, the value of third odd integer $\qquad \Rightarrow n + 4$
EZ Problem Set-Up $\Rightarrow$ In a set of three consecutive odd integers, seven times the middle integer is 85 more than the sum of the smallest and largest integers.

$$\Rightarrow 7(n + 2) = (n) + (n + 4) + 85 \qquad \text{[Set up the equation]}$$
$$\Rightarrow 7n + 14 = 2n + 89 \qquad \text{[Apply distributive property]}$$
$$\Rightarrow 5n + 14 = 89 \qquad \text{[Subtract } 2n \text{ from both sides]}$$
$$\Rightarrow 5n = 75 \qquad \text{[Subtract 14 from both sides]}$$
$$\Rightarrow n = 15 \qquad \text{[Divide both sides by 5]}$$

Value of the first (smallest) integer $\Rightarrow n = 15$
Value of the second (middle) integer $\Rightarrow n + 2 = 15 + 2 = 17$
Value of the third (biggest) integer $\Rightarrow n + 4 = 15 + 4 = 19$

Question #43: If $n + 2$ is the largest of five consecutive integers, what is the sum of the five integers?

Solution: Value of 5th integer $\Rightarrow n + 2$ [Given]
Value of 4th integer $\Rightarrow (n + 2) - 1 = n + 1$ [Subtract 1 from the 5th integer to find the 4th integer]
Value of 3rd integer $\Rightarrow (n + 1) - 1 = n$ [Subtract 1 from the 4th integer to find the 3rd integer]
Value of 2nd integer $\Rightarrow n - 1$ [Subtract 1 from the 3rd integer to find the 2nd integer]
Value of 1st integer $\Rightarrow (n - 1) - 1 = n - 2$ [Subtract 1 from the 2nd integer to find the 1st integer]
Sum of all five integers $\Rightarrow (n + 2) + (n + 1) + n + (n - 1) + (n - 2) = 5n$

Question #44: How many integers in the set of all integers from 1 to 100, inclusive, are not the square of an odd integer?

Solution: No. of integers from 1 to 100 $\Rightarrow 100 - 1 + 1 = 100$
No. of integers from 1 to 100 that are square of an integer $\Rightarrow 10$ (1, 4, 9, 16, 25, 36, 49, 64, 81, 100)
No. of integers from 1 to 100 that are square of an odd integer $\Rightarrow 5$ (1, 9, 25, 49, 81)
No. of integers from 1 to 100 that are not the square of an odd integer $\Rightarrow 100 - 5 = 95$

Question #45: How many distinct integers between 100 and 150, inclusive, can be evenly divisible by neither 2 nor 5?

Solution: No. of integers between 100 & 150 that are evenly divisible by 2 $\Rightarrow 50 \div 2 = 25 + 1 = 26$
No. of integers between 100 & 150 that are evenly divisible by 5 $\Rightarrow 50 \div 5 = 10 + 1 = 11$
No. of integers between 100 & 150 that are evenly divisible by 2 & 5 $\Rightarrow 6$ (duplicates)
(100, 110, 120, 130, 140, 150)
No. of integers between 100 & 150 that are evenly divisible by 2 or 5 $\Rightarrow 26 + 11 - 6 = 31$
No. of integers between 100 & 150 that are NOT evenly divisible by 2 & 5 $\Rightarrow 51 - 31 = 20$

Question #46: One positive integer is one-third of another integer. If the product of the two integers is 12, what is their sum?

Solution: Let the value of the two integers be x and y

One positive integer is one-third of another integer $\Rightarrow x = \dfrac{1}{3}y \qquad \Rightarrow$ Equation #1

Product of the two integers is 12 $\qquad \Rightarrow xy = 12 \qquad \Rightarrow$ Equation #2

Substitute the value of x from Equation #1 into #2 $\Rightarrow y\left(\dfrac{1}{3}y\right) = 12$ [Substitute $x = (1/3)y$]

$$\Rightarrow \frac{1}{3}y^2 = 12 \qquad \text{[Apply distributive property]}$$

$$\Rightarrow y^2 = 12 \times 3 = 36 \qquad \text{[Multiple both sides by 3]}$$

$$\Rightarrow y = 6 \qquad \text{[Square root both sides]}$$

Substitute the value of y in Equation #2 $\qquad \Rightarrow 6x = 12$

$$\Rightarrow x = 2 \qquad \text{[Divide both sides by 6]}$$

Sum of the two integers $\Rightarrow x + y = 2 + 6 = 8$

Question #47: If n is an odd integer, what is the sum of the smallest odd integer greater than $5n + 6$ and the largest odd integer less than $2n + 7$?

Solution: Value of the smallest odd integer greater than $5n + 6 \quad \Rightarrow 5n + 8$
Value of the largest odd integer less than $2n + 7 \qquad \Rightarrow 2n + 5$
Sum of the two integers $\Rightarrow (5n + 8) + (2n + 5) \Rightarrow 7n + 13$

Question #48: If $m = 2^3 \times 3^2 \times 6$, and n is a positive integer, what is the greatest number of values for n such that $\dfrac{m}{24n}$ is an integer?

Solution: Value of $\dfrac{m}{24n} = \dfrac{2^3 \bullet 3^2 \bullet 6}{24n} = \dfrac{2 \bullet 2 \bullet 2 \bullet 3 \bullet 3 \bullet 2 \bullet 3}{2 \bullet 2 \bullet 2 \bullet 3 \bullet n} = \dfrac{18}{n}$

For $\dfrac{18}{n}$ to be an integer, n can be any factor of 18.

Factors of 18 $\quad \Rightarrow$ 1, 2, 3, 6, 9, and 18
Greatest number of values for $n = 6$

Question #49: If x, y, and z are integers with $x < y < z$, and $y = 100$, what is the greatest value of $x + y - z$?
Solution: In order to get the greatest value of the given expression, z should be the smallest possible, and x should be the largest possible.
Since $y < z$, the smallest possible value of $z \quad \Rightarrow 101$
Since $x < y$, the largest possible value of $x \quad \Rightarrow 99$
Greatest value of $x + y - z \qquad \Rightarrow 99 + 100 - 101 = 98$

Question #50: How many positive integers less than 100 are NOT equal to squares of integers?
Solution: Total No. of positive integers that are less than 100 $\qquad\qquad \Rightarrow 99$
No. of positive integers less than 100 that are square of integers $\qquad \Rightarrow 9$ (from 1 through 9)
(For instance: $1^2 = 1$, $2^2 = 4$, ... $8^2 = 64$, $9^2 = 81$)
No. of positive integers less than 100 that are NOT squares of integers $\Rightarrow 99 - 9 = 90$

Question #51: How many distinct integers between 1 and 60 consist of the digit 2, the digit 5, or the digit 2 and 5?
Solution: List all the integers between 1 and 60 that consist of the digit 2, the digit 5, or the digit 2 and 5:
$\Rightarrow$ {2, 5};   {12, 15};   {20 through 29}; {32, 35};   {42, 45};   {50 through 59}
$\Rightarrow$ 2 +   2 +   10 +   2 +   2 +   10 $\Rightarrow 28$

Question #52: If x, y, and z are distinct positive integers such that $0 < x < y < z < 22$, where x is even, y is odd, and z is prime, what is the greatest possible value of $x + y + z$?
Solution: To find the greatest possible value of $x + y + z$, we have to use the greatest value of x, y, and z.
Greatest possible prime less than 22 is 19 $\qquad \Rightarrow$ Value of $z = 19$
Greatest possible odd number less than 19 is 17 $\quad \Rightarrow$ Value of $y = 17$
Greatest possible even number less than 17 is 16 $\Rightarrow$ Value of $x = 16$
Greatest possible value of $x + y + z \qquad\qquad \Rightarrow 16 + 17 + 19 = 52$

Question #53: If $x + y + z = -15$, and x, y, and z are each different negative integers, what is the smallest possible value of z?
Solution: In order to find the smallest possible value of z, the value of x and y should be largest possible
The two largest negative integers are -1 and -2. So, let $x = -1$ and $y = -2$.
Smallest possible value of $z \quad \Rightarrow x + y + z = -15 \qquad\qquad$ [Given]
$\qquad\qquad\qquad\qquad\qquad\quad \Rightarrow (-1) + (-2) + z = -15 \qquad$ [Substitute $x = -1$ and $y = -2$]

$$\Rightarrow (-3) + z = -15 \qquad \text{[Combine like-terms]}$$
$$\Rightarrow z = -12 \qquad \text{[Add 3 to both sides]}$$

Question #54: If m and n are positive integers, and $(17^m)^n = 17^{17}$, what is the average (arithmetic mean) of m and n?

Solution: Simplify the given equation $\Rightarrow (17^m)^n = 17^{17}$ [Given]
$$\Rightarrow 17^{mn} = 17^{17} \qquad \text{[Apply law of exponent]}$$
$$\Rightarrow mn = 17 \qquad \text{[Compare the exponents of common base]}$$

Since the only positive integers, whose product is 17 are 1 & 17 $\Rightarrow$ Value of $m = 17$ and $n = 1$
Average of m and $n \Rightarrow (17 + 1) \div 2 = 18 \div 2 = 9$

Question #55: Each of the 20 students in the students club contributed either a nickel or a quarter to the Alumni Fund. If the total amount collected was $2.20, how many students contributed a quarter?

Solution: Let, the No. of students who contributed nickels $\Rightarrow n$
Then, the No. of students who contributed quarter $\Rightarrow 20 - n$
Since each nickel is worth 5 cents $\Rightarrow$ Value of nickels in cents = $5n$
Since each quarter is worth 25 cents $\Rightarrow$ Value of quarters in cents = $25(20 - n) = 500 - 25n$
Total value of money collected $\Rightarrow$ $2.20 or 220 cents
EZ Problem Set-Up $\Rightarrow$ Value of nickels in cents + Value of quarters in cents = 220 cents
$$\Rightarrow 5n + 500 - 25n = 220 \qquad \text{[Substitute the value of nickels \& quarters in cents]}$$
$$\Rightarrow 20n = 280 \qquad \text{[Combine like-terms]}$$
$$\Rightarrow n = 14 \qquad \text{[Divide both sides by 20]}$$
No. of students who contributed nickels $\Rightarrow 14$
No. of students who contributed quarters $\Rightarrow 20 - 14 = 6$

LITERAL EXPRESSIONS:

Question #56: A certain union is divided into r regions. Each region has g groups. Each group has m members. How many members are there in the entire union?

Solution: No. of members in each group $\Rightarrow m$
No. of groups in each region $\Rightarrow g$
No. of members in each region $\Rightarrow mg$
No. of regions in the union $\Rightarrow r$
No. of members in the union $\Rightarrow mgr$

Question #57: A certain shipment contains t trucks. Each truck contains c containers. Each container contains p pallets. Each pallet contains b boxes. Each box contains 100 matchsticks. How many matchsticks are contained in half of the shipment?

Solution: No. of Matchsticks in 1 Box $\Rightarrow 100$
No. of Matchsticks in 1 Pallet $\Rightarrow b$ boxes = $100b$
No. of Matchsticks in 1 Container $\Rightarrow p$ pallets = $100pb$
No. of Matchsticks in 1 Truck $\Rightarrow c$ containers = $100pbc$
No. of Matchsticks in 1 Shipment $\Rightarrow t$ trucks = $100pbct$
No. of Matchsticks in ½ Shipment $\Rightarrow$ ½$(100pbct) = 50pbct$

Question #58: A certain worker can plant x trees in $\dfrac{1}{y}$ hours. At this rate, how many trees can the worker plant in y hours?

Solution: No. of Trees planted in $\dfrac{1}{y}$ hours $\Rightarrow x$

No. of Trees planted in 1 hour $\Rightarrow \dfrac{x}{\frac{1}{y}} = x \div \dfrac{1}{y} = x \bullet \dfrac{y}{1} = xy$

No. of Trees planted in y hours $\Rightarrow y(xy) = xy^2$

Question #59:   In a certain oil refinery, the level of oil in a tank increases at the rate of i inches in m minutes. At this rate, how many feet will the level increase in h hours?

Solution: Increase in Level in m minutes $\Rightarrow i$ inches

Increase in Level in 1 minute $\Rightarrow \dfrac{i}{m}$ inches

Increase in Level in 60 minutes $\Rightarrow \dfrac{60i}{m}$ inches

Increase in Level in 1 hour $\Rightarrow \dfrac{60i}{m}$ inches

Increase in Level in h hours $\Rightarrow \dfrac{60hi}{m}$ inches $= \dfrac{60hi}{m} \bullet \dfrac{1}{12}$ feet $= \dfrac{5hi}{m}$ feet

Question #60:   At the rate of y yards per s seconds, how many yards does a skater travel in m minutes?

Solution: No. of yards traveled in s seconds $\Rightarrow y$ yards

No. of yards traveled in 1 second $\Rightarrow \dfrac{y}{s}$ yards

No. of yards traveled in 1 minute $\Rightarrow \dfrac{y}{s} \times 60 = \dfrac{60y}{s}$ yards

No. of yards traveled in m minutes $\Rightarrow \dfrac{60y}{s} \times m = \dfrac{60ym}{s}$ yards

Question #61:   What is the number of seconds in h hours, m minutes, and s seconds?

Solution: No. of seconds in 1 hour $\Rightarrow 60 \times 60 = 3600$
No. of seconds in h hours $\Rightarrow 3600h$
No. of seconds in 1 minute $\Rightarrow 60$
No. of seconds in m minutes $\Rightarrow 60m$
No. of seconds in h hours + m minutes + s seconds $\Rightarrow 3600h + 60m + s$

Question #62:   How many quarters are equivalent to n nickels and d dimes?

Solution: Since, 1 Nickel = 5 cents $\Rightarrow n$ Nickels = $5n$ cents
Since, 1 Dime = 10 cents $\Rightarrow d$ Dimes = $10d$ cents
Therefore, n Nickels and d Dimes $\Rightarrow 5n + 10d$ cents

No. of Quarters in n Nickels and d Dimes $\Rightarrow \dfrac{5n + 10d}{25} = \dfrac{5n}{25} + \dfrac{10d}{25} = \dfrac{n}{5} + \dfrac{2d}{5} = \dfrac{n + 2d}{5}$

Question #63:   A jar contains r red marbles and b blue marbles. If 2 red marbles are added and 7 blue marbles are removed, then in terms of r and b, what fraction of the remaining marbles is red?

Solution: No. of Red Marbles in the jar $\Rightarrow r + 2$
No. of Blue Marbles in the jar $\Rightarrow b - 7$
Total No. of Marbles in the jar $\Rightarrow r + 2 + b - 7 = r + b - 5$

Fraction of marbles that are Red $\Rightarrow \dfrac{r + 2}{r + b - 5}$

Question #64:   The cost to rent a boat for a day is n dollars. If a group of 25 people decide to share the cost equally, but only 15 of them were actually able to contribute, then, in terms of n, how many more dollars does each person has to pay?

Solution: If all 25 people pay equally, then the cost per person $\Rightarrow \dfrac{n}{25}$ dollars

If only 15 people pay equally, then the cost per person $\Rightarrow \dfrac{n}{15}$ dollars

Difference between the costs per person $\Rightarrow \dfrac{n}{15} - \dfrac{n}{25} = \dfrac{5n}{75} - \dfrac{3n}{75} = \dfrac{2n}{75}$

Question #65: Peter has x more marbles than Sam has, and together they have a total of y marbles. How many marbles does Sam have?

Solution:
No. of marbles that Peter has $\Rightarrow P = x + S$
No. of marbles they both have $\Rightarrow P + S = y$
No. of marbles that Sam has $\Rightarrow S = y - P$
$\Rightarrow S = y - (x + S) = y - x - S$
$\Rightarrow 2S = y - x$
$\Rightarrow S = \dfrac{y - x}{2}$

Question #66: If a shopkeeper buys 100 identical radios for a total cost of r dollars, and then sells each radio for a price that was 20 percent above the original cost per radio, then, in terms of r, what was the selling price of each radio?

Solution:
Cost Price of 100 Radios $\Rightarrow r$ dollars

Cost Price of each Radio $\Rightarrow \dfrac{r}{100}$ dollars

Selling Price of each Radio $\Rightarrow 1.20$ times $\dfrac{r}{100} = \left(\dfrac{6}{5}\right)\dfrac{r}{100} = \dfrac{6r}{500}$

Question #67: In a certain party, 1/8 of the guests wore a red coat and 1/9 of the remaining guests wore a blue coat. If there were B guests who wore a blue coat, then, in terms of B, how many guests wore a red coat?

Solution:
Let the total No. of guests $\Rightarrow x$

No. of Red Coat Guests $\Rightarrow R = \dfrac{1}{8}x$

No. of Non-Red Coat Guests $\Rightarrow x - \dfrac{1}{8}x = \dfrac{7}{8}x$

No. of Blue Coat Guests $\Rightarrow B = \dfrac{1}{9}\left(\dfrac{7}{8}x\right) = \dfrac{7}{72}x$

$\Rightarrow x = \dfrac{72}{7}B$

No. of Red Coat Guests $\Rightarrow R = \dfrac{1}{8}\left(\dfrac{72}{7}B\right) = \dfrac{72}{56}B = \dfrac{9}{7}B$

Question #68: If a student scores an average (arithmetic mean) of x points per test for t tests and then scores y points in the next test, what is the student's average score for the $t + 1$ tests?

Solution:
Originally: Average score for t tests $\Rightarrow x$
No. of tests $\Rightarrow t$
Sum of score for n tests $\Rightarrow$ Average × Number $= xt$
After next test: New sum for $n + 1$ tests $\Rightarrow xt + y$
New No. of tests $\Rightarrow t + 1$
Average for $n + 1$ tests $\Rightarrow \dfrac{xt + y}{t + 1}$

Question #69: If the sum of two numbers that differ by 7 is n, then, in terms of n, what is the value of the greater of the two numbers?

Solution:
Let, the greater number $\Rightarrow x$
Then, the smaller number $\Rightarrow x - 7$
Sum of these two numbers is n $\Rightarrow x + (x - 7) = n$
$\Rightarrow 2x - 7 = n$
$\Rightarrow 2x = n + 7$
$\Rightarrow x = \dfrac{n + 7}{2}$

Question #70: If $n > 0$ and r is n percent of s, then, in terms of n, s is what percent of r?

Solution: Since r is n percent of s $\Rightarrow r = \dfrac{n}{100}s$

Find: s is what percent of r $\Rightarrow s = \dfrac{what}{100}r$

$\Rightarrow what = \dfrac{100s}{r} = \dfrac{100s}{\frac{ns}{100}} = \dfrac{100s}{1} \bullet \dfrac{100}{ns} = \dfrac{10,000}{n}$

Question #71: There are a applications that needs to be processed. After b of the applications has been processed, what percent of the applications are still not processed?

Solution:
Total No. of applications that need to be processed $\Rightarrow a$
Total No. of applications that has been processed $\Rightarrow b$
Total No. of applications that are still not processed $\Rightarrow a - b$
Percent of applications that are still not processed $\Rightarrow (a - b)$ is what percent of a
$\Rightarrow \dfrac{100(a - b)}{a}\%$

Question #72: A truck travels n miles per hour for 5 hours and then travels $\frac{1}{4}n$ miles per hour every hour thereafter. How many miles will the truck cover in 15 hours?

Solution:
No. of miles covered in first 5 hours $\Rightarrow n$ mph $\times 5 = 5n$

No. of miles covered in first 10 hours $\Rightarrow \dfrac{1}{4}n(10) = \dfrac{10}{4}n = \dfrac{5}{2}n$

Total Miles covered in 15 hours $\Rightarrow 5n + \dfrac{5}{2}n = \dfrac{10}{2}n + \dfrac{5}{2}n = \dfrac{15}{2}n = 7.5n$ miles

Question #73: At a certain bookstore, one-sixth of the books sold in a day were math books and one-half of the remaining books sold were English books. If n of the books sold were English books, then in terms of n, how many of the books sold were math books?

Solution: Let the total No. of books sold $\Rightarrow x$

No. of Math Books Sold $\Rightarrow \dfrac{1}{6}x$

No. of Remaining Books Sold $\Rightarrow x - \dfrac{1}{6}x = \dfrac{6}{6}x - \dfrac{1}{6}x = \dfrac{5}{6}x$

No. of English Books Sold $\Rightarrow n = \dfrac{1}{2} \bullet \dfrac{5}{6}x = \dfrac{5}{12}x$

$\Rightarrow n = \dfrac{5}{12}x$

$\Rightarrow x = \dfrac{12}{5}n$

No. of Math Books Sold $\Rightarrow \dfrac{1}{6} \bullet \dfrac{12}{5}n = \dfrac{2}{5}n$

Question #74: There are two cylindrical tanks, one big, and the other small. The volume of the bigger tank is x gallons and the volume of smaller tank is y gallons. The bigger tank is filled to its maximum capacity with oil, and the smaller tank is completely empty. If just enough oil is poured from the bigger tank to completely fill the smaller tank, what fraction of the bigger tank is now filled with oil?

Solution:
Before pouring: Oil in Larger Tank $\Rightarrow x$ gallons
Oil in Smaller Tank $\Rightarrow 0$ gallons
After pouring: Oil in Larger Tank $\Rightarrow x - y$ gallons
Oil in Smaller Tank $\Rightarrow y$ gallons

Fraction of Larger Tank that is still filled with oil $\Rightarrow \dfrac{\text{oil in larger tank after pouring}}{\text{oil in larger tank before pouring}} = \dfrac{x - y}{x}$

Question #75: In a certain company, there are *n* employees, and their average (arithmetic mean) salary is *m*. If there is only one manager in the company, and his salary is 8 times the average salary of all the other employees, then the manager's salary is what fraction of the total salary of all the employees in the company?

Solution:
No. of Employees in the Company $\Rightarrow n$
Average Salary of Employees $\Rightarrow m$
Sum of all Salaries excluding the Manager $\Rightarrow$ Number × Average = mn
Manager's Salary $\Rightarrow 8m$
Sum of all Salaries including Manager's Salary $\Rightarrow mn + 8m$

Manager's Salary as a Fraction of Total Salaries $\Rightarrow \dfrac{8m}{mn + 8m} = \dfrac{m(8)}{m(n+8)} = \dfrac{8}{n+8}$

AGE & WEIGHT PROBLEMS:

Question #76: If in 25 years, Monika will be six times as old as she was 10 years ago, how old is Monika now?

Solution:
Let, Monika's present age $\Rightarrow x$
Then, Monika's age in 25 years from now $\Rightarrow x + 25$
And, Monika's age 10 years ago $\Rightarrow x - 10$
EZ Problem Set-Up $\Rightarrow$ Monika's age 25 years later = 6(Monika's age 10 years ago)
$\Rightarrow x + 25 = 6(x - 10)$ [Set up the equation]
$\Rightarrow x + 25 = 6x - 60$ [Apply distributive property]
$\Rightarrow 25 = 5x - 60$ [Subtract x from both sides]
$\Rightarrow 5x = 85$ [Add 60 to both sides]
$\Rightarrow x = 17$ [Divide both sides by 5]

Question #77: Mary is six times as old as Tom, but in 20 years, Mary will be only twice as old as Tom. How old is Mary now?

Solution:
Organize all the given information in the following grid:
Let Tom's age now be *x*.

Year	Tom	Mary
Now	x	6x
20 years later	x + 20	6x + 20

EZ Problem Set-Up $\Rightarrow$ Mary's age after 20 years = 2(Tom's age after 20 years)
$\Rightarrow 6x + 20 = 2(x + 20)$ [Set up the equation]
$\Rightarrow 6x + 20 = 2x + 40$ [Apply distributive property]
$\Rightarrow 4x + 20 = 40$ [Subtract 2x from both sides]
$\Rightarrow 4x = 20$ [Subtract 20 from both sides]
$\Rightarrow x = 5$ [Divide both sides by 4]
Tom is now 5 years old.
Mary is now six times as old as Tom, or $6x \Rightarrow 6 \times 5 = 30$ years old

Question #78: If ½*x* years ago, Monika was 16, and ½*x* years from now she will be 2*x* years old, how old will she be 4*x* years from now?

Solution:
Monika's age ½x years ago $\Rightarrow 16$ [Given]
Monika's age now $\Rightarrow 16 + ½x$ [Add ½x]
Monika's age ½x years from now $\Rightarrow 16 + ½x + ½x = 16 + x$ [Again add ½x]
Monika's age ½x years from now will be 2x $\Rightarrow 16 + x = 2x$ [Given]
                                        $\Rightarrow x = 16$ [Subtract x from both sides]
Monika's age now $\Rightarrow 16 + ½x$ [As per above]
                                        $\Rightarrow 16 + ½(16)$ [Substitute x = 16]
                                        $\Rightarrow 16 + 8 = 24$ [Solve for the age]
Monika's age 4x years from now $\Rightarrow 24 + 4x$ [Monika's age now plus 4x]
                                        $\Rightarrow 24 + 4(16)$ [Substitute x = 16]
                                        $\Rightarrow 24 + 64 = 88$ [Solve for the age]

Question #79: In 1975, Monika was 4 times as old as Susan, but in 1985 Monika was only twice as old as Susan was. How old was Susan in 1990?

Solution: Organize all the given information in the following grid:

Let Susan's age in 1975 be x

Year	Monika	Susan
1975	$4x$	x
1985	$4x + 10$	$x + 10$

EZ Problem Set-Up $\Rightarrow$ Monika's age in 1985 = 2(Susan's age in 1985)

$\Rightarrow 4x + 10 = 2(x + 10)$ [Set up the equation]

$\Rightarrow 4x + 10 = 2x + 20$ [Apply distributive property]

$\Rightarrow 2x + 10 = 20$ [Subtract $2x$ from both sides]

$\Rightarrow 2x = 10$ [Subtract 10 from both sides]

$\Rightarrow x = 5$ [Divide both sides by 2]

Therefore, Susan's age in 1975 was 5 years. However, 5 is not the correct answer. The question asks for Susan's age in 1990. Substitute the value of x to find any age in any year. Since Susan's age was 5 in 1975, she will be (5 + 15) in 1990, so the correct answer is 20. The question may have asked for some other information, which can be easily determined by plugging in the value of x in the first table to form the following new table.

Year	Monika	Susan
1975	$4x = 20$	$x = 5$
1985	$4x + 10 = 30$	$x + 10 = 15$
1990	$30 + 5 = 35$	$15 + 5 = 20$
1995	$35 + 5 = 40$	$20 + 5 = 25$

Question #80: If the son is 27 years younger than his mother and one-seventh the age of his father, and the father is 9 years older than his mother; how old is the son?

Solution: Let, Son's age $\Rightarrow S$

And, Mother's age $\Rightarrow M$

And, Father's age $\Rightarrow F$

The son is 27 years younger than his mother $\Rightarrow S = M - 27$ $\Rightarrow$ Equation #1

The son is 1/7 the age of his father $\Rightarrow S = 1/7(F)$ $\Rightarrow$ Equation #2

The father is 9 years older than the mother $\Rightarrow F = M + 9$ $\Rightarrow$ Equation #3

Substitute the value of F from Eq #3 into #2 $\Rightarrow S = 1/7(M + 9)$ $\Rightarrow$ Equation #4

Equate Equation #1 and #4 $\Rightarrow M - 27 = 1/7(M + 9)$ [Equate the two values of S from #1 & #4]

$\Rightarrow 7(M - 27) = M + 9$ [Multiply both sides by 7]

$\Rightarrow 7M - 189 = M + 9$ [Apply distributive property]

$\Rightarrow 6M - 189 = 9$ [Subtract M from both sides]

$\Rightarrow 6M = 198$ [Add 189 to both sides]

$\Rightarrow M = 33$ [Divide both sides by 6]

Substitute the value of M into Equation #1 $\Rightarrow S = M - 27 = 33 - 27 = 6$

Substitute the value of M into Equation #3 $\Rightarrow F = M + 9 = 33 + 9 = 42$

Mother's Age $\Rightarrow M = 33$ years

Father's Age $\Rightarrow F = 42$ years

Son's Age $\Rightarrow S = 6$ years

WORK PROBLEMS:

Question #81: John earns $9.80 per hour on days other than weekends and one and a half times that rate on weekends. Last week he worked a total of 60 hours, including 8 hours on the weekend. What were his earnings for the week?

Solution: Hours Worked on Weekdays $\Rightarrow 60 - 8 = 52$

Hourly Rate on Weekdays $\Rightarrow \$9.80$

Earnings on Weekdays $\Rightarrow 52 \times \$9.80 = \$509.60$

Hours Worked on Weekend $\Rightarrow 8$

Hourly Rate on Weekends $\Rightarrow 1.5(\$9.80) = \$14.70$

Earnings on Weekend $\Rightarrow 8 \times \$14.70 = \$117.60$

Total Earning for the Week   ⇒ $509.60 + $117.60 = $627.20

Question #82: Photocopier A can make copies at a constant rate of 175 copies every 25 seconds working at its highest speed, and Photocopier B can make copies at a constant rate of 100 copies every 20 seconds working at its highest speed. If both photocopiers run simultaneously at their highest speed, how many seconds will it take them to make a total of 240 copies?

Solution:

Photocopier A makes 175 copies every 25 seconds	⇒ 175 ÷ 25 = 7 copies per second
Photocopier B makes 100 copies every 20 seconds	⇒ 100 ÷ 20 = 5 copies per second
Photocopier A & B working together can make	⇒ 7 + 5 = 12 copies per second
Photocopier A & B can make 12 copies in	⇒ 1 second
Photocopier A & B can make 1 copy in	⇒ $\dfrac{1}{12}$ seconds
Photocopier A & B can make 240 copies in	⇒ $\dfrac{1}{12}$ × 240 = 20 seconds

Question #83: A certain test is two hours long and has 120 questions. If a student completes 60 questions in 50 minutes, how many seconds does he have on an average for completing each of the remaining questions?

Solution: At the beginning ⇒ Total Test Duration = 2 hours = 120 minutes
⇒ Total No. of Questions = 120
After Completing 60 Questions in 50 min   ⇒ Remaining Time = 120–50=70 min = 70×60 = 4200 sec
⇒ Remaining Questions = 120 – 60 = 60
⇒ Average Time per Question = 4200 ÷ 60 = 70 seconds

Question #84: Jose can paint the first half of a house in two-fifths the time it takes him to paint the second half of the house. If it takes him 21 hours to paint the entire house, how many hours did he spend painting the first half of the house?

Solution: Let, the No. of hours spent paining the second half of the house ⇒ n hours

Then, the No. of hours spent painting the first half of the house ⇒ $\dfrac{2}{5}n$ hours

No. of hours spent paining the first half and the second half   ⇒ 21 hours
EZ Problem Set-Up ⇒ No. of hours spent paining the second half of the house + No. of hours spent painting the first half of the house = No. of hours spent paining the first half and the second half.

⇒ $n + \dfrac{2}{5}n = 21$	[Set up the equation]
⇒ $\dfrac{5}{5}n + \dfrac{2}{5}n = 21$	[Scale-Up the fractions to their LCD, which is 5]
⇒ $\dfrac{7}{5}n = 21$	[Combine like-terms]
⇒ $n = 21 \times \dfrac{5}{7} = 15$	[Multiply both sides by 5/7]

No. of hours spent paining the second half of the house ⇒ 15 hours
No. of hours spent paining the first half of the house   ⇒ 21 – 15 = 6 hours

Question #85: A certain job can be completed by four machines, working individually, in 2, 4, 6, and 8 hours, respectively. What is the greatest part of the job that can be done in one hour by two of the machines working together at their respective rates?

Solution: In order to get the greatest part of the job done, we need to use the fastest machines. The four machines can do the job in 2, 4, 6, and 8 hours respectively. Obviously, we should eliminate the last two (slower) machines and use the first two (faster) machines to do the job.
The first machine can do the job in 2 hours or ½ of the job in one hour.
The second machine can do the job in 4 hours or ¼ of the job in one hour.

Together, the first and the second machine can do the job in 2 + 4 hours or ½ + ¼ of the job in one

hour $\Rightarrow \dfrac{1}{2} + \dfrac{1}{4} = \dfrac{2}{4} + \dfrac{1}{4} = \dfrac{3}{4}$

Question #86:   If John can do one coat of paint for all his walls in 6 hours, and George can do one coat of paint for the same walls in 8 hours, how many hours will it take John and George to do two coats of paint for the same walls if they work together at these rates?

Solution: For One Coat of Paint $\Rightarrow \dfrac{1}{x} + \dfrac{1}{y} = \dfrac{1}{z}$ [Write the appropriate formula]

$\Rightarrow \dfrac{1}{6} + \dfrac{1}{8} = \dfrac{1}{z}$ [Substitute the known values]

$\Rightarrow \dfrac{4}{24} + \dfrac{3}{24} = \dfrac{1}{z}$ [Scale-up the fractions to their LCD, which is 24]

$\Rightarrow \dfrac{7}{24} = \dfrac{1}{z}$ [Combine like-terms]

$\Rightarrow 7z = 24$ [Cross-multiply]

$\Rightarrow z = \dfrac{24}{7}$ [Divide both sides by 7]

For Two Coats of Paint $\Rightarrow \dfrac{24}{7} \times 2 = \dfrac{48}{7} = 6\dfrac{6}{7}$

Question #87:   Working alone, a man can fence his yard in 12 hours, his older son can do it in 18 hours, and his younger son can do it in 24 hours. What is the ratio of the time it takes the man to fence the yard alone, working alone at his rate, to the time it takes the two sons to fence the yard, working together at their individual rates?

Solution: No. of hours it takes the Man alone to fence the yard = 12
No. of hours it takes the Older Son alone to fence the yard $\Rightarrow x = 18$
No. of hours it takes the Younger Son alone to fence the yard $\Rightarrow y = 24$
Let, the No. of hours it takes the Older and the Younger Son together to fence the yard = z

$\Rightarrow \dfrac{1}{x} + \dfrac{1}{y} = \dfrac{1}{z}$ [Write the appropriate formula]

$\Rightarrow \dfrac{1}{18} + \dfrac{1}{24} = \dfrac{1}{z}$ [Substitute the known values]

$\Rightarrow \dfrac{4}{72} + \dfrac{3}{72} = \dfrac{1}{z}$ [Scale-up the fractions to their LCD, which is 72]

$\Rightarrow \dfrac{7}{72} = \dfrac{1}{z}$ [Combine like-terms]

$\Rightarrow 7z = 72$ [Cross-multiply]

$\Rightarrow z = \dfrac{72}{7}$ [Divide both sides by 7]

Ratio of the time it takes the man to do the job to the time it takes the two sons to do the job:

$\Rightarrow \dfrac{12}{\frac{72}{7}} = 12 \div \dfrac{72}{7} = 12 \times \dfrac{7}{72} = \dfrac{7}{6}$

Question #88:   Henry and Jacob, working together, can finish a job in 6 hours. If Jacob can do the job by himself in 15 hours, what percent of the job does Henry do?

Solution: Jacob can finish the job working by himself in 15 hours.

This means, Jacob can do $\dfrac{1}{15}$ of the job working by himself in 1 hour.

And, in the 6 hours that they both work together, Jacob does $6 \times \dfrac{1}{15}$ of the job, which is $\dfrac{6}{15}$ of the job.

Henry does the remaining $1 - \dfrac{6}{15}$ of the job, which is $\dfrac{9}{15}$ of the job.

Henry does $\dfrac{9}{15} \times 100 = 60$ percent of the job.

Question #89: If six workers working at the same rate can do two-fifths of a job in 50 minutes, how many minutes would it take one worker working at the same rate to do one-tenths of the job?

Solution: No. of minutes it take 6 workers to do 2/5 of a job $\Rightarrow$ 50 minutes

No. of minutes it take 6 workers to do the whole job $\Rightarrow 50 \times \dfrac{5}{2} = 125$ minutes

No. of minutes it take 1 worker to do the whole job $\Rightarrow 125 \times 6 = 750$ minutes

No. of minutes it take 1 worker to do 1/10 of the job $\Rightarrow \dfrac{1}{10} \times 750 = 75$ minutes

Question #90: In a certain landscaping company, there are 16 workers, but exactly 5 of them actively work on the field at any given point in time. For an 8-hour workday, if each worker works exactly the same amount of time on the field, how many minutes does each worker work on the field?

Solution: Since the workday is 8 hours, or $8 \times 60 = 480$ minutes long, and there are always exactly 5 workers working on the field, there is a total of $480 \times 5 = 2,400$ worker-minutes of working time.
Now, since there are a total of 16 workers and each worker work exactly the same amount of time, the number of minutes each worker work on the field $\Rightarrow 2,400 \div 16 = 150$.

MOTION PROBLEMS:

Question #91: Robin is on a road trip driving from Morgantown to Yorktown. After driving for one and a half hours at an average speed of 80 miles per hour and taking a break, she still has 50 miles left to travel. What is her total driving distance between Morgantown and Yorktown?

Solution: From Morgantown to the point of break $\Rightarrow T_1 = 1.5$ hours
                                                         $\Rightarrow R_1 = 80$ miles per hour
                                                         $\Rightarrow D_1 = 80 \times 1.5 = 120$ miles
From point of break to Yorktown $\Rightarrow D_2 = 50$ miles
Total Distance from Morgantown to Yorktown $\Rightarrow D_1 + D_2 = 120 + 50 = 170$ miles

Question #92: A man drove 750 miles at an average speed of 50 miles per hour. How many miles per hour faster would he have to drive in order for the trip to take 5 hours less?

Solution: Organize all the given information in the following grid:

Original Trip	**Modified Trip**
$D_1 \Rightarrow 750$ m	$D_2 \Rightarrow 750$ m
$R_1 \Rightarrow 50$ mph	$T_2 \Rightarrow 15 - 5 = 10$ hrs
$T_1 \Rightarrow 750 \div 50 = 15$ hrs	$R_2 \Rightarrow 750 \div 10 = 75$ mph

Rate Difference $\Rightarrow R_2 - R_1 = 75$ mph $- 50$ mph $= 25$ mph
In order to cover the same trip in 5 hours less, the man will have to drive 25 mph faster.

Question #93: Two cars travel away from each other in opposite directions at 16 miles per hour and 56 miles per hour respectively. If the first car travels for 30 minutes and the second car for 15 minutes, how many miles apart will they be at the end of their trips?

Solution: Organize all the given information in the following grid:

First Car	**Second Car**
$R_1 \Rightarrow 16$ mph	$R_2 \Rightarrow 56$ mph
$T_1 \Rightarrow 30$ min $= 1/2$ hr	$T_2 \Rightarrow 15$ min $= 1/4$ hr
$D_1 \Rightarrow RT = 16 \times 1/2 = 8$ m	$D_2 \Rightarrow RT = 56 \times 1/4 = 14$ m

Total Distance between the two cars $\Rightarrow D_1 + D_2 = 8$ m $+ 14$ m $= 22$ miles
The two cars will be 22 miles apart at the end of their trips.

Question #94: A family is on a 90-mile trip. If they travel at an average speed of 75 miles per hour for the first 20 miles, and then at 25 miles per hour for the remainder of the trip, how many minutes longer will it take them than if they travel at 50 miles per hour for the entire trip?

Solution: Compare both scenarios when they travel at different rates and when they travel at the same rate:

Case #1: When the family travels at different rates for different parts of the entire trip:

First Part: $D_1 \Rightarrow 20$ miles   Second Part: $D_2 \Rightarrow 90 - 20 - 70$ miles

$\qquad\qquad$ $R_1 \Rightarrow 75$ mph $\qquad\qquad\qquad\qquad$ $R_2 \Rightarrow 25$ mph

$\qquad\qquad$ $T_1 \Rightarrow 20 \div 75 = \dfrac{4}{15}$ hrs = 16 min $\qquad$ $T_2 \Rightarrow 70 \div 25 = 2\dfrac{4}{5}$ hrs = 168 min

Total Travel Time $\Rightarrow T_1 + T_2 = 16 + 168 = 184$ minutes

Case #2: When the family travels at one same rate for the entire trip:

$D = 90$ miles

$R = 50$ mph

$T \Rightarrow 90 \div 50 = 1\dfrac{4}{5}$ hours = 108 minutes

Difference in travel time $\Rightarrow 184 - 108 = 76$ minutes

Question #95: For a certain trip, a car averages 60 miles per hour for the first 7 hours of the trip, and averages 80 miles per hour for each additional hour of the same trip. If the average speed for the entire trip is 75 miles per hour, how many hours long is the entire trip?

Solution: Organize all the given information in the following grid:

First Part of Trip   **Second Part of Trip**

$R_1 \Rightarrow 60$ mph $R_2 \Rightarrow 80$ mph

$T_1 \Rightarrow 7$ hours $T_2 \Rightarrow t$ hours

$D_1 \Rightarrow 60 \times 7 = 420$ miles $D_2 \Rightarrow 80t$ hours

Total Trip

Average Rate $\Rightarrow 75$ mph   [Given]

Total Distance $\Rightarrow 420 + 80t$ [Add the total distance]

Total Time $\Rightarrow \dfrac{420 + 80t}{75}$ [Find the total time]

EZ Problem Set-Up $\Rightarrow$ Time of First Part + Time of Second Part = Total Time of the Entire trip

$\qquad\qquad$ $\Rightarrow 7 + t = \dfrac{420 + 80t}{75}$ [Set up the equation]

$\qquad\qquad$ $\Rightarrow 75(7 + t) = 420 + 80t$ [Multiply both sides by 75]

$\qquad\qquad$ $\Rightarrow 525 + 75t = 420 + 80t$ [Apply distributive property]

$\qquad\qquad$ $\Rightarrow 5t + 420 = 525$ [Subtract 75t from both sides]

$\qquad\qquad$ $\Rightarrow 5t = 105$ [Subtract 420 from both sides]

$\qquad\qquad$ $\Rightarrow t = 21$ hours   [Divide both sides by 5]

Total time of the entire trip $\Rightarrow 7 + 21 = 28$ hours

Question #96: Anita walks from her home to her school in 50 minutes, and walks back along the same route to return home from school. If her average speed on the trip back home is twice as fast as her average speed on the trip to school, how many hours does she spend walking on the round trip?

Solution: Organize all the given information in the following grid:

Home to School   **School to Home**

$D_1 \Rightarrow d$ (assumption) $D_2 \Rightarrow d$ (same as home to school)

$T_1 \Rightarrow 50$ minutes $R_2 \Rightarrow 2\left(\dfrac{d}{50}\right) = \dfrac{d}{25}$ miles per minute

$R_1 \Rightarrow \dfrac{d}{50}$ miles per minute $T_2 \Rightarrow \dfrac{d}{\dfrac{d}{25}} = 25$ minutes

Total Time $\Rightarrow T_1 + T_2$

$\qquad\qquad$ $\Rightarrow 50 + 25 = 75$ minutes $= \dfrac{75}{60} = 1\dfrac{1}{4}$ hours

Question #97: A man runs from his home to his work at an average speed of 6 miles per hour, and then walks back home along the same route at an average of 3 miles per hour. If his whole journey took one hour, how many mile is his home from his work?

Solution: Organize all the given information in the following grid:

Outbound Trip (Home to Work)   **Inbound Trip (Work to Home)**

$R_1 \Rightarrow$ 6 mph $R_2 \Rightarrow$ 3 mph

$D_1 \Rightarrow n$ $D_2 \Rightarrow n$

$T_1 \Rightarrow n \div 6$ hrs $T_2 \Rightarrow n \div 3$ hrs

EZ Problem Set-Up $\Rightarrow$ Time of Outbound Trip (T_1) + Time of Inbound Trip (T_2) = 1 hr

$$\Rightarrow \frac{n}{6} + \frac{n}{3} = 1 \qquad \text{[Set up the equation]}$$

$$\Rightarrow \frac{n}{6} + \frac{2n}{6} = 1 \qquad \text{[Scale up the fractions to their LCD, which is 6]}$$

$$\Rightarrow \frac{3n}{6} = 1 \qquad \text{[Add the fractions with common denominator]}$$

$$\Rightarrow \frac{n}{2} = 1 \qquad \text{[Simplify the fraction to its lowest terms]}$$

$$\Rightarrow n = 2 \text{ miles} \qquad \text{[Multiply both sides by 2]}$$

Question #98: Two bikers are 20 miles apart and start biking towards each other along the same route. The first biker travels at a constant rate of 6 miles per hour and the second biker travels at a constant rate of 5 miles per hour. If the second biker starts his trip 24 minutes after the first biker, how far from his original starting point would he have traveled before the two bikers meet?

Solution: Organize all the given information in the following grid:

Biker 1   **Biker 2**

$R_1 \Rightarrow$ 6 mph $R_2 \Rightarrow$ 5 mph

$T_1 \Rightarrow t + 24$ min $T_2 \Rightarrow t$

$D_1 \Rightarrow 6(t + 24$ min$)$ $D_2 \Rightarrow 5t$

       $\Rightarrow 6(t + 24$ min$)$ $\Rightarrow 5t = d$

Let the distance covered by the second biker be d miles

EZ Problem Set-Up $\Rightarrow$ Distance covered by first biker = 20 miles – Distance covered by second biker

$\Rightarrow 6(t + 24$ min$) = 20 - d$ [Set up the equation]

$\Rightarrow 6(t + 0.4$ hrs$) = 20 - d$ [Convert the minutes to hours]

$\Rightarrow 6t + 2.4 = 20 - d$ [Apply distributive property]

$\Rightarrow 6t + 2.4 = 20 - 5t$ [Substitute $d = 5t$]

$\Rightarrow 11t + 2.4 = 20$ [Add $5t$ to both sides]

$\Rightarrow 11t = 17.6$ [Subtract 2.4 from both sides]

$\Rightarrow t = 1.6$ [Divide both sides by 11]

Biker 2 traveled $\Rightarrow 5t$ or 5×1.6 = 8 miles before the two bikers meet.

Biker 1 traveled $\Rightarrow 20 - 8$ = 12 miles before the two bikers meet.

MIXTURE PROBLEMS:

Question #99: If 10 gallons of apple juice that cost $5.00 per gallon is mixed with 15 gallons of grape juice that cost $7.00 per gallon, what is the cost per gallon of the resulting mixture?

Solution:

Total cost of the mixture $\Rightarrow 10(\$5.00) + 15(\$7.00)$ [Express the total cost of mixture]

                                    $\Rightarrow \$50 + \$105$ [Apply distributive property]

                                    $\Rightarrow \$155$ [Simplify the expression]

Total weight of the mixture $\Rightarrow 10 + 15$ [Express the total weight of mixture]

                                    $\Rightarrow 25$ gallons   [Simplify the expression]

Cost per gallon of the mixture $\Rightarrow \dfrac{\textit{Total Cost of Mixture}}{\textit{Total Weight of Mixture}}$ [Write the appropriate formula]

                                    $\Rightarrow \dfrac{155}{25}$ [Substitute the values]

⇒ $6.20   [Simplify the expression]

Question #100: A tank contains 10,000 gallons of a solution that is 9 percent calcium chloride by volume. If 2,000 gallons of water evaporates form the tank, what percent of the remaining solution will be calcium chloride?

Solution: Before Evaporation ⇒ Amount of liquid in the tank   ⇒ 10,000 gallons   [Given]

⇒ Percent of Calcium Chloride   ⇒ 9%   [Given]

⇒ Amount of Calcium Chloride   ⇒ 9% of 10,000   [Given]

⇒ 900 gallons   [Simplify the expression]

After Evaporation ⇒ Amount of liquid in the tank   ⇒ Before – Evaporation

⇒ 10,000 – 2,000   [Substitute the values]

⇒ 8,000 gallons   [Simplify the expression]

⇒ Amount of Calcium Chloride   ⇒ 900 gallons   [Same as before]

⇒ Percent of Calcium Chloride   ⇒ $\dfrac{900}{8,000} \times 100$ [Calculate the percent]

⇒ 11.25%   [Simplify the expression]

PART 6.0: LOGIC & STATS:

TOPICS COVERED:

- Pure Logic

- Permutation Combination

- Probability

- Sets

- Sequence & Patterns

- Miscellaneous Problems

- Stats – Averages

EZ REFERENCE: -To review logic & stats concepts, please refer to our EZ Review Logic & Stats.
-To practice medium-to-difficult level questions, please refer to our EZ Practice Advanced Workbook.

PRACTICE EXERCISE:

PURE LOGIC:

Question #1: In a certain flower shop, there are five different types of flowers, two of which are red, two are blue, and one is green. How many different combinations of bunches of three flowers can be made so that each flower is of a different color?

Question #2: Newton has a pile of coins that he is trying to arrange in even stacks. If he stacks them in piles of 8, he has 2 coins left over. If he stacks them in piles of 7, he has 5 coins left over. After trying a few more combinations, he gives up, and stacks the coins in two even stacks. What is the least number of coins that he may have in each stack?

PERMUTATION & COMBINATION:

Question #3: A man finds that by wearing different combinations of shirts and pants that he owns, he can make up 75 different outfits. If he owns 15 different shirts, how many pants does he own?

Question #4: A woman finds that by wearing different combinations of shirts, pants, and jackets that she owns, she can make up 192 different outfits. If she owns 16 different shirts and 6 different pants, how many jackets does she own?

Question #5: How many four-digit numbers are there that do not contain the digits 6 and 9?

Question #6: In a certain furniture sale, there are 6 kinds of sofas, 9 kinds of chairs, 2 kinds of tables, and 8 kinds of shelves. In how many ways can a person decorate his house, if he wants to buy one sofa, one chair, and either a table or a shelf?

Question #7: A certain runway model has a collection of 8 shirts and 9 pants. How many dressing combinations of a shirt and a pant can she make if she doesn't want to wear 2 specific shirts with 5 specific pants?

Question #8: How many 10-letter words can be generated by using the computer binary language of 0/1 only?

Question #9: If there are 7 cars but only 6 empty spots in a parking lot, how many numbers of different ways can those 7 cars be parked in 6 empty spots in the parking lot?

Question #10: In how many ways can 9 books be arranged on a bookshelf if 2 of the books are identical and 5 of the other books are identical?

Question #11: For a certain championship, there are 7 teams and each team plays each of the other teams exactly once. If each game is played by 2 teams, what is the total number of games played?

Question #12: In a certain team, there are 12 players and each player shakes hand with each of the other players exactly once. If each handshake is between 2 players, what is the total number of handshakes?

Question #13: There is a group of 7 people, 6 boys and 1 girl who needs to be seated in a row of 7 seats in a theater. In how many ways can the 7 people be seated if the girl won't sit on the either end or in the middle?

PROBABILITY:

Question #14: If two fair dice are thrown and the same number comes up on each of the dice, what is the probability that the sum of the two numbers is 7?

Question #15: There are 100 people in a line. Sam is 21st person and Tom is 92nd person. If a person on line is chosen at random, what is the probability that the person is standing between Sam and Tom?

Question #16:   Peter and Tina tossed a coin 10 times, and each time the coin lands as "heads". After the tenth toss, Tina makes a bet that the coin will land as "tails" on the eleventh toss. What is the probability of Tina winning the bet?

Question #17:   If a fair coin is tossed four times, what is the probability that on at least one of the tosses the coin will turn up tails?

Question #18:   If one student is chosen randomly from a group of nine students, then one student is again chosen randomly from the same group of nine students, what is the probability that two different students will be chosen?

Question #19:   A jar has 6 marbles, one each of color red, blue, green, yellow, orange, and purple. If 5 marbles are removed from the jar, what is the probability that the purple marble was removed?

Question #20:   In a certain election, there are 7 male candidates and 5 female candidates. If three candidates are elected, what is the probability that all three candidates will be males?

Question #21:   Two integers are to be randomly selected from the two sets given below, one integer form set X and one integer form set Y. What is the probability that the sum of the two integers will be even?
Set X: {1, 2, 3, 4}
Set Y: {5, 6, 7, 8}

Question #22:   Two integers are to be randomly selected from the two sets given below, one integer form set X and one integer form set Y. What is the probability that the product of the two integers will be odd?
Set X: {1, 2, 3, 4}
Set Y: {5, 6, 7, 8}

Question #23:   What is the probability that when a pair of six-sided dice is thrown, the sum of the numbers equals 5?

Question #24:   What is the probability that when a pair of six-sided dice is thrown, the sum of the numbers is at least 10?

Question #25:   On one side of the coin, the number 5 is written, and on the other side, the number 7 is written. What is the probability that the sum of three tosses will be 17?

Question #26:   A big jar contains 25 postcards, each with a different integer from 1 to 25 written on it. Blindfolded, if one of the postcards is drawn at random, what is the probability that the number written on the postcard will be a multiple of 3 or 5?

Question #27:   If a number is chosen at random from set X, what is the probability that the number is in the intersection of set X and set Y?
Set X = {1, 2, 4, 6, 8, 9, 12, 15}
Set Y = {8, 9, 11, 16}

Question #28:   What is the probability that the sum of two dice is greater than 9 given that the first dice is a 6?

Question #29:   Folded paper notes numbered consecutively from 101 through 850 are placed in a box. If a paper note is picked randomly, what is the probability that it will have a number written on it which has a hundreds digit of 7?

Question #30:   From the set of numbers {1, 2, 3, 4, 5, 6, 7}, one number is picked and then replaced, and then another number is again picked. If the sum of the two numbers picked is 8, what is the probability that the two numbers included the number 7 as one of the numbers picked?

Question #31:   In a standard deck of 52 cards, numbered from 1 to 13, with 4 cards of each number, 16 more cards with the number 8 on them are added to the deck. After shuffling the cards, what is the probability of picking a card with the number 8 on it?

Question #32: A certain jar contains 21 balls. After drawing 6 red balls from the jar without putting them back, the probability of drawing the next red ball is 1/5. How many red balls were in the jar in the beginning?

Question #33: A certain jar contains 2 red marbles, 2 blue marbles, 2 green marbles, and 2 yellow marbles. If two marbles are randomly picked from the jar, what is the probability that neither one of them will be red?

Question #34: In a certain jar, there are n red balls, $5n + 10$ blue balls and 2 green balls. What is the probability of drawing a red or a green ball?

Question #35: A social club consists of m male and f females. If 7 males and 5 females join the club, and if one member is selected at random from the expanded club to become the new president of the club, then what is the probability of selecting a male president?

SETS:

Question #36: If Set-R contains all positive odd integers less than 100 and Set-S contains the square roots of the integers in Set-R, how many elements are in the intersection of the two sets?

Question #37: If Set-P contains 7 distinct numbers and Set-Q contains 5 distinct letters, how many elements are in the union and intersection of the two sets?

Question #38: There are 15 people in group X, and 16 people in group y. If 7 people are in both groups, how many people are only in one of the groups?

Question #39: In a certain club, if 75 percent of the members participate in indoor activities, 65 percent participate in outdoor activities, and 20 percent participate in neither of the activities, what percent participate in both types of activities?

Question #40: In a certain association, 110 members participate in gardening and 90 members participate in fishing. If 20 members participate in both gardening and fishing, what is the ratio of the number of members who participate only in gardening to the number of members who participate in only fishing?

Question #41: In a school, there are 175 students who are enrolled in Math, English, or Science. There are 70 students who are in Math, 80 are in English, and 90 are in Science. There are 15 students who are enrolled in all three of the courses. How many of the students are enrolled in exactly all three courses: Math, English, and Science?

SEQUENCE & PATTERNS:

Question #42: If $\dfrac{9}{11}$ is converted into a decimal form, what is the 95th digit to the right of the decimal point?

Question #43: If $\dfrac{11}{7}$ is converted into a decimal form, what is the 67th digit to the right of the decimal point?

Question #44: At a certain fundraiser, colored ribbons are given out in the order, red, blue, blue, green, green, green, yellow, yellow, yellow, yellow, red, blue, blue, green, green, green, yellow, yellow, yellow, yellow. If this pattern continues, how many blue ribbons will be given out when a total of 75 ribbons have been given out?

Question #45: The first term of a sequence of numbers is 1. Subsequently, every even term in the sequence is found by subtracting 2 from the previous term, and every odd term in the sequence is found by adding 9 to the previous term. What is the difference between the 95th and 97th terms in this sequence?

Question #46: What is the sum of the first 200 terms of the sequence given below that repeats itself in sets of four? {1, 2, 7, 9, 1, 2, 7, 9, 1, 2.......}

Question #47:   A certain list is made up of 15 consecutive multiples of 7. If the first term is 56, what is the value of the middle term?

Question #48:   The first term in a sequence is *n*, and each term after the first term is 5 times the preceding term. If the sum of first 5 terms is 7810, what is the value of the first term in the sequence?

Question #49:   The first term of a sequence is 24 and the second term is 8. The next term and each term after that is the average (arithmetic mean) of the two terms immediately preceding it. What is the value of the first term in the sequence that is not an integer?

Question #50:   The first term of a sequence is 1. The next term and each term after that is 1 more than twice the term immediately preceding it. What is the value of the smallest term in the sequence that is greater than 100?

Question #51:   If it is now the month of June, what month will it be 101 months from now?

Question #52:   If today is Sunday, what day will it be 699 days from today?

Question #53:   In the sequence given below, what is the sum of the first 200 terms?
1, 2, 3, 4, 5, 6, 1, 2, 3, 4, 5, 6, ...

MISCELLANEOUS PROBLEMS:

Question #54:   By how many degrees does the angle formed by the hour hand and the minute hand of a clock increase from 9:57 AM to 9:58 AM?

Question #55:   In the correctly worked out addition problem given below, each letter represents a different digit. What is the value of *A*?

```
  2A
+ A2
 BBC
```

Question #56:   In the correctly worked out addition problem given below, each letter represents a different digit. What is the number *ABC*?

```
  2C
  9C
+CC
 ABC
```

Question #57:   If all the letters represent single digits in the correctly worked computation shown below, what is the value of *A* + *B* + *C* + *D*?

```
  A  6  8  5  7
  5  B  1  2  5
  7  2  C  7  6
+ 5  8  6  D  1
1 9  9  9  9  9
```

Question #58:   If all the letters represents single digits in the correctly worked computation shown below, what is the value of *X* + *Y* + *Z*?

```
  X  7  6  9
  5  Y  5  5
+ 8  5  Z  5
1 9  9  9  9
```

STATS – AVERAGES:

Question #59: In a class of 10 students, the average score was 75. When the highest and lowest scores were dropped, the average score of the remaining 8 students was 79. What was the lowest most possible score in the class? (maximum score = 100)

Question #60: If the temperature readings at noon for four consecutive days are +26°, –1°, +27°, –2°, what must the reading be at noon on the fifth day for the average (arithmetic mean) noon temperature of all five days to be +11°?

Question #61: $\frac{1}{8}$ is the average (arithmetic mean) of $\frac{1}{6}$ and what number?

Question #62: A student averaged a score of 70 in 8 tests over a series of 10 tests. What does the average score of the other tests have to be if the average score of the entire series equals 75?

Question #63: The average of 7 numbers is 5. If two of the numbers are 11 and 14, what is the average of the remaining numbers?

Question #64: In a certain company, the average (arithmetic mean) salary of 15 employees is $50,000. If 9 of the employees have a salary of $25,000 each, what is the average salary of the other 6 employees?

Question #65: If a man drives the first 2 hours at 90 mile per hour, then due to traffic delays the next 2 hours at 80 miles per hour, then due to construction delays the next 2 hours at 70 miles per hour, and then due to speed limits the next 2 hours at 60 miles per hour. What is his average speed for the entire trip?

Question #66: What is the average (arithmetic mean) of $(x + 10)^2$ and $(x - 10)^2$?

Question #67: What is the average (arithmetic mean) of $(8x^2 + 6x + 2)$, $(7x^2 + 2x + 5)$, and $(6x^2 + 7x - 1)$?

Question #68: If $x + y = 5$, $y + z = 8$, and $z + x = 9$, what is the average (arithmetic mean) of x, y, and z?

Question #69: If the average (arithmetic mean) of 10, 18, 24, 28, and n is equal to n, what is the value of n?

Question #70: If the average (arithmetic mean) of 11, 18, and n is between 15 and 17, inclusive, what is the greatest possible value of n?

Question #71: If the average of m, n, and another number is A, then what is the value of that another number?

Question #72: If the average of (arithmetic mean) of n and –5 is 10, then what is the value of n?

Question #73: The average (arithmetic mean) of two numbers is a. If one of the numbers is 10, what is the other number?

Question #74: If the average (arithmetic mean) of a, b, and 10 is 100, what is the average of a and b?

Question #75: If the average (arithmetic mean) of 7, 9, and 11 equals the average of 6, 9, and n, what is the value of n?

Question #76: If the average (arithmetic mean) of n and 2 is equal to the average of n, 5, and 6, what is the value of n?

Question #77: If $10a + 10b = 50$, what is the average (arithmetic mean) of a and b?

Question #78: The average (arithmetic mean) of two numbers is A. If one of the numbers is n, what's the other number?

Question #79: The average (arithmetic mean) of two numbers is $6n - 1$. If one of the numbers is n, then what is the value of the other number?

Question #80: The average (arithmetic mean) of 3 numbers is 19, and the smallest of these numbers is 5. If the other two numbers are equal, what is the value of each one of the other two numbers?

Question #81: The average (arithmetic mean) of 10, 50, and 90 is 15 less than the average of 25, 75, and what number?

Question #82: If the average (arithmetic mean) of p and q is 25 and the average of r and q is 60, what is the value of $r - p$?

Question #83: If $p + q = 3(r + s)$, what is the average (arithmetic mean) of p, q, r, and s?

Question #84: If the average (arithmetic mean) of 20, 70, and 90 is 5 more than the average of 10, 80, and n, what is the value of n?

Question #85: If the average (arithmetic mean) of x and y is 6 and the average of x, y, and z is 9, what is the value of z?

Question #86: In a group of 60 workers, the average (arithmetic mean) daily salary is $80 per worker. If some of the workers earn $75 a day and the rest earn $100 a day, how many workers earn $100 a day?

Question #87: For a certain concert, fifteen tickets were sold at an average price of $8 a ticket. If some of the tickets were sold at $10 each and the rest at $5 each, how many tickets were sold at $5 price?

Question #88: The average (arithmetic mean) of eight numbers is 12. If 2 is subtracted from each of six of the numbers, what is the new average?

Question #89: The average (arithmetic mean) of 8 positive numbers is 7. If the average of least and greatest of these numbers is 10, what is the average of the other 6 numbers?

Question #90: The average (arithmetic mean) of x and y is 25. If $z = 10$, what is the average of x, y, and z?

Question #91: If the average (arithmetic mean) of a, b, c, d, and e is 95, and the average of a, b, and e is 100, what is the average of c and d?

Question #92: A big cargo container has only two sizes of boxes, large and small. If 80 percent of the boxes are large and the remaining 20 percent are small, and if the average weight of each large box is 80 pounds and the average weight of each small box is 20 pounds, what is the average weight, in pounds, of all the boxes in the cargo container?

Question #93: In a group of 5 people, each person was given a blank card on which they were supposed to write a positive integer. If the average (arithmetic mean) of all five of those integers is 15, what is the greatest possible integer that could be one of the cards?

Question #94: In a group of 5 people, each person was given a blank card on which they were supposed to write a positive integer. If the average (arithmetic mean) of all five of those integers is 15, and if no two cards can have the same number, what is the greatest possible integer that could be one of the cards?

Question #95: A student's grade in a course is determined by 8 quizzes and 1 exam. If the exam counts twice as much as each of the quizzes, what fraction of the final grade is determined by the exam?

Question #96: If A is the average (arithmetic mean) of the first 5 prime numbers and B is the median of first 5 prime numbers, what is the value of $A - B$?

Question #97: If the median of the numbers in Set A below is equal to the median of the numbers in Set B below, what is the value of n?
Set A: {11, 12, 18, 19}
Set B: {7, 9, n, 20, 21}

Question #98: If the average (arithmetic mean) of the set of numbers arranged in increasing order given below is equal to the median of the same set of numbers given below, then what is the value of n?
{5, 7, 11, 12, n}

Question #99: A company wants to draw a pie chart representing their expenditures. After the final break-up of all the expenses, 25% of the expenses were for rent, 20% for salaries, 15% for insurance, 10% for technology, 10% for utilities, and the remaining were miscellaneous expenses. What should be the degree measure of the sector representing miscellaneous expenses?

Question #100: The family budget of a certain family is represented on a pie chart. If the size of each sector of the pie chart is proportional to the amount of the budget it represents, how many degrees of the pie chart should be used to represent an item that is 16 percent of the total budget?

PRACTICE EXERCISE – QUESTIONS & ANSWERS WITH EXPLANATIONS:

PURE LOGIC:

Question #1: In a certain flower shop, there are five different types of flowers, two of which are red, two are blue, and one is green. How many different combinations of bunches of three flowers can be made so that each flower is of a different color?

Solution: We need to make bunches of three flowers so that each flower is of different type and color.
There are two types of red flowers, namely, $r1$ and $r2$.
There are two types of blue flowers, namely, $b1$ and $b2$.
There is one type of green flower, namely, $g1$.
List all 3-flower combinations so that each flower is of different color: $r1b1g1$, $r1b2g1$, $r2b1g1$, $r2b2g1$
Alternately $\Rightarrow$ (2 red) × (2 blue) × (1 green) = 4
$\Rightarrow$ No. of different combinations of bunches of three flowers that can be made so that each flower is of a different color = 4

Question #2: Newton has a pile of coins that he is trying to arrange in even stacks. If he stacks them in piles of 8, he has 2 coins left over. If he stacks them in piles of 7, he has 5 coins left over. After trying a few more combinations, he gives up, and stacks the coins in two even stacks. What is the least number of coins that he may have in each stack?

Solution: If the coins are stacked in piles of 8, and there are 2 left over $\Rightarrow$ this means that the total number of coins could be any multiple of 8 plus 2, such as, 10, 18, 26, 34, 42, 50, etc.
If the coins are stacked in piles of 7, and there are 5 left over $\Rightarrow$ this means that the total number of coins could be any multiple of 7 plus 5, such as, 12, 19, 26, 33, 40, 47, 54, etc.
Since we are looking for the least number of coins, the smallest number that works for both is 26, which works for both, the 8-coin stack with remainder 2 and 7-coin stack with remainder 5. If there were 26 total coins, then each stack would have 13 coins each.

PERMUTATION & COMBINATION:

Question #3: A man finds that by wearing different combinations of shirts and pants that he owns, he can make up 75 different outfits. If he owns 15 different shirts, how many pants does he own?

Solution: Different Types of Shirts × Different Types of Pants = Total No. of Combinations
$\Rightarrow$ Different Types of Pants × 15 = 75
$\Rightarrow$ Different Types of Pants = 75 ÷ 15 = 5

Question #4: A woman finds that by wearing different combinations of shirts, pants, and jackets that she owns, she can make up 192 different outfits. If she owns 16 different shirts and 6 different pants, how many jackets does she own?

Solution: Different Types of Shirts × Different Types of Pants × Different Types of Pants = Total Combinations
$\Rightarrow$ Different Types of Jackets × 16 × 6 = 192
$\Rightarrow$ Different Types of Jackets = 192 ÷ (16 × 6) = 192 ÷ 96 = 2

Question #5: How many four-digit numbers are there that do not contain the digits 6 and 9?

Solution: List all the options for each digit:

No. of options for the first digit	$\Rightarrow$ 7 (choices: 10 – 0, 6, and 9)
No. of options for the second digit	$\Rightarrow$ 8 (choices: 10 – 6, and 9)
No. of options for the third digit	$\Rightarrow$ 8 (choices: 10 – 6, and 9)
No. of options for the fourth digit	$\Rightarrow$ 8 (choices: 10 – 6, and 9)
Total No. of options for the four-digit numbers	$\Rightarrow$ 7 × 8 × 8 × 8 = 3,584

Question #6: In a certain furniture sale, there are 6 kinds of sofas, 9 kinds of chairs, 2 kinds of tables, and 8 kinds of shelves. In how many ways can a person decorate his house, if he wants to buy one sofa, one chair, and either a table or a shelf?

Solution:

No. of ways to choose a sofa	$\Rightarrow$ 6
No. of ways to choose a chair	$\Rightarrow$ 9

No. of ways to choose a table $\Rightarrow 2$
No. of ways to choose a shelf $\Rightarrow 8$
No. of ways to choose a table or a shelf $\Rightarrow 2 + 8 = 10$
Total No. of ways to choose 1 sofa, 1 chair, 1 table or 1 shelf $\Rightarrow (6) \times (9) \times (2 + 8) = 6 \times 9 \times 10 = 540$

Question #7: A certain runway model has a collection of 8 shirts and 9 pants. How many dressing combinations of a shirt and a pant can she make if she doesn't want to wear 2 specific shirts with 5 specific pants?

Solution:
No. of total combinations of a shirt and a pant $\Rightarrow (8) \times (9) = 72$
No. of restricted combinations of a shirt and a pant $\Rightarrow (2) \times (5) = 10$
No. of possible combinations of a shirt and a pant $\Rightarrow 72 - 10 = 62$

Question #8: How many 10-letter words can be generated by using the computer binary language of 0/1 only?
Solution: Since every letter must be chosen from 0 or 1 only, every letter has only two options.
Total No. of options for a 10-letter words $\Rightarrow 2^{10} = 1,024$

Question #9: If there are 7 cars but only 6 empty spots in a parking lot, how many numbers of different ways can those 7 cars be parked in 6 empty spots in the parking lot?

Solution:
Large Group = Total No. of cars $\Rightarrow m = 7$
Small Group = Total No. of empty spots $\Rightarrow n = 6$
No. of different ways of parking 7 cars in 6 spots:

$$\text{Permutation} \Rightarrow {}_mP_n \quad \Rightarrow \frac{m!}{(m-n)!}$$

$$\Rightarrow {}_7P_6 \quad \Rightarrow \frac{7!}{(7-6)!} = \frac{7!}{1!} = 7 \times 6 \times 5 \times 4 \times 3 \times 2 = 5,040$$

Logically thinking, any one of the 7 cars could be parked in the first spot, leaving 6 cars, any one of which could be parked in the second spot, and so no, for a total of $7 \times 6 \times 5 \times 4 \times 3 \times 2 = 5,040$ possible outcomes.

Question #10: In how many ways can 9 books be arranged on a bookshelf if 2 of the books are identical and 5 of the other books are identical?

Solution: This is a permutation question; however, we must take into account the fact that 2 of the books are identical and 5 of the other books are identical.

$$\text{No. of Different Arrangements} \quad \Rightarrow \frac{9!}{2!5!} = \frac{9 \times 8 \times 7 \times 6 \times 5!}{2!5!} = \frac{9 \times 8 \times 7 \times 6}{2 \times 1} = 1512$$

Question #11: For a certain championship, there are 7 teams and each team plays each of the other teams exactly once. If each game is played by 2 teams, what is the total number of games played?

Solution: No. of different games played:

$$\text{Combination} \Rightarrow {}_mC_n \Rightarrow \frac{m!}{n!(m-n)!}$$

$$\Rightarrow \frac{7!}{2!(7-2)!} = \frac{7!}{2!5!} = \frac{7 \times 6 \times 5!}{2! \, 5!} = \frac{7 \times 6}{2 \times 1} = \frac{42}{2} = 21$$

Alternately: All games are between two teams and no team can play by itself or with itself. This means that each of the 7 teams need to play with 6 other teams instead of 7 teams. Moreover, since each game is between 2 teams, each game needs to be counted only once instead of twice for each team that plays the game $\Rightarrow \dfrac{7 \times 6}{2} = 21$ games

Question #12: In a certain team, there are 12 players and each player shakes hand with each of the other players exactly once. If each handshake is between 2 players, what is the total number of handshakes?

Solution: No. of different handshakes:

$$\text{Combination} \Rightarrow {}_mC_n \Rightarrow \frac{m!}{n!(m-n)!}$$

$$\Rightarrow \frac{12!}{2!(12-2)!} = \frac{12!}{2!10!} = \frac{12 \times 11 \times \cancel{10\,!}}{2!\,\cancel{10}\,!} = \frac{12 \times 11}{2 \times 1} = \frac{132}{2} = 66$$

Alternately: All handshakes are between two players and no player can shake hands by itself or with itself. This means that each of the 12 players needs to shake hands with 11 other players instead of 12 players. Moreover, since each handshake is between 2 players, each handshake needs to be counted only once instead of twice for each player that shakes hands.

$$\Rightarrow \frac{12 \times 11}{2} = 66 \text{ handshakes}$$

Question #13: There is a group of 7 people, 6 boys and 1 girl who needs to be seated in a row of 7 seats in a theater. In how many ways can the 7 people be seated if the girl won't sit on the either end or in the middle?

Solution: Total No. of People $\Rightarrow$ 7; 6 boys and 1 girl who cant be seated on either end or in the middle.
Total No. of Seating Options for the Girl $\Rightarrow$ 7 – (2 for the two ends) – 1 (for the middle) = 4
Total No. of Seating Options for the Boys $\Rightarrow$ 7 – 1 (for the girl) = 6! = 720
Total No. of Seating Options for all 7 people $\Rightarrow$ 4 × (6!) = 4 × 720 = 2,880

PROBABILITY:

Question #14: If two fair dice are thrown and the same number comes up on each of the dice, what is the probability that the sum of the two numbers is 7?

Solution: If two fair dice are thrown and the same number appears on both, the sum will always be 2 times the number shown on either of the dice and thus must be an even number. Since 7 is an odd number, the sum cannot be 7. Therefore, the probability of that happening is zero.

Question #15: There are 100 people in a line. Sam is 21st person and Tom is 92nd person. If a person on line is chosen at random, what is the probability that the person is standing between Sam and Tom?

Solution: No. of people between Sam and Tom $\Rightarrow$ 92 – 21 – 1 = 70

Probability that the person chosen is standing between Sam and Tom $\Rightarrow \dfrac{70}{100} = \dfrac{7}{10}$

Question #16: Peter and Tina tossed a coin 10 times, and each time the coin lands as "heads". After the tenth toss, Tina makes a bet that the coin will land as "tails" on the eleventh toss. What is the probability of Tina winning the bet?

Solution: The probability of the outcome of a toss of a coin is completely independent of the previous outcomes and the probability of a coin landing as heads or tails is always ½ for any flip.
Probability of Tina winning the bet = ½ or 50%

Question #17: If a fair coin is tossed four times, what is the probability that on at least one of the tosses the coin will turn up tails?

Solution: Note that a tossed coin will turn up as tails at least once is the same as it will not turn up heads every time.

Probability that the coin will turn up as heads in one toss $\Rightarrow \dfrac{1}{2}$

Probability that the coin will turn up as heads in four tosses $\Rightarrow \dfrac{1}{2} \times \dfrac{1}{2} \times \dfrac{1}{2} \times \dfrac{1}{2} = \dfrac{1}{16}$

In all four tosses, the probability of not getting heads all four times or not getting heads at least once or getting tails at least once $\Rightarrow 1 - \dfrac{1}{16} = \dfrac{15}{16}$

Question #18: If one student is chosen randomly from a group of nine students, then one student is again chosen randomly from the same group of nine students, what is the probability that two different students will be chosen?

Solution: Probability of Randomly Picking One Student $\Rightarrow \dfrac{1}{9}$

Probability of Randomly Picking the Same Student Again $\Rightarrow \dfrac{1}{9} \times \dfrac{1}{9} = \dfrac{1}{81}$

Probability of picking the same student twice + Probability of not picking the same student twice = 1
Probability of Picking Two Different Students = 1 − Probability of picking the same student twice

$\Rightarrow 1 - \dfrac{1}{81} = \dfrac{81}{81} - \dfrac{1}{81} = \dfrac{80}{81}$

Question #19:   A jar has 6 marbles, one each of color red, blue, green, yellow, orange, and purple. If 5 marbles are removed from the jar, what is the probability that the purple marble was removed?

Solution: Probability that purple marble is left in the jar $\Rightarrow \dfrac{1}{6}$

Probability that purple marble is removed from the jar $\Rightarrow 1 - \dfrac{1}{6} = \dfrac{5}{6}$

Question #20:   In a certain election, there are 7 male candidates and 5 female candidates. If three candidates are elected, what is the probability that all three candidates will be males?

Solution: Probability of the first male candidate $\Rightarrow \dfrac{7}{12}$

Probability of the second male candidate $\Rightarrow \dfrac{6}{11}$

Probability of the third male candidate $\Rightarrow \dfrac{5}{10}$

Probability that all three candidates elected drawn will be male $\Rightarrow \dfrac{7}{12} \times \dfrac{6}{11} \times \dfrac{5}{10} = \dfrac{7}{44}$

Question #21:   Two integers are to be randomly selected from the two sets given below, one integer form set X and one integer form set Y. What is the probability that the sum of the two integers will be even?
Set X: {1, 2, 3, 4}
Set Y: {5, 6, 7, 8}

Solution: Total No. of different pairs of numbers, one form set X and one from set Y $\Rightarrow$ (4) (4) = 16
Total No. of pairs that has an even sum (1+5), (1+7), (2+6), (2+8), (3+5), (3+7), (4+6), (4+8) $\Rightarrow$ 8
Notice that since for the sum of two integers to be even, either both should be odd or both should be even; hence, there will be equal number of even and odd pairs.

Probability that the sum of the two integers will be even $\Rightarrow \dfrac{8}{16} = \dfrac{1}{2}$

Question #22:   Two integers are to be randomly selected from the two sets given below, one integer form set X and one integer form set Y. What is the probability that the product of the two integers will be odd?
Set X: {1, 2, 3, 4}
Set Y: {5, 6, 7, 8}

Solution: Total No. of different pairs of numbers, one form set X and one from set Y $\Rightarrow$ (4) (4) = 16
Total No. of pairs that has an odd product (1 × 5), (1 × 7), (3 × 5), (3 × 7) $\Rightarrow$ 4
Notice that since for the product of two integers to be odd, both integers should be odd; hence, there will be only four such pairs.

Probability that the sum of the two integers will be odd $\Rightarrow \dfrac{4}{16} = \dfrac{1}{4}$

Question #23:   What is the probability that when a pair of six-sided dice is thrown, the sum of the numbers equals 5?
Solution: Total No. of different pairs of numbers, one from each dice $\Rightarrow 6 \times 6 = 36$
Total No. of pairs that has a sum of 5: (1 + 4), (2 + 3), (3 + 2), (4 + 1) $\Rightarrow$ 4

Probability of the two dice adding up to 5 $\Rightarrow \dfrac{4}{36} = \dfrac{1}{9}$

Question #24: What is the probability that when a pair of six-sided dice is thrown, the sum of the numbers is at least 10?

Solution: Total No. of different pairs of numbers, one from each dice $\Rightarrow 6 \times 6 = 36$

Total No. of pairs that has a sum of at least 10: (5 + 5), (5 + 6), (6 + 5), (6 + 6) $\Rightarrow 4$

Probability of the two dice adding up to at least 10 $\Rightarrow \dfrac{4}{36} = \dfrac{1}{9}$

Question #25: On one side of the coin, the number 5 is written, and on the other side, the number 7 is written. What is the probability that the sum of three tosses will be 17?

Solution: Total No. of Options for 1 toss $\Rightarrow 2$ (either 5 or 7)

Total No. of Options for 3 tosses $\Rightarrow 2 \times 2 \times 2 = 8$

No. of options where the sum of three tosses will be 17 $\Rightarrow 3$ (557), (575), (755)

Probability that the sum of three tosses will be 17 $\Rightarrow \dfrac{3}{8}$

Question #26: A big jar contains 25 postcards, each with a different integer from 1 to 25 written on it. Blindfolded, if one of the postcards is drawn at random, what is the probability that the number written on the postcard will be a multiple of 3 or 5?

Solution: Total No. of Numbers written on the postcards $\Rightarrow 25 - 1 + 1 = 25$

No. of postcards with a multiple of 3 written on them $\Rightarrow 8$ (3, 6, 9, 12, *15*, 18, 21, 24)

No. of postcards with a multiple of 5 written on them $\Rightarrow 5$ (5. 10, *15*, 20, 25)

Total No. of postcards with a multiple of 3 or 5 written on them $\Rightarrow 8 + 5 = 13 - 1$

                                        (the number 15 is counted twice) = 12

Probability that the drawn postcard will have a number written on it, which is a multiple of 3 or 5 $\Rightarrow \dfrac{12}{25}$

Question #27: If a number is chosen at random from set *X*, what is the probability that the number is in the intersection of set *X* and set *Y*?

Set $X = \{1, 2, 4, 6, 8, 9, 12, 15\}$

Set $Y = \{8, 9, 11, 16\}$

Solution: Intersection Set *X* and Set $Y = \{8, 9\}$

Probability of picking a number from set *X*, which is also in the intersection of set *X* & set $Y \Rightarrow \dfrac{2}{8} = \dfrac{1}{4}$

Question #28: What is the probability that the sum of two dice is greater than 9 given that the first dice is a 6?

Solution: Given that the value of the first dice is fixed as a 6, there are a total of 6 possibilities for the two dice;

Namely: (6, 1), (6, 2), (6, 3), (6, 4), (6, 5), (6, 6)

Out of the 6 possibilities, there are 3 that sum up to more than 9; namely: (6, 4), (6, 5), (6, 6)

Probability that the sum of two dice is greater than 9 given that the first dice is a 6 $\Rightarrow \dfrac{3}{6} = \dfrac{1}{2}$

Question #29: Folded paper notes numbered consecutively from 101 through 850 are placed in a box. If a paper note is picked randomly, what is the probability that it will have a number written on it which has a hundreds digit of 7?

Solution: Total No. of paper notes $\Rightarrow (850 - 101) + 1 = 750$

Total No. of paper notes with hundreds digit 7 $\Rightarrow (799 - 700) + 1 = 100$

Probability that a randomly picked paper note will have a number written on it which has a hundreds digit of 7 $\Rightarrow \dfrac{100}{750} = \dfrac{2}{15}$

Question #30: From the set of numbers $\{1, 2, 3, 4, 5, 6, 7\}$, one number is picked and then replaced, and then another number is again picked. If the sum of the two numbers picked is 8, what is the probability that the two numbers included the number 7 as one of the numbers picked?

Solution: Total No. of options for the two picked numbers so that their sum is $8 \Rightarrow 7$

List: (1, 7), (2, 6), (3, 5), (4, 4), (5, 3), (6, 2), (7, 1)

Total No. of options for the two picked numbers so that their sum is 8 and one of the number is $7 \Rightarrow 2$

List: (1, 7), (7, 1)

Probability that two picked numbers included the number 7 $\Rightarrow \dfrac{2}{7}$

Question #31: In a standard deck of 52 cards, numbered from 1 to 13, with 4 cards of each number, 16 more cards with the number 8 on them are added to the deck. After shuffling the cards, what is the probability of picking a card with the number 8 on it?

Solution:
No. of Cards in the deck $\Rightarrow$ 52 (standard) + 16 (new) = 68
No. of Cards with the number 8 $\Rightarrow$ 4 (standard) + 16 (new) = 20

Probability of picking a card with the number 8 on it $\Rightarrow \dfrac{20}{68} = \dfrac{5}{17}$

Question #32: A certain jar contains 21 balls. After drawing 6 red balls from the jar without putting them back, the probability of drawing the next red ball is 1/5. How many red balls were in the jar in the beginning?

Solution:
No. of Ball in the jar in the beginning $\Rightarrow$ 21
No. of Ball in the jar after drawing 6 red balls $\Rightarrow$ 21 − 6 = 15

Probability of drawing a red ball out of 15 balls $\Rightarrow \dfrac{1}{5}$

No of red ball remaining after drawing 6 red balls $\Rightarrow \dfrac{1}{5} \times 15 = 3$

Total No. of red balls in the jar in the beginning $\Rightarrow$ 6 + 3 = 9

Question #33: A certain jar contains 2 red marbles, 2 blue marbles, 2 green marbles, and 2 yellow marbles. If two marbles are randomly picked from the jar, what is the probability that neither one of them will be red?

Solution:
Probability that the first marble picked will be not be red $\Rightarrow \dfrac{6}{8}$

Probability that the second marble picked will not be red $\Rightarrow \dfrac{5}{7}$

Probability that neither one of the picked marbles will be red $\Rightarrow \dfrac{6}{8} \times \dfrac{5}{7} = \dfrac{30}{56} = \dfrac{15}{28}$

Question #34: In a certain jar, there are n red balls, $5n + 10$ blue balls and 2 green balls. What is the probability of drawing a red or a green ball?

Solution:
No. of Red Balls $\Rightarrow n$
No. of Blue Balls $\Rightarrow 5n + 10$
No. of Green Balls $\Rightarrow 2$
Total No of Balls $\Rightarrow (n) + (5n + 10) + 2 = 6n + 12$

Probability of drawing a Red or a Green Ball $\Rightarrow \dfrac{n+2}{6n+12} = \dfrac{n+2}{6(n+2)} = \dfrac{1}{6}$

Question #35: A social club consists of m male and f females. If 7 males and 5 females join the club, and if one member is selected at random from the expanded club to become the new president of the club, then what is the probability of selecting a male president?

Solution:
Total No. of Males in the Original Club $\Rightarrow m$
Total No. of Females in the Original Club $\Rightarrow f$
Total No. of Members in the Original Club $\Rightarrow m + f$
Total No. of Males in the Expanded Club $\Rightarrow m + 7$
Total No. of Females in the Expanded Club $\Rightarrow f + 5$
Total No. of Members in the Expanded Club $\Rightarrow m + 7 + f + 5 = m + f + 12$

Probability of randomly selecting a Male $\Rightarrow \dfrac{total\ number\ of\ males}{total\ number\ of\ members} = \dfrac{m+7}{m+f+12}$

SETS:

Question #36: If Set-R contains all positive odd integers less than 100 and Set-S contains the square roots of the integers in Set-R, how many elements are in the intersection of the two sets?

Solution: Set R: $\{1, 3, 5, 7, 9, 11, 13, 15, 17, 19, ...\}$

Set S: $\left\{\sqrt{1}, \sqrt{3}, \sqrt{5}, \sqrt{7}, \sqrt{9}, \sqrt{11}, \sqrt{13}, \sqrt{15}, \sqrt{17}, \sqrt{19}, ...\sqrt{25}, ...\sqrt{49}, ...\sqrt{81}, ...\sqrt{99}\right\}$

$R \cap S \Rightarrow \{1, 3, 5, 7, 9\}$

No. of element in the intersection of the two sets $\Rightarrow$ 5 elements

Question #37: If Set-P contains 7 distinct numbers and Set-Q contains 5 distinct letters, how many elements are in the union and intersection of the two sets?

Solution: Since Set-P and Set-Q contain different kinds of elements, so the union set contains every element that is in either set.

$\Rightarrow P \cup Q = 7 + 5 = 12$

Since Set-P and Set-Q contain different kinds of elements, there are no elements that are common in both sets, so the intersection set contains nothing.

$\Rightarrow P \cap Q = 0$

Question #38: There are 15 people in group X, and 16 people in group y. If 7 people are in both groups, how many people are only in one of the groups?

Solution:
No. of people who are in group X $\Rightarrow$ 15
No. of people who are in group Y $\Rightarrow$ 16
No. of people who are in both groups $\Rightarrow$ 7
No. of people who are only in group X $\Rightarrow 15 - 7 = 8$
No. of people who are only in group Y $\Rightarrow 16 - 7 = 9$
No. of people who are only in one of the groups $\Rightarrow 8 + 9 = 17$

Question #39: In a certain club, if 75 percent of the members participate in indoor activities, 65 percent participate in outdoor activities, and 20 percent participate in neither of the activities, what percent participate in both types of activities?

Solution:
Let the No. of members who participate in both types of activities $\Rightarrow x$
Then, No. of members who participate in only Indoor Activities $\Rightarrow (75\% - x)$
And, No. of members who participate in only Outdoor Activities $\Rightarrow (65\% - x)$
No. of members who participate in neither of the Activities $\Rightarrow 20\%$
Total No. of members who participate in Indoor/Outdoor Activities $\Rightarrow 100\% - 20\% = 80\%$
EZ Problem Set-Up $\Rightarrow$ Indoor only + Outdoor only + Indoor & Outdoor = Total Members
$\Rightarrow (75\% - x) + (65\% - x) + x = 80\%$
$\Rightarrow 140\% - x = 80\%$
$\Rightarrow x = 60\%$
Percent of students who participate in both Indoor & Outdoor activities $\Rightarrow 60\%$

Question #40: In a certain association, 110 members participate in gardening and 90 members participate in fishing. If 20 members participate in both gardening and fishing, what is the ratio of the number of members who participate only in gardening to the number of members who participate in only fishing?

Solution:
No. of member who participate in Gardening $\Rightarrow 110$
No. of member who participate in Fishing $\Rightarrow 90$
No. of member who participate in both Gardening & Fishing $\Rightarrow 20$
No. of member who participate in only Gardening $\Rightarrow 110 - 20 = 90$
No. of member who participate in only Fishing $\Rightarrow 90 - 20 = 70$
Ratio of the number of members who participate only in gardening to the number of members who participate in only fishing $\Rightarrow 90:70 = 9:7$

Question #41: In a school, there are 175 students who are enrolled in Math, English, or Science. There are 70 students who are in Math, 80 are in English, and 90 are in Science. There are 15 students who are enrolled in all three of the courses. How many of the students are enrolled in exactly two courses?

Solution: Let: No. of students enrolled in Math & English $\Rightarrow a$

No. of students enrolled in Math & Science $\Rightarrow b$
No. of students enrolled in English & Science $\Rightarrow c$
No. of students enrolled in exactly two courses $\Rightarrow a + b + c$
No. of students enrolled in all three courses $\Rightarrow 15$
Total No. of students $\Rightarrow 175$

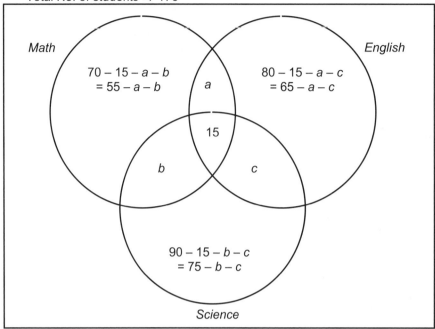

Then, No. of students enrolled in Math $\Rightarrow 55 - a - b$
And, No. of students enrolled in English $\Rightarrow 65 - a - c$
And, No. of students enrolled in Science $\Rightarrow 75 - b - c$
EZ Problem Set-Up $\Rightarrow$ Only Math + Only English + Only Science + Any 2 + All 3 = Total
$\Rightarrow (55 - a - b) + (65 - a - c) + (75 - b - c) + (a + b + c) + 15 = 175$
$\Rightarrow 195 - (a + b + c) + 15 = 175$
$\Rightarrow 210 - (a + b + c) = 175$
$\Rightarrow (a + b + c) = 35$
No. of students who are enrolled in exactly two courses $\Rightarrow 35$

SEQUENCE & PATTERNS:

Question #42:   If $\dfrac{9}{11}$ is converted into a decimal form, what is the 95th digit to the right of the decimal point?

Solution: $\Rightarrow \dfrac{9}{11} = 0.818181818181$

Notice that every odd-numbered digit to the right of the decimal point is 8, and every even-numbered digit to the right of the decimal point is 1.
The 95th (odd-numbered) digit to the right of the decimal point = 8

Question #43:   If $\dfrac{11}{7}$ is converted into a decimal form, what is the 67th digit to the right of the decimal point?

Solution: $\Rightarrow \dfrac{11}{7} = 1.571428571428571428571428571428$

Notice that there is a repeated pattern of "571428" indefinitely.
In order to find the digit of the 67th term in this pattern, divide 67 by 6, which results in a quotient of 11 ($6 \times 11 = 66$) and a remainder of 1.
The 66th digit to the right of the decimal point is 8, and the 67th digit to the right of the decimal point must be the next digit, which is 5.

Question #44: At a certain fundraiser, colored ribbons are given out in the order, red, blue, blue, green, green, green, yellow, yellow, yellow, yellow, red, blue, blue, green, green, green, yellow, yellow, yellow, yellow. If this pattern continues, how many green ribbons will be given out when a total of 75 ribbons have been given out?

Solution: The given pattern of red, blue, blue, green, green, green, yellow, yellow, yellow, yellow forms a repeated pattern in sets of 10 $\Rightarrow$ 1 (red) + 2(blue) + 3(green) + 4(yellow) = 10.
For the first 10 ribbons distributed, there will be 3 green ribbons given out.
Likewise, for the first 70 ribbons distributed, there will be 3 × 7 = 21 green ribbons given out.
For the 71st through 75th ribbons distributed, there will be only 2 green ribbons given out (74th & 75th).
In all, there will be 21 + 2 = 23 green ribbons given out in the first 75 ribbons distributed.

Question #45: The first term of a sequence of numbers is 1. Subsequently, every even term in the sequence is found by subtracting 2 from the previous term, and every odd term in the sequence is found by adding 9 to the previous term. What is the difference between the 95th and 97th terms in this sequence?

Solution: Write out the first few terms in the sequence: 1, −1, 8, 6, 15, 13, 22, 20, 29
Recognize the pattern; difference between every other term is a constant 7 $\Rightarrow$ 97th term–95th term = 7

Question #46: What is the sum of the first 200 terms of the sequence given below that repeats itself in sets of four?
{1, 2, 7, 9, 1, 2, 7, 9, 1, 2.......}

Solution: Sum of first 4 terms $\Rightarrow$ 1 + 2 + 7 + 9 = 19
Sets of 4 terms in 200 terms $\Rightarrow$ 200 ÷ 4 = 50
Sum of first 200 terms $\Rightarrow$ 19 × 50 = 950

Question #47: A certain list is made up of 15 consecutive multiples of 7. If the first term is 56, what is the value of the middle term?

Solution: If there are a total of 15 terms in a sequence, the middle term is the 8th term.
List the terms: 56, 63, 70, 77, 84, 91, 98, 105 $\Rightarrow$ the value of the middle or the 8th term is 105

Question #48: The first term in a sequence is n, and each term after the first term is 5 times the preceding term. If the sum of first 5 terms is 7810, what is the value of the first term in the sequence?

Solution: Write the first five terms in the sequence $\Rightarrow n, 5n, 25n, 125n, 625n$
EZ Problem Set-Up $\Rightarrow$ Sum of first 5 terms is 7,810.
$\Rightarrow n + 5n + 25n + 125n + 625n = 7810$
$\Rightarrow 781n = 7810$
$\Rightarrow n = 10$
Value of n, the first term in the sequence $\Rightarrow$ 10

Question #49: The first term of a sequence is 24 and the second term is 8. The next term and each term after that is the average (arithmetic mean) of the two terms immediately preceding it. What is the value of the first term in the sequence that is not an integer?

Solution: Start writing out the terms in the sequence until a non-integer comes up:
$\Rightarrow 24, 8, \dfrac{24+8}{2} = 16, \dfrac{8+16}{2} = 12, \dfrac{16+12}{2} = 14, \dfrac{12+14}{2} = 13, \dfrac{14+13}{2} = \dfrac{27}{2}$
$\Rightarrow$ 24, 8, 16, 12, 14, 13, 13.5
Value of the first term in the sequence that is not an integer $\Rightarrow$ 13.5

Question #50: The first term of a sequence is 1. The next term and each term after that is 1 more than twice the term immediately preceding it. What is the value of the smallest term in the sequence that is greater than 100?

Solution: Start writing out the terms in the sequence until the smallest term greater than 100 comes up:
$\Rightarrow$ 1, 2(1) + 1 = 3, 2(3) + 1 = 7, 2(7) + 1 = 15, 2(15) + 1 = 31, 2(31) + 1 = 63, 2(63) + 1 = 127
$\Rightarrow$ 1, 3, 7, 15, 31, 63, 127
Value of the smallest term in the sequence that is greater than 100 $\Rightarrow$ 127

Question #51: If it is now the month of June, what month will it be 101 months from now?

Solution: Since there are 12 months in a year, after every 12 months it will again be June, that is, after 12, 24, 36, 48, 60 ... months, it will be June.
Since 101 ÷ 12 = 8 with a remainder of 5, it will be June after 12 × 8 = 96 months, and then count 5 more months from then, and it will be November after 101 months.

Question #52: If today is Sunday, what day will it be 699 days from today?
Solution: Since there are 7 days in a week, after every 7 days it will again be Sunday, that is, after 7, 14, 21, 28, 35, 42, 49, 56... days, it will be Sunday.
Since 699 ÷ 7 = 99 with a remainder of 6, it will be Sunday after 7 × 99 = 693 days, and then count 6 more days from then, and it will be Saturday after 699 days.

Question #53: In the sequence given below, what is the sum of the first 200 terms?
1, 2, 3, 4, 5, 6, 1, 2, 3, 4, 5, 6, ...
Solution: Since the first 6 terms are repeated indefinitely, divide 200 by 6, which give 33 and a remainder of 2.
So, there are 33 sets of 6 repeated terms (1, 2, 3, 4, 5, 6) plus 2 more terms (1, 2) in the first 200 terms.

Sum of first 6 terms	$\Rightarrow 1 + 2 + 3 + 4 + 5 + 6 = 21$
Sum of 33 sets of 6 terms	$\Rightarrow 21 \times 33 = 693$
Sum of first 2 terms	$\Rightarrow 1 + 2 = 3$
Sum of first 200 terms	$\Rightarrow$ Sum of 33 sets of 6 terms + Sum of first 2 terms
	$\Rightarrow 693 + 3 = 696$

MISCELLANEOUS PROBLEMS:

Question #54: By how many degrees does the angle formed by the hour hand and the minute hand of a clock increase from 9:57 AM to 9:58 AM?
Solution: The hour-hand makes a complete revolution of 360°, once every 12 hours.
  ⇒ Hence, in every 1 hour it goes forward 360° ÷ 12 = 30°.
  ⇒ And, in every 1 minute it advances through 30° ÷ 60 = 0.5°.
The minute-hand makes a complete revolution of 360°, once every 60 minutes.
  ⇒ Hence, in every 5 minutes it goes forward 360° ÷ 12 = 30°.
  ⇒ And, in every 1 minute it advances through 360° ÷ 60 = 6°.
⇒ In the minute from 9:57 AM to 9:58 AM, or any other minute for that matter, the difference between the hands increases by 6 – 0.5 = 5.5°.
It is not necessary, and would have been more time-consuming to determine the angles between the hands at 9:57 and 9:58.

Question #55: In the correctly worked out addition problem given below, each letter represents a different digit. What is the value of A?
```
  2A
+ A2
────
 BBC
```
Solution: Two 2-digit numbers will add up to at most something in the 100's, so B = 1.
Rewrite the problem again, replacing B with 1:
```
  2A
+ A2
────
 11C
```
Now, if A ≤ 7, then A + 2 in each column would be a one-digit number, since we know that sum is a three-digit number, A has to be at least 8, or it could be 9. Let's see if 8 works.
Rewrite the problem again, replacing A with 8:
```
  28
+ 82
────
 110
```
Value of A = 8

Question #56: In the correctly worked out addition problem given below, each letter represents a different digit. What is the number ABC?
```
  2C
```

Solution:

$$9C$$
$$+CC$$
$$\overline{ABC}$$

Since C can't be 0, and the only other digit C that multiplied by 3 or added three times, ends in C is 5
$\Rightarrow 5 + 5 + 5 = 15$
Rewrite the problem again, replacing C with 5:

$$25$$
$$95$$
$$+ 55$$
$$\overline{AB5}$$

Next, fill in the other numbers:

$$25$$
$$95$$
$$+ 55$$
$$\overline{175}$$

Value of number ABC = 175

Question #57: If all the letters represent single digits in the correctly worked computation shown below, what is the value of $A + B + C + D$?

```
  A  6  8  5  7
  5  B  1  2  5
  7  2  C  7  6
+ 5  8  6  D  1
──────────────
1 9  9  9  9  9
```

Solution: Add the digits vertically down, form equations, and solve for the missing digits:

Sum of units digits	$\Rightarrow 7 + 5 + 6 + 1 = 19$
	Carry over to tens digit = 1
Sum of tens digits	$\Rightarrow 1 + (5 + 2 + 7 + D) = 19$
	$\Rightarrow D = 4$
	Carry over to hundreds digit = 1
Sum of hundreds digits	$\Rightarrow 1 + (8 + 1 + C + 6) = 19$
	$\Rightarrow C = 3$
	Carry over to thousands digit = 1
Sum of thousands digits	$\Rightarrow 1 + (6 + B + 2 + 8) = 19$
	$\Rightarrow B = 2$
	Carry over to ten-thousands digit = 1
Sum of ten-thousands digits	$\Rightarrow 1 + (A + 5 + 7 + 5) = 19$
	$\Rightarrow A = 1$
	Carry over to hundred-thousands place = 1
Sum of hundred thousands	$\Rightarrow 1$
Sum of $A + B + C + D$	$\Rightarrow 1 + 2 + 3 + 4 = 10$

Question #58: If all the letters represents single digits in the correctly worked computation shown below, what is the value of $X + Y + Z$?

```
  X  7  6  9
  5  Y  5  5
+ 8  5  Z  5
────────────
1 9  9  9  9
```

Solution: Add the digits vertically down, form equations, and solve for the missing digits:

Sum of units digits	$\Rightarrow 9 + 5 + 5 = 19$
	Carry over to tens digit = 1
Sum of tens digits	$\Rightarrow 1 + (6 + 5 + Z) = 19$
	$\Rightarrow Z = 7$
	Carry over to hundreds digit = 1
Sum of hundreds digits	$\Rightarrow 1 + (7 + Y + 5) = 19$
	$\Rightarrow Y = 6$
	Carry over to thousands digit = 1
Sum of thousands digits	$\Rightarrow 1 + (X + 5 + 8) = 19$

$\Rightarrow X = 5$
Carry over to ten-thousands digit = 1
Sum of ten-thousands digits $\Rightarrow 1$
Sum of $X + Y + Z$ $\Rightarrow 5 + 6 + 7 = 18$

STATS – AVERAGES:

Question #59: In a class of 10 students, the average score was 75. When the highest and lowest scores were dropped, the average score of the remaining 8 students was 79. What was the lowest most possible score in the class? (Maximum score = 100)

Solution: Total Score of 10 Students $\Rightarrow 10 \times 75 = 750$
Total Score of 8 Students $\Rightarrow 8 \times 79 = 632$
Total Score of the 2 Students (Highest & Lowest) $\Rightarrow 750 - 632 = 118$
Since the highest score is 100, the lowest possible score $\Rightarrow 118 - 100 = 18$

Question #60: If the temperature readings at noon for four consecutive days are +26°, –1°, +27°, –2°, what must the reading be at noon on the fifth day for the average (arithmetic mean) noon temperature of all five days to be +11°?

Solution: Mean of all 5 Temperature Readings $\Rightarrow +11°$
Sum of all 5 Temperature Readings $\Rightarrow 11° \times 5 = 55°$
Sum of 4 Temperature Readings $\Rightarrow 26° - 1° + 27° - 2° = 50°$
Temperature Reading on the Fifth Day $\Rightarrow$ Sum of all 5 Readings – Sum of 4 Readings
                                      $\Rightarrow 55° - 50° = 5°$

Question #61: $\frac{1}{8}$ is the average (arithmetic mean) of $\frac{1}{6}$ and what number?

Solution: Let the other number = n
EZ Problem Set-Up $\Rightarrow$ Mean$\Rightarrow$ Sum ÷ Number

$$\Rightarrow \frac{\frac{1}{6} + n}{2} = \frac{1}{8} \qquad \text{[Set up the equation]}$$

$$\Rightarrow \frac{1}{6} + n = \frac{1}{4} \qquad \text{[Multiply both sides by 2]}$$

$$\Rightarrow n = \frac{1}{12} \qquad \text{[Subtract 1/6 from both sides]}$$

Question #62: A student averaged a score of 70 in 8 tests over a series of 10 tests. What does the average score of the other tests have to be if the average score of the entire series equals 75?

Solution: Mean of 8 Tests $\Rightarrow 70$
Sum of 8 Tests $\Rightarrow$ Mean of 8 Tests × 8
                   $\Rightarrow 70 \times 8 = 560$
Mean of 10 Tests $\Rightarrow 75$
Sum of 10 Tests $\Rightarrow$ Mean of 10 Tests × 10
                   $\Rightarrow 75 \times 10 = 750$
Sum of 2 Tests $\Rightarrow$ Sum of 10 Tests – Sum of 8 Tests
                   $\Rightarrow 750 - 560 = 190$
Mean of 2 Tests $\Rightarrow$ Sum of 2 Tests ÷ 2
                   $\Rightarrow 190 \div 2 = 95$

Question #63: The average of 7 numbers is 5. If two of the numbers are 11 and 14, what is the average of the remaining numbers?

Solution: Mean of 7 Numbers $\Rightarrow 5$
Sum of 7 Numbers $\Rightarrow$ Mean × Number
                   $\Rightarrow 7 \times 5 = 35$
Sum of 2 Numbers $\Rightarrow 11 + 14 = 25$

Sum of 5 Numbers $\Rightarrow$ Sum of 7 Numbers − Sum of 2 Numbers
                   $\Rightarrow$ 35 − 25 = 10
Mean of 5 Numbers $\Rightarrow$ Total Sum of Remaining Numbers ÷ Total No. of Remaining Numbers
                   $\Rightarrow$ 10 ÷ 5 = 2

Question #64: In a certain company, the average (arithmetic mean) salary of 15 employees is $50,000. If 9 of the employees have a salary of $25,000 each, what is the average salary of the other 6 employees?

Solution:

Mean of 15 employees $\Rightarrow$ $50,000
Sum of 15 employees $\Rightarrow$ *Mean × Number*
                       $\Rightarrow$ $50,000 × 15 = $750,000
Mean of 9 employees $\Rightarrow$ $25,000
Sum of 9 employees $\Rightarrow$ *Mean × Number*
                       $\Rightarrow$ $25,000 × 9 = $225,000
Sum of 6 employees $\Rightarrow$ Sum of 15 employees − Sum of 9 employees
                       $\Rightarrow$ $750,000 - $225,000 = $525,000
Mean of 6 employees $\Rightarrow$ *Sum ÷ Number*
                       $\Rightarrow$ $525,000 ÷ 6 = $87,500

Alternate Method: This problem can also be solved by using the weighted average formula.
Let the average of the salary of 6 employees = x
EZ Problem Set Up $\Rightarrow$ *Sum of products ÷ Sum of Weights = Weighted Mean*

$\Rightarrow \dfrac{9(\$25,000) + 6(x)}{15} = \$50,000$ [Set up the equation]

$\Rightarrow \$225,000 + 6x = \$750,000$ [Cross multiply]

$\Rightarrow 6x = \$525,000$ [Subtract $225,000 from both sides]

$\Rightarrow x = \$87,500$ [Divide both sides b y 6]

Question #65: If a man drives the first 2 hours at 90 mile per hour, then due to traffic delays the next 2 hours at 80 miles per hour, then due to construction delays the next 2 hours at 70 miles per hour, and then due to speed limits the next 2 hours at 60 miles per hour. What is his average speed for the entire trip?

Solution: Weighted Mean $\Rightarrow$ *sum of products ÷ sum of weights*
$\Rightarrow$ [2(90) + 2(80) + 2(70) + 2(60)] ÷ [2 + 2 + 2 + 2] = 600 ÷ 8 = 75

Question #66: What is the average (arithmetic mean) of $(x + 10)^2$ and $(x − 10)^2$?

Solution: Mean $\Rightarrow$ *Sum ÷ Number*   [Write the formula for calculating arithmetic mean]

$\Rightarrow \dfrac{(x+10)^2 + (x-10)^2}{2}$ [Substitute the known values]

$\Rightarrow \dfrac{(x^2 + 20x + 100) + (x^2 - 20x + 100)}{2}$ [Apply distributive property]

$\Rightarrow \dfrac{2x^2 + 200}{2}$ [Combine like-terms]

$\Rightarrow \dfrac{2(x^2 + 100)}{2}$ [Factor out 2 from the numerator]

$\Rightarrow x^2 + 100$ [Cancel-out the common terms]

Question #67: What is the average (arithmetic mean) of $(8x^2 + 6x + 2)$, $(7x^2 + 2x + 5)$, and $(6x^2 + 7x − 1)$?

Solution: Mean $\Rightarrow$ *Sum ÷ Number*   [Write the formula for calculating arithmetic mean]

$\Rightarrow \dfrac{(8x^2 + 6x + 2) + (7x^2 + 2x + 5) + (6x^2 + 7x - 1)}{3}$ [Substitute the known values]

$\Rightarrow \dfrac{21x^2 + 15x + 6}{3}$ [Combine like-terms]

$\Rightarrow \dfrac{3(7x^2 + 5x + 2)}{3}$ [Factor out 3 from the numerator]

$\Rightarrow 7x^2 + 5x + 2$ [Cancel-out the common terms]

Question #68: If $x + y = 5$, $y + z = 8$, and $z + x = 9$, what is the average (arithmetic mean) of x, y, and z?

Solution: Solve the given equations simultaneously:

$$
\begin{array}{lll}
x + y & = 5 & \Rightarrow \text{Equation \#1} \\
y + z & = 8 & \Rightarrow \text{Equation \#2} \\
+ \quad z + x & = 9 & \Rightarrow \text{Equation \#3} \\
\hline
2x + 2y + 2z & = 22 & \text{[Add all the three equations]} \\
\Rightarrow 2(x + y + z) & = 22 & \text{[Factor out 2 on the left side]} \\
\Rightarrow x + y + z & = 11 & \text{[Divide both sides by 2]}
\end{array}
$$

$$\Rightarrow \frac{x + y + z}{3} = \frac{11}{3} \qquad \text{[Divide both sides by 3]}$$

Average of x, y, and z $\Rightarrow \dfrac{11}{3}$

Question #69: If the average (arithmetic mean) of 10, 18, 24, 28, and n is equal to n, what is the value of n?

Solution: EZ Problem Set-Up $\Rightarrow$ Mean of 10, 18, 24, 28, and n is equal to n.

$$\Rightarrow \frac{10 + 18 + 24 + 28 + n}{5} = n \quad \text{[Set up the equation]}$$

$$
\begin{array}{ll}
\Rightarrow 10 + 18 + 24 + 28 + n = 5n & \text{[Cross multiply]} \\
\Rightarrow 80 + n = 5n & \text{[Combine like-terms]} \\
\Rightarrow 4n = 80 & \text{[Subtract } n \text{ from both sides]} \\
\Rightarrow n = 20 & \text{[Divide both sides by 4]}
\end{array}
$$

Question #70: If the average (arithmetic mean) of 11, 18, and n is between 15 and 17, inclusive, what is the greatest possible value of n?

Solution: For the greatest possible value of n, the average must also be the greatest possible, which is 17.

EZ Problem Set-Up $\Rightarrow$ Mean of 11, 18, and n is 17.

$$
\begin{array}{ll}
\Rightarrow (11 + 18 + n) \div 3 = 17 & \text{[Set up the equation]} \\
\Rightarrow (11 + 18 + n) = 51 & \text{[Multiply both sides by 3]} \\
\Rightarrow 29 + n = 51 & \text{[Combine like-terms]} \\
\Rightarrow n = 22 & \text{[Subtract 29 from both sides]}
\end{array}
$$

Question #71: If the average of m, n, and another number is A, then what is the value of that another number?

Solution: Let that another number $= x$

EZ Problem Set-Up $\Rightarrow$ Mean of m, n, and x is A.

$$\Rightarrow \frac{m + n + x}{3} = A \qquad \text{[Set up the equation]}$$

$$
\begin{array}{ll}
\Rightarrow m + n + x = 3A & \text{[Cross multiply]} \\
\Rightarrow x = 3A - m - n & \text{[Subtract } m + n \text{ from both sides]}
\end{array}
$$

Question #72: If the average of (arithmetic mean) of n and -5 is 10, then what is the value of n?

Solution: EZ Problem Set-Up $\Rightarrow$ Mean of n and -5 is 10.

$$\Rightarrow \frac{n + (-5)}{2} = 10 \qquad \text{[Set up the equation]}$$

$$
\begin{array}{ll}
\Rightarrow n + (-5) = 20 & \text{[Cross multiply]} \\
\Rightarrow n = 25 & \text{[Add 5 to both sides]}
\end{array}
$$

Question #73: The average (arithmetic mean) of two numbers is a. If one of the numbers is 10, what is the other number?

Solution: Let that other number be n

EZ Problem Set-Up $\Rightarrow$ Mean of 10 and n is a.

$$\Rightarrow a = \frac{10 + n}{2} \qquad \text{[Set up the equation]}$$

$$\Rightarrow 2a = 10 + n \qquad \text{[Cross multiply]}$$

$$\Rightarrow n = 2a - 10 \qquad \text{[Subtract 10 from both sides]}$$

Question #74: If the average (arithmetic mean) of a, b, and 10 is 100, what is the average of a and b?

Solution: EZ Problem Set-Up $\Rightarrow$ Mean of a, b, and 10 is 100.

$$\Rightarrow \frac{a + b + 10}{3} = 100 \qquad \text{[Set up the equation]}$$

$$\Rightarrow a + b + 10 = 300 \qquad \text{[Cross multiply]}$$

$$\Rightarrow a + b = 290 \qquad \text{[subtract 10 from both sides]}$$

$$\Rightarrow \frac{a + b}{2} = 145 \qquad \text{[Divide both sides by 2]}$$

Question #75: If the average (arithmetic mean) of 7, 9, and 11 equals the average of 6, 9, and n, what is the value of n?

Solution: EZ Problem Set-Up $\Rightarrow$ Mean of 6, 9, and n = Mean of 7, 9, and 11

$$\Rightarrow \frac{6 + 9 + n}{3} = \frac{7 + 9 + 11}{3} \qquad \text{[Set up the equation]}$$

$$\Rightarrow \frac{6 + 9 + n}{3} = 9 \qquad \text{[Simplify the right hand side]}$$

$$\Rightarrow 15 + n = 27 \qquad \text{[Cross multiply]}$$

$$\Rightarrow n = 12 \qquad \text{[Subtract 15 from both sides]}$$

Question #76: If the average (arithmetic mean) of n and 2 is equal to the average of n, 5, and 6, what is the value of n?

Solution: EZ Problem Set-Up $\Rightarrow$ Mean of n and 2 is equal to the mean of n, 5, and 6.

$$\Rightarrow \frac{n + 2}{2} = \frac{n + 5 + 6}{3} \qquad \text{[Set up the equation]}$$

$$\Rightarrow 3(n + 2) = 2(n + 5 + 6) \qquad \text{[Cross multiply]}$$

$$\Rightarrow 3n + 6 = 2n + 10 + 12 \qquad \text{[Apply distributive property]}$$

$$\Rightarrow 3n + 6 = 2n + 22 \qquad \text{[Combine like-terms]}$$

$$\Rightarrow n + 6 = 22 \qquad \text{[Subtract $2n$ from both sides]}$$

$$\Rightarrow n = 16 \qquad \text{[Subtract 6 from both sides]}$$

Question #77: If $10a + 10b = 50$, what is the average (arithmetic mean) of a and b?

Solution:
$$\Rightarrow 10a + 10b = 50 \qquad \text{[Given]}$$

$$\Rightarrow 10(a + b) = 10(5) \qquad \text{[Factor out 10 from both sides]}$$

$$\Rightarrow a + b = 5 \qquad \text{[Divide both sides by 10]}$$

$$\Rightarrow \frac{a + b}{2} = \frac{5}{2} \qquad \text{[Divide both sides by 2]}$$

Mean of a and b $\Rightarrow 2.5$

Question #78: The average (arithmetic mean) of two numbers is A. If one of the numbers is n, what's the other number?

Solution:
Average of two numbers $\Rightarrow A$
One of the numbers $\qquad \Rightarrow n$
Let the other number $\qquad \Rightarrow x$

EZ Problem Set-Up $\Rightarrow$ Average of two numbers = $\dfrac{\text{one number} + \text{other number}}{2}$

$$\Rightarrow A = \frac{n + x}{2} \qquad \text{[Set up the equation]}$$

$$\Rightarrow n + x = 2A \qquad \text{[Cross multiply]}$$

$$\Rightarrow x = 2A - n \qquad \text{[Subtract n from both sides]}$$

Question #79: The average (arithmetic mean) of two numbers is $6n - 1$. If one of the numbers is n, then what is the value of the other number?

Solution: Let the other number = x

EZ Problem Set-Up $\Rightarrow$ Mean of x and n is $6n - 1$

$$\Rightarrow \frac{x+n}{2} = 6n - 1 \qquad \text{[Set up the equation]}$$

$\Rightarrow x + n = 2(6n - 1)$ [Cross multiply]

$\Rightarrow x + n = 12n - 2$ [Apply distributive property]

$\Rightarrow x = 11n - 2$ [Subtract n from both sides]

Question #80:   The average (arithmetic mean) of 3 numbers is 19, and the smallest of these numbers is 5. If the other two numbers are equal, what is the value of each one of the other two numbers?

Solution: Let the other two numbers be n each

EZ Problem Set-Up $\Rightarrow$ Mean of 5, n, and n is 19.

$$\Rightarrow 19 = \frac{5+n+n}{3} \qquad \text{[Set up the equation]}$$

$\Rightarrow 57 = 5 + 2n$ [Cross multiply]

$\Rightarrow 2n = 52$ [Subtract 5 from both sides]

$\Rightarrow n = 26$ [Divide both sides by 2]

Question #81:   The average (arithmetic mean) of 10, 50, and 90 is 15 less than the average of 25, 75, and what number?

Solution: Average of 10, 50, and 90 $\Rightarrow \dfrac{10+50+90}{3} = \dfrac{150}{3} = 50$

EZ Problem Set-Up $\Rightarrow$ Average of 10, 50, and 90 is 50, which is 15 less than the average 25, 75, and what number (50 is 15 less of 65).

$$\Rightarrow \frac{25+75+n}{3} = 65 \qquad \text{[Set up the equation]}$$

$$\Rightarrow \frac{100+n}{3} = 65 \qquad \text{[Combine like-terms]}$$

$\Rightarrow 100 + n = 195$ [Cross multiply]

$\Rightarrow n = 95$ [Subtract 100 from both sides]

Question #82:   If the average (arithmetic mean) of p and q is 25 and the average of r and q is 60, what is the value of $r - p$?

Solution: Mean of p and q = 25 $\Rightarrow$ Sum of p and q = 25 × 2 = 50 $\Rightarrow p + q = 50$ $\Rightarrow$ Equation #1

Mean of r and q = 60 $\Rightarrow$ Sum of r and q = 60 × 2 = 120 $\Rightarrow r + q = 120$ $\Rightarrow$ Equation #2

Subtract Equation #1 from Equation #2

$$
\begin{array}{r}
r + q = 120 \\
- (p + q = 50) \\
\hline
r - p = 70
\end{array}
$$

Value of $r - p \Rightarrow 70$

Question #83:   If $p + q = 3(r + s)$, what is the average (arithmetic mean) of p, q, r, and s?

Solution: Mean $\Rightarrow$ Sum ÷ Number   [Write the formula for calculating arithmetic mean]

$$\Rightarrow \frac{p+q+r+s}{4} \qquad \text{[Substitute the known values]}$$

$$\Rightarrow \frac{3(r+s)+r+s}{4} \qquad \text{[Substitute } p + q = 3(r + s)]$$

$$\Rightarrow \frac{3r+3s+r+s}{4} \qquad \text{[Apply distributive property]}$$

$$\Rightarrow \frac{4r+4s}{4} \qquad \text{[Combine like-terms]}$$

$$\Rightarrow \frac{4(r+s)}{4} \qquad \text{[Factor out 4 from the numerator]}$$

$\Rightarrow r + s$ [Cancel-out the common terms]

Question #84: If the average (arithmetic mean) of 20, 70, and 90 is 5 more than the average of 10, 80, and n, what is the value of n?

Solution: EZ Problem Set-Up $\Rightarrow$ (Mean of 20, 70, and 90) = (Mean of 10, 80, and n) + 5

$$\Rightarrow \frac{20+70+90}{3} = \frac{10+80+n}{3} + 5 \qquad \text{[Set up the equation]}$$

$$\Rightarrow \frac{180}{3} = \frac{90+n}{3} + 5 \qquad \text{[Combine like-terms]}$$

$$\Rightarrow 60 = \frac{90+n}{3} + 5 \qquad \text{[Do the division]}$$

$$\Rightarrow 55 = \frac{90+n}{3} \qquad \text{[Subtract 5 from both sides]}$$

$$\Rightarrow 90 + n = 165 \qquad \text{[Cross multiply]}$$

$$\Rightarrow n = 75 \qquad \text{[Subtract 90 from both sides]}$$

Question #85: If the average (arithmetic mean) of x and y is 6 and the average of x, y, and z is 9, what is the value of z?

Solution: Mean of x and y is 6 $\Rightarrow \dfrac{x+y}{2} = 6$ [Set up the equation]

$\Rightarrow x + y = 12$ [Cross multiply] $\Rightarrow$ Equation #1

Mean of x, y, and z is 9 $\Rightarrow \dfrac{x+y+z}{3} = 9$ [Set up the equation]

$\Rightarrow x + y + z = 27$ [Cross multiply] $\Rightarrow$ Equation #2

Solve the equations simultaneously $\Rightarrow \quad x \ + y + \quad z \ = 27$ $\Rightarrow$ Equation #2
$\Rightarrow -(x \ + y \qquad\quad = 12)$ $\Rightarrow$ Equation #1
$\Rightarrow \qquad\qquad\qquad z \ = 15$ [Subtract Equation #1 from #2]

Question #86: In a group of 60 workers, the average (arithmetic mean) daily salary is $80 per worker. If some of the workers earn $75 a day and the rest earn $100 a day, how many workers earn $100 a day?

Solution: Average daily salary of 60 workers $\Rightarrow$ $80
Total Salary received $\Rightarrow 60 \times 80 = \$4,800$
Some workers earn $75 a day and some workers earn $100 a day
Let, the No. of workers who earn $75 a day $\Rightarrow n$
Then, the No. of workers who earn $100 a day $\Rightarrow 60 - n$
EZ Problem Set-Up $\Rightarrow$ Total income from $75-workers + Total income from $100-workers = 4,800
$\Rightarrow 75n + 100(60 - n) = 4,800$ [Set up the equation]
$\Rightarrow 75n + 6,000 - 100n = 4,800$ [Apply distributive property]
$\Rightarrow -25n + 6,000 = 4,800$ [Combine like-terms]
$\Rightarrow -25n = -1,200$ [Subtract 6,000 from both sides]
$\Rightarrow n = 48$ [Divide both sides by –25]
No. of workers earning $75 a day $\Rightarrow 48$
No. of workers earning $100 a day $\Rightarrow 60 - 48 = 12$

Question #87: For a certain concert, fifteen tickets were sold at an average price of $8 a ticket. If some of the tickets were sold at $10 each and the rest at $5 each, how many tickets were sold at $5 price?

Solution: Total No. of tickets sold $\Rightarrow 15$
Mean price per ticket $\Rightarrow$ $8
Total proceeds from sale of tickets $\Rightarrow$ Total No. of tickets sold $\times$ Mean price per ticket
$\Rightarrow (15)\,(8) = 120$
Let, the total No. of $10 tickets sold $\Rightarrow n$
Then, the total No. of $5 tickets sold $\Rightarrow 15 - n$
EZ Problem Set-Up $\Rightarrow n$ tickets at the rate of $10 + (15 - n)$ tickets at the rate of $5 = Total Sales
$\Rightarrow 10(n) + 5(15 - n) = (15)\,(8)$ [Set up the equation]
$\Rightarrow 10n + 75 - 5n = 120$ [Apply distributive property]
$\Rightarrow 5n + 75 = 120$ [Combine like-terms]
$\Rightarrow 5n = 45$ [Subtract 75 from both sides]

$\Rightarrow n = 9$ [Divide both sides by 5]

No. of tickets sold for $10 each $\Rightarrow 9$

No. of tickets sold for $5 each $\Rightarrow 15 - n = 15 - 9 = 6$

Question #88: The average (arithmetic mean) of eight numbers is 12. If 2 is subtracted from each of six of the numbers, what is the new average?

Solution:

Original Numbers	$\Rightarrow 8$
Original Mean	$\Rightarrow 12$
Original Sum	$\Rightarrow$ *Mean × Number*
	$\Rightarrow 8 \times 12 = 96$

Subtract 2 from each of the 6 numbers $\Rightarrow 2 \times 6 = 12$

New Sum	$\Rightarrow$ *Original Sum* $- 12$
	$\Rightarrow 96 - 12 = 84$
New Mean	$\Rightarrow$ *Sum ÷ Number*
	$\Rightarrow 84 \div 8 = 10.5$

Question #89: The average (arithmetic mean) of 8 positive numbers is 7. If the average of least and greatest of these numbers is 10, what is the average of the other 6 numbers?

Solution:

No. of terms	$\Rightarrow 8$
Mean of 8 numbers	$\Rightarrow 7$
Sum of 8 numbers	$\Rightarrow$ *Number × Mean*
	$\Rightarrow 7 \times 8 = 56$
Mean of least & greatest number	$\Rightarrow 10$
Sum of least & greatest number	$\Rightarrow$ *Mean × Number*
	$\Rightarrow 10 \times 2 = 20$
Sum of other 6 numbers	$\Rightarrow$ Sum of 8 numbers – Sum of least and greatest number
	$\Rightarrow 56 - 20 = 36$
Mean of other 6 numbers	$\Rightarrow$ Sum of other 6 numbers $\div 6$
	$\Rightarrow 36 \div 6 = 6$

Question #90: The average (arithmetic mean) of x and y is 25. If $z = 10$, what is the average of x, y, and z?

Solution:

Mean of x and y	$\Rightarrow 25$
Sum of x and y	$\Rightarrow$ *Mean × Number*
	$\Rightarrow 25 \times 2 = 50$
Sum of x, y, and z	$\Rightarrow$ Sum of x and y + value of z
	$\Rightarrow 50 + 10 = 60$
Mean of x, y, and z	$\Rightarrow$ *Sum ÷ Number*
	$\Rightarrow 60 \div 3 = 20$

Question #91: If the average (arithmetic mean) of a, b, c, d, and e is 95, and the average of a, b, and e is 100, what is the average of c and d?

Solution:

Mean of a, b, c, d, & e	$\Rightarrow 95$
Sum of a, b, c, d, & e	$\Rightarrow$ *Mean × Number*
	$\Rightarrow 95 \times 5 = 475$
Mean of a, b, and e	$\Rightarrow 100$
Sum of a, b, and e	$\Rightarrow$ *Mean × Number*
	$\Rightarrow 100 \times 3 = 300$
Sum of c and d	$\Rightarrow$ (Sum of a, b, c, d, and e) – (Sum of a, b, and e)
	$\Rightarrow 475 - 300 = 175$
Mean of c and d	$\Rightarrow$ *Sum ÷ Number*
	$\Rightarrow 175 \div 2 = 87.5$

Question #92: A big cargo container has only two sizes of boxes, large and small. If 80 percent of the boxes are large and the remaining 20 percent are small, and if the average weight of each large box is 80 pounds and the average weight of each small box is 20 pounds, what is the average weight, in pounds, of all the boxes in the cargo container?

Solution: Weighted Mean $\Rightarrow$ *sum of products ÷ sum of weights*   [Write the formula to calculate weighted mean]

$$\Rightarrow \frac{80\%(80) + 20\%(20)}{100\%(1)}$$ [Substitute the known values]

$$\Rightarrow \frac{64 + 4}{1}$$ [Simplify the percents]

$\Rightarrow$ 68 pounds   [Simplify the fraction]

Question #93:   In a group of 5 people, each person was given a blank card on which they were supposed to write a positive integer. If the average (arithmetic mean) of all five of those integers is 15, what is the greatest possible integer that could be one of the cards?

Solution: Mean of 5 integers $\Rightarrow$ 15
Sum of 5 integers $\Rightarrow$ 15 × 5 = 75
Since we want one of the five values to be the greatest, the rest of the four values must be the least possible. The least value that any card can have is 1, so let's assume that four of the cards had 1 written on them, which adds up to 4. Therefore, the fifth card can have at most 75 – 4 = 71.
Greatest possible integer that could be one of the cards $\Rightarrow$ 71

Question #94:   In a group of 5 people, each person was given a blank card on which they were supposed to write a positive integer. If the average (arithmetic mean) of all five of those integers is 15, and if no two cards can have the same number, what is the greatest possible integer that could be one of the cards?

Solution: Mean of 5 integers $\Rightarrow$ 15
Sum of 5 integers $\Rightarrow$ 15 × 5 = 75
Since we want one of the five values to be the greatest, the rest of the four values must be the least possible. The least value that any card can have is 1 but no two cards can have the same integer, so let's suppose that the first card had 1, the second card had 2, the third card had 3, and the fourth card had 4 on them, which add up to 1 + 2 + 3 + 4 = 10. Therefore, the fifth card can have at most 75 – 10 = 65.
Greatest possible integer that could be one of the cards $\Rightarrow$ 65

Question #95:   A student's grade in a course is determined by 8 quizzes and 1 exam. If the exam counts twice as much as each of the quizzes, what fraction of the final grade is determined by the exam?

Solution: The final grade is determined by $\Rightarrow$ 8 Quizzes & 1 Exam
Since the exam counts twice as much as each quiz $\Rightarrow$ 1 Exam = 2 Quizzes
Now the final grade is determined by $\Rightarrow$ 8 Quizzes & 2 Quizzes = 10 Quizzes

Exam represents 2 Quizzes, so the fraction of the final grade is determined by the exam $\Rightarrow \dfrac{2}{10} = \dfrac{1}{5}$

Question #96:   If A is the average (arithmetic mean) of the first 5 prime numbers and B is the median of first 5 prime numbers, what is the value of $A - B$?

Solution: List of first 5 prime nos. $\Rightarrow$ 2, 3, 5, 7, 11

Mean of first 5 prime nos. $\Rightarrow A \quad = \dfrac{2 + 3 + 5 + 7 + 11}{5} = \dfrac{28}{5} = 5.6$

Median of first 5 prime nos. $\Rightarrow B \quad = 5$
Value of $A - B$ $\Rightarrow$ 5.6 – 5.0 = 0.6

Question #97:   If the median of the numbers in Set A below is equal to the median of the numbers in Set B below, what is the value of n?
Set A: {11, 12, 18, 19}
Set B: {7, 9, n, 20, 21}

Solution: Median of Set A $\Rightarrow$ *Mean of Two Middle Terms – for even number of terms*
                   $\Rightarrow$ (12 + 18) ÷ 2 = 30 ÷ 2 = 15
Median of Set B $\Rightarrow$ *Middle Term – for odd number of terms*
                   $\Rightarrow n$
Median of Set A = Median of Set B = n = 15

Question #98: If the average (arithmetic mean) of the set of numbers arranged in increasing order given below is equal to the median of the same set of numbers given below, then what is the value of n?
{5, 7, 11, 12, n}

Solution: Median $\Rightarrow$ *Middle Term – for odd number of terms*
$\quad\quad\quad\quad\;\Rightarrow 11$

EZ Problem Set-Up $\Rightarrow$ Mean of the terms = Median of the terms

$\quad\quad\Rightarrow \dfrac{5+7+11+12+n}{5} = 11$ $\quad\quad$ [Set up the equation]

$\quad\quad\Rightarrow \dfrac{35+n}{5} = 11$ $\quad\quad\quad\quad\quad\quad$ [Simplify the left side]

$\quad\quad\Rightarrow 35 + n = 55$ $\quad\quad\quad\quad\quad$ [Cross-multiply]

$\quad\quad\Rightarrow n = 20$ $\quad\quad\quad\quad\quad\quad\quad$ [Subtract 35 from both sides]

Question #99: A company wants to draw a pie chart representing their expenditures. After the final break-up of all the expenses, 25% of the expenses were for rent, 20% for salaries, 15% for insurance, 10% for technology, 10% for utilities, and the remaining were miscellaneous expenses. What should be the degree measure of the sector representing miscellaneous expenses?

Solution: Miscellaneous Expenses $\quad\quad\quad\quad\Rightarrow 100\% - (25\%+20\%+15\%+10\%+10\%) = 100\% - 80\% = 20\%$
Total Degree Measure in Pie-Chart $\quad\Rightarrow 360°$
Degree Measure for a 20% Sector $\quad\;\Rightarrow$ 20% of 360° = 0.20 × 360° = 72°

Question #100: The family budget of a certain family is represented on a pie chart. If the size of each sector of the pie chart is proportional to the amount of the budget it represents, how many degrees of the pie chart should be used to represent an item that is 16 percent of the total budget?

Solution: Total No. of Degree in a Pie Chart $\Rightarrow 360°$
No. of Degrees of the Pie Chart to represent an item that is 16% of the total $\Rightarrow$ 16% of 360 = 57.6°

EZ SOLUTIONS ORDERS & SALES:

ORDERS & SALES INFORMATION: EZ Solutions products and services can be ordered via one of the following methods:

🖥 ON-LINE ORDERS:
On-line Orders can be placed 24/7 via internet by going to: www.EZmethods.com

✉ E-MAIL ORDERS:
E-Mail Orders can be placed 24/7 via internet by emailing: orders@EZmethods.com

☎ PHONE ORDERS:
Phone Orders can be placed via telephone by calling: (Please check our website for most updated information)

📠 FAX ORDERS:
Fax Orders can be placed via fax by faxing: (Please check our website for most updated information)

📧 MAIL ORDERS:
Mail Orders can be placed via regular mail by mailing to the address given below:
EZ Solutions
Orders Department
P.O. Box 10755
Silver Spring, MD 20914
USA

OTHER OPTIONS: EZ Solutions books are also available at most major bookstores.

Institutional Sales: For volume/bulk sales to bookstores, libraries, schools, colleges, universities, organization, and institutions, please contact us. Quantity discount and special pricing is available.

EZ SOLUTIONS PRODUCTS & SERVICES:

LIST OF EZ TEST PREP SERIES OF BOOKS:

EZ Solutions Test Prep Series Books are available for the following sections:
- EZ Solutions – Test Prep Series – General – Test Taker's Manual
- EZ Solutions – Test Prep Series – Math Review – Arithmetic
- EZ Solutions – Test Prep Series – Math Review – Algebra
- EZ Solutions – Test Prep Series – Math Review – Applications
- EZ Solutions – Test Prep Series – Math Review – Geometry
- EZ Solutions – Test Prep Series – Math Review – Word Problems
- EZ Solutions – Test Prep Series – Math Review – Logic & Stats
- EZ Solutions – Test Prep Series – Math Practice – Basic Workbook
- EZ Solutions Test Prep Series – Math Practice – Advanced Workbook
- EZ Solutions – Test Prep Series – Math Strategies – Math Test Taking Strategies
- EZ Solutions – Test Prep Series – Math – Data Sufficiency
- EZ Solutions – Test Prep Series – Verbal Section – Reading Comprehension
- EZ Solutions – Test Prep Series – Verbal Section – Sentence Correction/Completion
- EZ Solutions – Test Prep Series – Verbal Section – Vocabulary
- EZ Solutions – Test Prep Series – Verbal Section – Grammar
- EZ Solutions – Test Prep Series – Verbal Section – Critical Reasoning
- EZ Solutions – Test Prep Series – Verbal Section – Writing Skills

Note: Most of these books have already been published and others will be released shortly.

EZ Solutions Test Prep Series Books are available for the following standardized tests:
- EZ Solutions GMAT Test Prep Series of Books
- EZ Solutions GRE Test Prep Series of Books
- EZ Solutions SAT Test Prep Series of Books
- EZ Solutions ACT Test Prep Series of Books
- EZ Solutions LSAT Test Prep Series of Books
- EZ Solutions PRAXIS Test Prep Series of Books
- EZ Solutions POWER MATH/ENGLISH Test Prep Series of Books